Front Cover

The painting on the front cover is a detail from *St. John the Evangelist on the Island of Patmos*. It was painted in 1485 by Domenico Ghirlandaio. It is located in the Museum of Fine Arts in Budapest, Hungary.

In the scroll in John's left hand are the Latin words, "IN PRINCIPIO ERAT VERBUM", in English, "In the beginning was the Word." These are the first words of John's Gospel.

John is shown on the Greek island of Patmos, in the Aegean Sea, where he wrote the Book of Revelation, also known as the Apocalypse. John is shown in the painting holding a book that is opened to a page with the word "APOCALIPSE", in English, "Apocalypse." It is the last book in the Bible.

"You may have read fictional biographies of the Apostles. However, *The Gospel of Love* is the only historical fictional autobiography that I have read of any of them.

Dan Lynch wrote this story of the life of the beloved disciple of Jesus, St. John the Evangelist, from John's personal point of view. Solidly based on the Bible, it is presented in such a way as to make it easy for the beginner to relate John's world to ours.

You will experience John's life as if you were with him nearly 2000 years ago. You will experience John's innermost thoughts and doubts as he struggles to accept Jesus Christ as the Messiah, the Son of Man and the Son of God, and His teachings that constitute the Gospel of Love. You will see John's transformation from tempestuousness to tranquility as he gradually comes to know and believe in the love that God has for all of us.

More importantly, you will come away with a deeper understanding of how the Gospel of Love, taught by Jesus, affected John's character and growth in sanctity and how its reading can do the same for you.

Nothing is so important in life as to grow in holiness by fulfilling the first and second laws of the Gospel: love of God who is love itself and love of neighbor as oneself made in the image and likeness of God. Nothing in life is so sad as not to have become a saint by loving God and neighbor as Jesus does.

Our thanks to Dan Lynch for this inspiring work!"

Fr. Peter M. Damien Fehlner F.F.I., S.T.D., Author and
Theologian

The Ten Secrets of the Blessed Virgin Mary

"Once again Dan Lynch has given us a simple, clear presentation, this time on the much discussed apparitions of Our Lady at Medjugorje. His argumentation in favor of authenticity deserves a serious hearing. For the goals of Our Lady at Medjugorje touch not only local issues, but have worldwide implications and should be pondered in relation to previous apparitions of Mary, for instance, at Fatima, at Amsterdam (Our Lady of All Nations), and elsewhere."

Fr. Peter M. Damien Fehlner F.F.I., S.T.D., Author
and Theologian

"I praise Dan Lynch for his work at articulating an understanding of the ten secrets of Medjugorje. I also appreciate his use of favorable comments from persons of authority in the Church in assisting people to 'Not Be Afraid.' "

Fr. Charles Becker
Leader of pilgrimages to Medjugorje

"In the days of Fatima no one would have believed what has come of the world today. Our Lady's message in 1917 and 93 years later in Medjugorje has not changed. The message of Our Lady is the eternal message of the Gospels – prayer, fasting, conversion, penance, confession, Eucharist. Dan Lynch reminds us of the many apparitions of Our Lady and her heartfelt warning to 'turn away from sin and be faithful to the Gospel.' Only in embracing Our Lady's call will the world be saved from the road of self-destruction. In his book, Dan gives a concise presentation of Our Lady's messages and how we can practically respond in today's world. I pray that all who come in contact with this little book will take seriously the warning of our heavenly mother, embrace her messages and find true peace within their souls."

Father Jay Finelli
The iPadre Catholic Podcast & Videocast

"Dan Lynch has done a masterful job conveying the messages of the Queen of Peace in a simple and readable style for people of all ages."

"Medjugorje is the extension of the messages of Fatima, and what Dan has written are the keys to peace of mind and soul and will provide people answers in the midst of any storm."

Ted Flynn, Author

Saints of the States

"Too few of the faithful in our great country are aware of the lives and sacrifices of the American Saints. Thank you for your latest book, *Saints of the States*."

> Most Reverend Robert J. Baker
> Bishop of the Diocese of Birmingham
> Co-author, *Cacique, A Novel of Florida's Heroic Mission History*

Our Lady of Guadalupe, Hope for the World

"This book will instruct, encourage and inspire a wide variety of people in the Church and outside the Church. You may be a pro-life activist looking for signs of progress. You may be a priest seeking new ways to call your people to deeper faith. You may be a son or daughter of the Virgin Mary eager to find new ways to honor her. You may be someone considering abortion or wounded by it, and looking for hope. You may be away from the Church looking for a way back, or someone without any background in Catholicism but interested in finding out more. Whoever you are, give this book some of your time, and it will repay you abundantly."

> Fr. Frank Pavone, National Director Priests for Life

Our Lady of Guadalupe, Mother of Hope Video

"Stirring, gripping, comprehensive with moving testimonies!"

> Reviews by producers, Ted Flynn, Dr. Tom Petrisko, Drew Mariani and Ignatius Press

Our Lady of America, Our Hope for the States

"Are there sound grounds for hope about the immediate future of the USA? Without doubt the messages of Our Lady of America to Sr. Mary Ephrem certainly do offer such grounds. This simple, yet detailed sketch of the historical background and of the context of these messages makes perfectly clear why this is so and why Our Lady has chosen the States for a particular role in the salvation of souls, and what will be the consequences of not corresponding with her requests. Dan Lynch once again has succeeded in making crystal clear why the Immaculate Virgin is not simply a pious extra for us, but someone who must be at the very heart of our lives, socially as well as personally."

Fr. Peter M. Damien Fehlner F.F.I., S.T.D., Author
and Theologian

Teresita's Choices

"This book is a drama with many surprising twists and turns. While feminists claim that a key aspect of feminism is to 'listen to the voices of women', ironically, those who support abortions fail to listen to the voices of those women who testify to the pain and devastation that it brings. Teresita is one of those voices."

Fr. Frank Pavone
National Director Priests for Life

"This book highlights the devastation of abortion, yet gives hope that Our Lord can heal even the most devastating wounds. No doubt an inspiring book of hope. Thank you for this encouraging book."

Judie Brown
American Life League

The Call to Total Consecration

"I used Dan Lynch's book as a resource for my talk on the Total Consecration. Of the many books that I have received, this is one of the very few that I actually read and enjoyed!"

Scott Hahn, Author and Professor of Theology
and Scripture at Franciscan University of
Steubenville

THE GOSPEL
OF LOVE

Dan Lynch

Published by:

John Paul Press
144 Sheldon Road
St. Albans, VT 05478
www.JKMI.com

Dedication

The Gospel of Love is dedicated to Servant of God Sister Marie de Mandat-Grancey as a participation with Pope Francis in his New Evangelization. It is a response to his call for us to personally encounter Jesus Christ, who is the King of All Nations. May His reign be recognized on Earth!

Sister Marie was a Daughter of Charity born in France on September 13, 1837. In 1886, her order sent her as a missionary nun to Smyrna, near Ephesus, Turkey. While she was there, she read the writings of Blessed Anne Catherine Emmerich. Blessed Catherine was a German mystic nun who saw visions of the life of the Blessed Virgin Mary and of the house that St. John the Evangelist built for her in Ephesus.

Sister Marie encouraged two French Vincentian priests to use Blessed Catherine's writings as a "guidebook" and to go on an expedition in an attempt to find Mary's last home. They discovered the remains of a house on July 29, 1891. The site and the house corresponded accurately to Blessed Catherine's description.

On December 1, 1891, Archbishop Timoni of Smyrna declared in a formal document that those remains were truly the remains of the house inhabited by the Blessed Virgin Mary. Sister Marie purchased Mary's House in her own name on November 15, 1892. She restored it and made it a place of pilgrimage. Sister Marie went to see the house for the very first time on December 12, 1892, the Feast of Our Lady of Guadalupe.

Sister Marie preserved, promoted, protected, and developed the Shrine that is known today as Mary's House (in Turkish, *Meryem Ana Evi*). God in His providence chose her to be the humble soul who would give Mary's House, built by St. John the Evangelist, to the Church and to the world.

Sister Marie was responsible for the finding of Mary's House. For that reason, some of the original 1ˢᵗ century stones found during the excavation of Mary's House were sent back to her birthplace at the de Mandat-Grancey Chapel in the Chateau Grancey in Burgundy, France. These stones came from the hearth of Mary's House, the very heart of her home, and thus can be considered as its cornerstone.

The symbol of the cornerstone is applied to Jesus as the cornerstone of His Church. (See Matthew 21:42; Ephesians 2:20). We build our faith around this cornerstone.

Sister Marie was a prayerful, virtuous soul filled with radiant, invincible faith. She and her family had special devotion to St. John through the centuries. They named the family's Collegiate Chapel in honor of St. John.

Sister Marie promoted devotion to Mary at the Shrine in Ephesus until her death on May 31, 1915. Her devotion was so great that she touched the hearts of Christians and Muslims alike, drawing them together to the Shrine. To this day, Muslims and Christians honor Mary in prayer together in Mary's House. This is a sign of hope for peace between Muslims and Christians in these times of terrorism.

Hopefully, Servant of God Sister Marie de Mandat-Grancey will be canonized as a saint for our times. Let us pray for her canonization and through her the prayer that is on the following page.

Sister MARIE de MANDAT-GRANCEY

September 13th, 1837 -
May 31st, 1915
SERVANT OF GOD

We Thank God
For Giving us the privilege of
Sister Marie de Mandat-Grancey.

Through her great generosity
She acquired the property at Ephesus,
The Home of Mary and
Saint John the Evangelist.

We ask God and Sister Marie
To continue to Bless the cornerstone
Given to her, "Around this Cornerstone
We build our faith and the powers of
darkness will not prevail."

We pray for God's will to be
Completely fulfilled through the
Intercession of Sister Marie.
Amen

WWW.SISTERMARIE.COM

Report any spiritual or physical
favors granted in her name to:
Cause of Sr. Marie de Mandat-Grancey, DC
P.O. Box 419037
Kansas City, Missouri 64141-6037

Imprimatur: ✝ W Giuseppe G. Bernardini
Archbishop of Izmir, Turkey
October 6, 2004

Appendix

Foreword

The *Gospel of Love* is unlike any other book about St. John the Evangelist. It's an accurate, historical fictional autobiography written from John's own point of view. While reading your way through it, you will feel like you are right there with John in 1st century Israel and Ephesus.

As you progress through each chapter, you will attain an insight into the intimate circle of Jesus Christ, which St. John and the other Apostles embodied. Each interjection of John's interior thoughts will give you an opportunity to stretch your own knowledge of the life and ministry of Jesus, and of the biblical characters, stories, and prophecies from the Old and New Testaments.

You will understand the meanings of the prophetic words of the Prophets and learn who they were, where they fit into biblical history and what they prophesied about the coming Messiah. You will learn about Mosaic Law and the ancient Jewish traditions. You will acquire a meticulous background of the Greek and Roman religions and cultures. Dan Lynch's informed connotations of Scripture and the revelations of the Kingdom of God provide the stepping-stones of the pathway to eternal life itself!

The epic biblical stories from the Gospel of St. John are familiar to most of us, but now they have supplementary elements composed into each account, which give a broader, richer depiction of their meaning, especially through the eyes of St. John. Dan Lynch does this brilliantly by detailing factual components in each chapter while inserting his own deep understanding and expertise of the Bible.

This added attention to detail imparts specific scriptures linking them to the fulfillment of the Prophets (Isaiah, Malachi, Simeon,

Micah, Elisha, Moses, Ezekiel, Jeremiah, Zechariah, etc.) who foretell the coming of Jesus as the Messiah. These enrichments create a unique opportunity to recognize the indicated meanings of these Prophets as they relate to the Messiah. This is truly a gift for the reader to behold.

While reading *The Gospel of Love*, you will also gain a profound awareness of the teachings of Jesus Christ, as taught to St. John. Each reflection through St. John's eyes will carry you to a new level of understanding of the broader delineation of God's plan for humankind. Throughout the book there are many occasions to relate to St. John along his journey through the numerous thoughts and questions that come to his mind, which he expounds upon. There is a great deal of knowledge presented to the reader with each of these occasions. They reveal many hidden mysteries that you probably never knew about.

Swiftly and effortlessly, Dan Lynch will propel you with his distinctive writing style into the Holy Land. While traveling to and from Galilee, Jerusalem, Jericho, Capernaum, Nazareth, Samaria, Cana, etc., it is exciting to learn the historical significance of these places that Dan adds as they relate to the Messiah.

Along your excursion with St. John through the Holy Land, you will recognize biblical quotations that are familiar to your eyes and ears. It is fascinating to learn their context as Dan clarifies their meaning and presents their origin in the Gospel of John: "Do whatever He tells you." (John 2:5); "The Good Shepherd" (John 10:11); "The Light of the World" (John 9:5); "The Bread of Life" (John 6:35); "The Resurrection and Life" (John 11:25-26); and "No greater love has man than this." (John 15:13).

Dan Lynch writes through the eyes and ears of St. John. He divulges tremendous biblical insight. You will have the sensation that St. John is personally guiding you and clarifying for you the firsthand knowledge that he acquired from Jesus Himself and is bestowing it upon you! Dan uses his unique ability to speak through the experiences of St. John's lifelong journey, clearly giving a new way to process St. John's Gospel.

Dan Lynch introduces us to the young St. John at the age of 13, in the year 19 A.D., as a Galilee fisherman who is working with his brother, St. James, his father, Zebedee, and his father's partner, Peter. The journey will end in Ephesus, Asia Minor, at John's ripe old age of 92, in the year 98 A.D. There is certainly an abundance of material on St. John for you to discover regarding his life between the ages of 13 and 92.

St. John was the only Apostle to be with Jesus and His Mother at the Crucifixion on Mount Calvary in Jerusalem. As Jesus was dying on the Cross, He desired to be sure that His Mother would be cared for, so He gave His Mother to St. John with the words, "Woman, Behold your Son. Behold, your Mother." (John 19:26-27). That is the moment that Mary became the spiritual Mother to John and to all people. "From that hour the disciple took her into his own home." (John 19:27).

Dan's book reveals that in 42 A.D., St. John left Jerusalem with Mary to bring her to the safety of Ephesus. There he built a stone home for her in the shape of a cross on Nightingale Hill. This was Mary's dwelling place where she spent the last nine years of her life.

St. John continued his ministry in Ephesus, where he preached the Gospel of Love until his death.

I hope that you will read and reread this book many times. It will continue to inspire fresh thoughts to ponder in your mind, heart, and soul and bring you closer to God. May St. John spiritually be with you as you take this journey through the Gospel of Love!

This is a fabulous book! I really hope that it inspires many people to share it with their friends and relatives.

When I read my Foreword aloud to my 91-year-old mother, she said, "I want to read that book just from listening to what you said about it."

Dan did such a wonderful job. I thank him for all that he did for so many of us to learn more about our rich faith! Once the dots are connected and you truly understand the meaning of the various Bible verses, everything seems to make more sense. That is what Dan did in *The Gospel of Love*. Bravo Dan!

Erin von Uffel, DM (Dame in the Order of Malta)
Vice Postulator of the cause for the canonization of
Sister Marie de Mandat-Grancey
President of the Sister Marie de Mandat-Grancey
Foundation
December 12, 2014, Feast of Our Lady of Guadalupe

Author's Preface

I made a journey to Ephesus in Turkey in the first year of the third millennium. It was in September, 2001, just after the September 11 terrorist attacks on America by militant Muslims. I flew to Muslim Turkey on an almost empty airplane. Many people were afraid to fly for fear of more airplanes being hijacked.

I went to Ephesus to pray for reconciliation and peace with Muslims. I also wanted to do some research for a possible book to write about the Apostle St. John. I wanted to write a novel about John's life with Jesus and His mother Mary — from his first meeting of Jesus in Galilee to his last mission and death in Ephesus.

I stayed at a hotel in the nearby city of Selcuk. The name of the hotel was the Kalehen (Castle House) Hotel. It was located at the base of Ayasuluk Hill on which sat a Crusader Castle and the ruins of St. John's Basilica, where I was told St. John was buried.

I had read that in the year 42 A.D., St. John and the Blessed Virgin Mary fled from a persecution in Jerusalem and came to Ephesus, where he built a house for her and that the remains of this house still exist. It is called Mary's House and many Muslims and Christians come there to pray together.

However, later I read that some so-called experts argued that John and Mary had never lived and died in Ephesus, and that John didn't even write the Gospel that was named after him. They said that an unknown person called "The Beloved Disciple" wrote it and that he wasn't even an apostle. This "Beloved Disciple" supposedly only wrote about the *tradition* that was passed on by John's *community* — not what the Apostle John himself had really seen and heard, as it says in the Gospel named after him. They also said that there was no evidence that John had died in Ephesus.

So, I started to research whether St. John and Mary had lived in Ephesus, whether Mary actually lived and died in Mary's House in Ephesus and whether St. John wrote his Gospel in Ephesus and died there. I learned a lot about what the so-called experts didn't know or what they had ignored.

Most scholars agreed that John took care of Jesus' mother Mary after the death of Jesus. This was in fulfillment of His commission to John from the Cross, "Son, behold your Mother!" (John 19:27).

In 1891, some priests discovered what the Church later determined was the actual house of Mary in Ephesus.

In 1907, the Vatican declared that the author of the Fourth Gospel was, in fact, the Apostle John.

From my research, I believed that Mary had lived in Ephesus and that John personally wrote his Gospel.

Later, I found the Scripture where Jesus Himself had told John to write. John wrote:

> I, John, your brother, who share with you in Jesus the tribulation and the kingdom and the patient endurance, was on the island called Patmos on account of the word of God and the testimony of Jesus. I was in the Spirit on the Lord's Day, and I heard behind me a loud voice like a trumpet saying, "Write what you see in a book." (Revelation 1:9-11).

So, St. John *was* a writer. And the island of Patmos was just off the coast of Selcuk, where I was staying near Ephesus — more evidence for me that he not only personally wrote his Gospel but that he wrote it at Ephesus. I began to read down the page with more excitement what John had written in the Book of Revelation:

> Then I turned to see the voice that was speaking to me, and on turning, I saw seven golden lampstands, and in the midst of the lampstands one like a Son of Man, clothed with a long robe and with a golden girdle round His breast; His head and His hair were

white as white wool, white as snow; His eyes were like a flame of fire, His feet were like burnished bronze, refined as in a furnace, and His voice was like the sound of many waters; in His right hand He held seven stars, from His mouth issued a sharp two-edged sword, and His face was like the sun shining in full strength.

When I saw Him, I fell at His feet as though dead. But He laid His right hand upon me, saying, "Fear not, I am the first and the last, and the living one; I died, and behold I am alive for evermore, and I have the keys of Death and Hades. Now *write* what you see, what is and what is to take place hereafter. (Revelation 1:12-19).

So, John had received his commission to write on the nearby island of Patmos from Jesus Himself. This increased the likelihood that he personally wrote his Gospel and his Letters at Ephesus. It also substantiated the claim that he taught there. Now I was really intrigued.

When I got home to Vermont, I did some further research on St. John and Ephesus in an effort to verify what I had found out while I was there.

I learned that, in the early 1820s, Blessed Sister Catherine Emmerich saw visions of the life of the Blessed Virgin Mary and of her house in Ephesus. Blessed Catherine was a German mystic nun who was bed-ridden with the stigmata. She had never left Germany. Her visions were extraordinarily extensive and detailed. They contained facts and places that she could not have naturally known. She described her visions in detail to her secretary, Clemens Brentano. He later published a book.

Blessed Catherine said that, after Our Lord's ascension into heaven, Mary lived on Mount Zion in Jerusalem, then in Bethany, and then was taken by St. John to Ephesus, where she lived for nine years in a house that he had built for her. Several Christian families had already settled there in caves or rustic huts in a scattered village, where they lived a simple, natural life.

Servant of God Sister Marie de Mandat-Grancey was sent as a missionary nun to the French Naval Hospital in Smyrna, Turkey in 1886. While she was there, she read about Sister Catherine's visions. She persuaded two scholarly Vincentian priests, Fathers Poulin and Jung, to see whether they could confirm Blessed Catherine's description of Mary's House from the evidence on the ground.

So the two priests went into the mountains on July 29, 1891. After searching they came upon some natives who led them to a small ruined house near the summit of an isolated peak. The site and the house corresponded accurately to Blessed Catherine's description.

They saw Ephesus on one side of the house and the island of Samos on the other side. They saw the terrace gardens, the old ruins, the stones, the trees, and the spring, all exactly as Blessed Catherine had described them.

On their second expedition to the house, the priests discovered that its insides also corresponded accurately to Blessed Catherine's description. The house had two rooms, one in front of the other and the back room was finished with a rounded back and a window on one side only, just as Blessed Catherine had described them.

The priests learned that the natives were descended from the early Christians of Ephesus and that the house had been venerated since that time. They called the house *Panaya Kapulu* — "The House of the Holy Virgin".

The original house was shaped like a T on the ground. The upper left top was a cloakroom that was not restored. The upper right top was Mary's "bedroom." The chapel in the front was once Mary's "living room." It measures 20' wide by 50' deep and the attached "bedroom" measures 12'x12'.

Within two years, archaeologists discovered that the foundations of the house dated to the first century. Later archeological excavations corresponded with Blessed Catherine's description and diagrams. They proved that her visions, in fact, showed reality.

Sister Marie purchased Mary's House in her own name on

November 15, 1892. She restored it and made it a place of pilgrimage for all people, especially Christians and Muslims. During the restoration, some stones from the hearth built by John were found. Some of these were sent to Sister Marie's birthplace in France.

Archbishop Timoni of Izmir convened a commission to investigate the discovery of Mary's House. He composed a lengthy document dated December 1, 1891 that was signed by every member of the commission. It listed in detail the priests' findings and showed how they conformed exactly to the descriptions of Blessed Catherine. The document concluded, "The ruins are truly the remains of the House inhabited by the Virgin Mary."

So, I came to believe that Mary had actually lived in Ephesus. If she did, then most probably John did as well. Then I did some more research. I learned that my belief so far was consistent with the stories of the early Church Fathers and the constant tradition of the Church.

The unanimous testimony of Tertullian, St. Polycarp, St. Irenaeus, Origen, Eusebius and St. Jerome, as well as numerous inferences drawn from the *Acts of the Apostles,* affirms that the Apostle John went to Ephesus soon after the ascension of Jesus to heaven, at a time when Mary must have been still alive.

The earliest known basilica built in honor of the Mother of God was at Ephesus. In that very church, the Council of Ephesus defined the first Marian dogma in the year 431. It declared that Mary was the Mother of God. The Fathers of the Council wrote a letter that links the names of Mary and John together in such a way that indicates that both of them had lived in Ephesus.

At that time, no church would be built and dedicated in honor of a saint unless he or she had lived there or died there as a martyr, which gave to the place its special importance. So Mary must have lived in Ephesus in order to have the basilica built and dedicated there in her honor. Today there are still archeological remains of this basilica called the Council Church.

Finally, I learned that in the 18th century Pope Benedict XIV accepted the accumulated evidence and wrote in his *Treatise on the Holy Mysteries* that "St. John, *departing for Ephesus, took Mary with him* and it was there that the Blessed Mother took her flight to heaven."

Then I learned from Eusebius' chronicle that St. John died in peace at Ephesus, in the third year of the reign of the Roman Emperor Trajan and the hundredth year of the Christian era, at the age of approximately 92. He was buried in a graveyard on Ayasuluk Hill, in what is now the city of Selcuk, where I had stayed below the Crusader Castle on that same hill. The dust of John's tomb was carried away out of devotion and was famous for miracles, as St. Austin, St. Ephrem, and St. Gregory of Tours mentioned.

A wooden basilica was built over St. John's tomb in the 4th century. In the 6th century, with help from Emperor Justinian and his wife, Theodora, a larger basilica was built. The ruins of this church are still visible today. It even contains a fresco of St. John and is known as St. John's Basilica and is also located on Ayasuluk Hill.

From 1920 to 1921, the Greek archeologist, Sotiriu, during his excavations of St. John's Basilica, removed a skeleton from the tomb that could be the body of St. John.

This was enough for me. It wasn't just visions or tradition, but *three physical archeological remains* – Mary's House, the Council Church and St. John's Basilica – that proved to me that St. John and Mary lived in Ephesus, that John preached there, wrote his Gospel there and that they both died there.

Some people believed that Mary died in Jerusalem. However, on April 18, 1896, Pope Leo XIII discontinued, for all time, indulgences formerly attached to the supposed tomb of Mary in Jerusalem.

On August 18, 1961, St. John XXIII granted a plenary indulgence, for all time, to all pilgrims to Mary's House in Ephesus.

I felt like God had helped me to figure out a great mystery. I had no more doubts as to the authenticity of John's life in Ephesus and so I began to write *The Gospel of Love* – from John's personal point of view.

Author's Note to Readers

The Gospel of Love is historical fictional autobiography. It is the story of how St. John the Apostle and Evangelist, the beloved disciple of Jesus King of All Nations, transformed from a tempestuous son of thunder to a gentle son of Mary, mother of Jesus.

From His Cross, Jesus gave His mother to John to be his own mother. This historical novel tells the story of John's search and struggle to come to the belief that Jesus Christ was the prophesied Messiah, the Lord and Savior, the Son of Man and Son of God, the King of Love and the King of All Nations, and his belief in eternal life through the forgiveness of his sins.

John tells from his own point of view how he came to know and to believe in the love that God has for us.

The book raises challenging questions in the New Evangelization in our secular culture, much like the pagan Roman culture, about the nature of searching for love, truth and peace, struggling with faith and transformation towards salvation and eternal life.

The book is based on history. It refers to real events in real times with real places and people. However, the work as a whole is a work of fiction, and some events, the thoughts and reflections of individuals, and some of the dialogue were created by me.

The current style of designating time, days, months, dates, seasons and distances did not exist during the time of Christ. For the convenience of the reader, I have used the current style.

The Scripture quotations from the Old Testament are from various sources. I paraphrased some of them to fit the context in which I used them or to be more reader-friendly. My style of citations to the Old Testament was not prevalent during the Apostle John's lifetime. I used it only to help the reader find the source. I chose not to add distracting footnotes or other explanations as to which particular translation I used or which ones I paraphrased.

I gratefully acknowledge and thank Lori Rainville who formatted this book and Randy Pratt and Debbie Kopp who edited it. Without their help, the book would still be stored in my computer!

This is my prayer for the book:

> O God, who through the blessed Apostle John have unlocked for us the secrets of your Word, grant, we pray, that we may grasp with proper understanding what he has so marvelously brought to our ears. Through our Lord Jesus Christ, your Son, who lives and reigns with you in the unity of the Holy Spirit, one God, for ever and ever. Amen.
>
> *Collect from Divine Office for the Feast of St. John the Apostle and Evangelist December 27*

May you come to know and to believe in the love that God has for you! God is love, and whoever lives in love lives in God and God in him." (1 John 4:16).

Thank you for reading my book.

Dan Lynch

John's Prologue

This is the story of how I, John, Apostle of Jesus Christ, came to believe, know, love and serve the one true God, our Lord and Savior Jesus Christ, true God and true man, who came not to condemn us, but to save us by laying down His life for us and loving us to the end.

His love was unconditional and wholly directed to the good of each person. His love was also sacrificial. He gave the best He had and all that He had. He gave His very life for us in order to secure for us eternal life with Him.

Jesus was the model for His own teaching, "No greater love has a man than to lay down his life for his friends." Through His great sacrificial death, He obtained for us the forgiveness of our sins and our eternal life, which is to know the one true God and His only Son, Jesus Christ.

I came to know and believe that God is love and that he who lives in love, lives in God and God in him. He called us to love one another, as He loved us. We are able to do this by His grace; for all human love is a cooperation of His divine grace and our free will in acts of love.

What was from the beginning, what I heard, what I saw with my own eyes and what I looked upon and touched with my own hands concerns Jesus Christ, the Word of life; for the life was made visible. I saw it and testify to it and proclaim to you the eternal life that was with the Father and was made visible to me. What I saw and heard, I now proclaim to you, so that you too may have fellowship with the Father and with His Son, Jesus Christ. I am writing this so that your joy may be complete.

"Boanerges," that's what He called my brother James and me because of our fervid and impetuous temperaments. My name is

John, but when I wrote my Gospel I called myself in humility "the Beloved Disciple" to hide my identity. "Boanerges" means "Sons of Thunder". On the day that I met Him, I began my transformation to a gentle and spiritual son of Mary, His Mother.

The angel Gabriel told Mary to call her son "Jesus," which means "God saves," because He would save people from their sins. That's what He did for me.

I met Him one day at the River Jordan. I asked Him where He lived and He said, "Come and see." So I followed Him and I never turned back. I have no regrets, because He preached the Gospel of Love. He had the words of eternal life. Where else could I go but to Him? He was the only man who ever claimed to be God and clearly proved it.

He proved that He was God by doing only what God could do: healing the sick, the blind, the deaf and the lame; calming the sea and walking on water; delivering people from demonic possession; bringing people to reformation and conversion from within; raising people from death; promising eternal life through His forgiveness of sins; and truly suffering, dying and rising from the dead as He had prophesied. I saw all of this with my own eyes. I talked and ate with Him after He rose from the dead. I tell you all of this so that you too may respond to His Gospel of Love and enter the Kingdom of God.

The Gospel of Love is the good news of the Kingdom of God. I heard this good news and entered the Kingdom of God, the realm of the sovereign God who is love and in which we live in His love for us and our love for one another.

A kingdom of the world consists of a geographic area and its inhabitants, the subjects of the king's authority. A worldly king has all legislative, judicial and executive authority to rule his subjects. He punishes for disobedience.

The Kingdom of God is not of this world. It is a supernatural kingdom. All men and women live in the natural world of humanity, but all are called to live in the supernatural Kingdom of God, under the King of Love, with love for Him and for one another for our eternal happiness. If we love Him, we will follow His commandments to love God and one another as He loved us and to lay down our lives for one another in this Kingdom of love, peace, joy and happiness that only God, our true sovereign, can give to us.

God the Father is love and He loved us so much that He sent His Son, Jesus Christ, as the Savior of the world, and as our King of Love, so that we might receive His merciful gift of eternal life through His forgiveness of our sins. If we do not repent and seek His forgiveness, He justly punishes us and sends us to the fire of eternal damnation, chosen by our own free will.

We enter the Kingdom of God through baptism, whereby we renounce Satan and all his works and consecrate ourselves to God. All in the Kingdom of God recognize Jesus as the King of Love and the King of All Nations who reigns over them and over all nations. He lives in us and reigns over our minds and hearts.

And so I was baptized, entered the Kingdom of God and was transformed from a Son of Thunder to a Son of Mary. This is my story. I tell it so that you may come to believe that Jesus Christ is Lord and Savior, the Messiah, the Son of Man and Son of God, the King of Love and the King of All Nations, and that, through that belief, you may have eternal life in Him.

1. The Teacher's Chair

"My little children, love one another!" I said this as I sat in the Teacher's Chair in a public square in Ephesus in Asia Minor. It was in the year 97 and I was 91 years old. My disciples had carried me there, as I was no longer able to walk very far. Some of them shaded my head from the sun as I squinted into the throng gathering around me. My chair would always attract a good crowd in the mid-morning. It gave the townspeople and travelers a break from their morning routines.

I began to preach to the small crowd. "Beloved, let us love one another; for love is of God, and he who loves is born of God and knows God. He who does not love does not know God; for God is love. In this the love of God was made manifest among us, that God sent His only Son into the world, so that we might live through Him. In this is love, not that we loved God, but that He loved us and sent His Son to be the expiation for our sins. Beloved, if God so loved us, we also ought to love one another. No man has ever seen God; if we love one another, God lives in us and His love is perfected in us."

"By this we know that we live in Him and He in us," I explained, "This is His divine indwelling because He has given us of His own Spirit. And we have seen and testify that the Father

1

has sent His Son as the Savior of the world. Whoever confesses that Jesus is the Son of God, God lives in him, and he in God. So we know and believe the love God has for us. God is love, and he who lives in love, lives in God, and God lives in him. In this is love perfected with us, that we may have confidence for the Day of Judgment, because as He is, so are we in this world."

I counseled them, "There is no fear in love, but perfect love casts out fear. For fear has to do with punishment, and he who fears is not perfected in love. We love, because He first loved us."

I told them, "If anyone says, 'I love God,' and hates his brother, he is a liar; for he who does not love his brother whom he has seen, cannot love God whom he has not seen. And this commandment we have from Him, that he who loves God should love his brother also."

I noticed a young Greek man approaching me from the edge of the crowd and I quickly concluded as I had begun, "So, my little children love one another."

He asked me, "Why do you keep repeating, 'My little children love one another?' "

"Because it is the Lord's commandment and if you keep it, that alone suffices. That is what the Master taught us."

"And who is the Master?" he asked.

"Jesus Christ, the Son of the living God."

"We Greeks have many gods, but none of them are alive. Who is the living God?"

"The one and only real true God who became a man just like you and me," I answered, "to teach us how to live and how to love. He didn't come to condemn the world but to save it. He gave His life in self-surrender for love of us. He loves you just as you are. For God so loved the world that He gave His only Son, that whoever believes in Him should not perish but have eternal life."

"And what is 'eternal life?' "

"Eternal life is to know the one true God and Jesus Christ, His Son. You can have eternal life by becoming like Him, by following His way."

"There are many ways," he rejoined.

"Yes, there are many ways, young man, but there is only one Way with a capital 'W' and His name is Jesus Christ. He said, 'I am the Way, the Truth and the Life.' "

"But what is truth?"

I thought that the young man had a lot of questions, but this showed an openness that indicated that he was really seeking the truth. So I continued to patiently answer him. "Truth is that which really is and there is only one real Truth and His name is Jesus."

"There's *your* truth and there's *my* truth and they don't have to be the same. We Greeks use our heads. We reason. Reason teaches us everything."

"Yes, but you all use your so-called reason to reach different results. For example, for some of you, infanticide is acceptable. For others, it is evil. You supposedly use the same reason to say that infanticide is good or that infanticide is evil. But you can't have it both ways."

"Well, it differs for each person who can reach different results using the same process."

"That's because the process is defective. It isn't enlightened by divine truth. With divine truth you reach *the same* result using the same process because you have the guide of divine truth to educate and inform your conscience so you can tell right from wrong."

"Tell me more," he said as he began to open his heart to my words.

"What is your name?" I asked.

"Odysseus," he replied.

"That's an appropriate name," I said. "He was a Greek king who journeyed for ten years and you seem to be on a journey

3

yourself. Let what you have heard from the beginning live in you."

"But I've never heard it from the beginning."

"Yes you have, but you haven't listened. God instills in us the need to search and find the meaning of man and the meaning of life. We are rational beings and can use our reason alone, as you Greeks do, to come to the knowledge of God from looking at His creation. Our hearts were made for Him alone and they are ever restless until they rest in Him. He is our end — eternal life in Him. Jesus, true God and true man is the Way, the Truth and the Life. God created us to know, love and serve Him in this world and to be happy with Him in the next world of heaven. He has destined us for Himself."

"Jesus reveals the meaning of man to himself. We are dignified because we are created in the image of God, for Himself. God created man in His image with an immortal soul with an intellect, will and emotions to know the truth, to do good and to appreciate beauty. He instilled the natural moral law into our intellect so that through reason we can come to know Him and His moral law. He confirmed this by giving Moses the Ten Commandments."

"Man is the crown of God's creation," I continued, "and man has God's authority to subdue Earth with dominion over all minerals, plants and animals for our use and not abuse. The psalmist said, 'Heaven is the heaven of the Lord, but the earth He has given to the children of men.' " (Psalm 115).

"God gave us freedom to love Him, not forcing us but subjecting us to a law to obey Him. The first parents of the human family, Adam and Eve, did not obey Him. They freely chose to defy God's will. As a result, all of human nature was distorted and became prone to sin. They lost the grace of God and His preternatural gifts of immortality and integrity, which is the absence of passion. They passed on their fallen human nature to all of us with our suffering and death, darkened intellects, weakened wills and subjection to our passions. But God promised them and us a redeemer who would redeem our human nature and grant us grace to do His will to do good and to receive eternal life in happiness with Him. This redeemer is

4

Jesus Christ and He gave us the Gospel or Good News of Love."

"I never realized…," Odysseus said with an open mouth.

"Meditate on what I've said and come back tomorrow morning and we'll begin again. The sun is getting too high for me today."

"I will sir, and thank you for your words of light."

This ended another one of my teaching mornings. As my disciples carried me home I thought, *So many still do not know the Master! I remember when I was a young man just like Odysseus. I too searched for the truth on my journey. I was a faithful Jew but I wasn't satisfied with a religion that had become all rules and laws. The Pharisees, our teachers, had taken the heart out of our religion. They taught all of the laws except the most important one of all – the Master's new law of love – "Love one another as I have loved you," He said, "for no greater love has a man for his friends than to lay down his life for them."*

I remembered that my own search for truth started when I was a young man and I responded to the thunderous voice of John the Baptist who said, "Repent!" I resolved not to sin and to follow him. That was the beginning of my transformation and my eventual following of the Master. As an old man I realized that there were so many who did not know the Master. That's why I began these teachings, so that after I died, others would know Jesus as I knew Him when I lived. I called this *The Gospel of Love*. The story began in my youth, in the year 19, when I was just 13 years old.

2. My Youth

"John, be careful! You're tangling the net." It was too late to heed my father's thunderous voice as it came to our boat over the water of the Sea of Galilee. He stood with his fishing team on the south shore of Bethsaida, holding his team's end of the net.

The dragnet was operated by two teams. Dad's team held one end of the net on the shore while our team took the rest of it out in the boat. My job was to help to let the net out gently and carefully as the rest of our team rowed the boat to stretch the net and circle it back to the shore in the hopes of trapping some fish in it.

The net was like a wall. It was 300 feet long and 12 feet high, with ropes attached to each end. Stone weights on its bottom held the net down in the water and corks on top kept it floating. The net was difficult to set without tangling it.

I was only 13 years old. This was my first time setting the dragnet and I wasn't doing it to Dad's satisfaction, or to mine. It was winter and the cool water drove the schools of fish in towards shore which gave us a better chance to catch them in the net. The fish were called musht, meaning "comb", because of the comb-like appearance of their spiny dorsal fins. They weighed up to two pounds and made excellent table fare. These fish provided my father, Zebedee, a living with the help of my older brother James and now me.

I was sitting in the stern trying to help some of the men to set the net. James and the rest of our team manned the oars. "John," he said, more gently than my father, "don't let out any more of the net. Let's get this mess untangled and give it another try. Don't mind Dad. You know he's a perfectionist and nobody can do as good a job as he can. Now take your time and do it right. We're going to row away from the shore and then turn around in a semicircle and row back towards shore. You help to gently let out the net. Let it out so that the corks float on the top of the water and the weights bring the bottom of the net down so that it sets right and traps the fish that we hope are still here—if we haven't scared them away with all of our commotion."

This time I did it right and James and our team rowed the boat back to shore, about 100 feet away from my father. We jumped out of the boat and grabbed our end of the net and pulled it as we walked towards my father's team, which stood waiting holding their end of the net. Our teams met and successfully corralled a school of fish. My father's stern face broadened into a smile as he saw the fish flopping at his feet.

Our dragnet was made of mesh squares which were sized so that the fish could swim their heads into them, but not their whole bodies, thereby trapping them in the mesh. After we hauled the whole net onto the shore, we had to pick each fish out of the net, one at a time. Then we had to sort them into piles of clean and unclean fish. Under Jewish law, fish without scales and fins were regarded as unclean and had to be discarded.

As I sorted the fish, I felt a sense of satisfaction at having successfully completed such a good catch on my very first day with Dad. I felt happy living near the shores of the beautiful Sea of Galilee. I thought how wonderful it was to be a Jew, a part of the Chosen People of God.

I remembered what Moses told my ancestors, "You are a people sacred to the Lord, your God; He has chosen you from all the nations on the face of the earth to be a people peculiarly His own." (Deuteronomy 7:6).

God had been very good to us. He gave us the Covenant through Abraham, the Law through Moses, the Temple through King Solomon, and His teachings and warnings through the Prophets. I learned all of this at our local synagogue, since we had only made annual pilgrimages to the Temple in far-off Jerusalem. Sacrifices were only made in the Temple, but Scripture was taught in all of the synagogues.

As I picked out the fish, I reflected on how God had chosen us through the Patriarch Abraham, our Father in faith, gave him the Covenant and promised him that He would be our God and that we would be His people.

My father taught me that He also promised Abraham that this land would be the Promised Land and that his descendants would be as numerous as the sands of the seashore upon which I stood. God fulfilled His promises to Abraham who, at a seemingly impossible old age, had a son, Isaac, who had a son, Jacob, who had 12 sons, who were the Patriarchs of the 12 tribes of Israel.

I continued to reflect on how God was faithful to His promise to be our God. He freed the descendants of the Patriarchs who were enslaved in Egypt for over 200 years. He guided them, through Moses, in their Exodus from Egypt across the Red Sea where He miraculously parted the waters. He gave them the Law of the Ten Commandments on Mount Sinai and led them throughout their 40 years in the desert to the Promised Land, which they entered under Joshua. God gave us judges and then kings to rule us. Our greatest king was King David. His son, King Solomon, built the Temple.

Our Scriptures had prophesied that the scepter, a symbol of a king's rule and authority, would not depart from the tribe of Judah, one of Jacob's sons, until the time of the Messiah King. (See Genesis 49:10). However, our rulers from the tribe of Judah, in the line of King David, had come to an end with the rulers of Rome's governors and the Herod kings. They were not from the tribe of Judah and not in the line of King David. Because the scepter had departed from the tribe of Judah, our people were expecting the coming of the Messiah King and the fulfillment of the prophecy.

9

However, it was the year 19 and we were still waiting for the expected Messiah, the Christ, the anointed of God, our great King. Rome had changed the name of the region of Judah to Judea and it was now ruled by Valerius Gratus, a Roman governor, while my region of Gaulanitis, northeast of Galilee, was ruled by King Herod Philip, son of King Herod the Great. I wondered when the Messiah would come. I longed for him to come in my lifetime and fulfill all of the messianic prophecies. We expected a great King who would conquer our enemies and gather Israel as a light to all nations.

I had memorized most of the prophecies. He will be a great King in the line of King David, the government will be upon his shoulders and he will be named "Mighty God" and "Prince of Peace." (Isaiah 9:6). God promised us that there will be no end to the greatness of his government and peace. He will reign on David's throne and over his kingdom, establishing and upholding it with justice and righteousness from that time on and forever. (Isaiah 9:7).

He will "raise a signal to all nations and gather the outcasts of Israel." (Isaiah 11:12). God promised him that he will "make all nations his heritage and the ends of the earth his possession. He will be a powerful King who will break them with a rod of iron and dash them in pieces like a potter's vessel." (Psalm 2:8-9). God will make his enemies his footstool, will extend the scepter of his sovereign might from Zion, the mount in Jerusalem, and he will rule over his enemies. (Psalm 110:1-2).

How I prayed that day would soon come and that the Messiah King would liberate us from our Roman oppression and rule over our enemies.

I remembered the book of Sirach and the prayer that the Messiah would come as the King of All Nations to put all of the nations in dread of him, to gather the scattered tribes of Jacob, to fill the Temple with His glory and to fulfill the prophecies so that all the nations would know that the God of all nations and the universe is the eternal God:

Come to our aid, O God of the universe, look upon us, show us the light of your mercies, and put all the nations in dread of you!

Thus they will know, as we know, that there is no God but you, O Lord.

Give new signs and work new wonders.

Gather all the tribes of Jacob, that they may inherit the land as of old.

Show mercy to the people called by your name; Israel, whom you named your firstborn.

Take pity on your holy city, Jerusalem, your dwelling place.

Fill Zion with your majesty, your Temple with your glory.

Give evidence of your deeds of old; fulfill the prophecies spoken in your name.

Reward those who have hoped in you, and let your prophets be proved true.

Hear the prayer of your servants, for you are ever gracious to your people; and lead us in the way of justice.

Thus it will be known to the very ends of the earth that you are the eternal God. (Sirach 36:1, 4-5A, 10-17).

After we picked these fish out of the net, we gathered the clean ones into baskets and brought them to the cleaning table. There we gutted, split and salted them and laid them in the sun on the drying tables to be sold in the local market.

We usually brought our fish fresh and wet to Magdala for gutting, cleaning, salting and drying. Then the fish would be packed in baskets for export and we would take them on wagons pulled by mules to shops in Jerusalem, or to a seaport where they would be loaded on ships and taken to Rome. Dried fish from

Galilee was considered a delicacy among the Roman aristocracy.

Because of my frequent trips to Jerusalem to sell our fish, I got to know some priests, including the High Priest, Caiaphas. I also learned how the Pharisees, Scribes and Sadducees strictly interpreted the Jewish Law for the people in an attempt to regulate their lives in ways that they themselves did not follow.

As we were bantering with one another, while cleaning this catch of fish for our local market, we were interrupted by someone calling out to my father.

"Hey Zebedee! It looks like you had a good day."

"It would have been better if you were here to help us. I had to use my boy with the nets for the first time and he slowed us down."

"He'll learn soon enough Zeb. Be patient with him."

I felt embarrassed as my father's partner stood up for me. His name was Simon. His brother, Andrew, was a friend of mine who was quiet and reserved, unlike his louder brother. Neither one of us looked forward to lives as fishermen. We thought that there must be more to life than just working for money, like many of the fishermen, or for power, like many of our religious leaders, or for glory, like our King Herod Philip.

My father, brother and I were fishermen. The city people of Jerusalem looked down on us as country simpletons. Unlike the fine and smooth hands of many of the fancy city people, our hands were rough and scarred from our fishing nets, the spines of the fish and our hard labor.

We lived from day to day, dependent on our fishing, without any financial security. We looked for a leader who would bring us economic prosperity and independence. We all hoped that the Messiah King would come and restore the Kingdom of Israel to us and expel the Romans, who had conquered us under Pompey in 63 BC.

Some of the people in Jerusalem were landed gentry. They were wealthy and lived in beautiful houses with heated baths, tiled floors and beautiful mosaics decorating their walls. The High

12

Priest lived there, along with many of the Sanhedrin, the 71-member religious Council of elders and wise men. They were the ultimate religious authority and assured public order. The priests officiated at the sacred functions, primarily sacrifices, in the Temple.

Although Jerusalem was controlled by the Romans, we lived under our own religious Law. Life was good for the Jews in Jerusalem, so they tended to support the Roman Empire. They did not want their lives upset by appearances of any messianic figures.

The High Priest had the most power among the Jewish aristocracy and acted as the religious and political leader. He led the Sanhedrin and commanded a force of armed guards. However, the Romans did not leave all matters in the hands of the Jewish leadership. The Romans appointed a governor who was called a "procurator." He maintained a cohort (brigade) of Roman legionnaires on duty at all times to keep a constant vigil over the entire city and, in particular, the Temple.

In accordance to our Law, my family made annual pilgrimages to the Temple in Jerusalem to celebrate the Feasts of Passover, Tabernacles and Pentecost. It was about a four-day journey south and west from Bethsaida. Jerusalem was a crowded city of approximately 80,000 inhabitants, crammed into about 450 acres.

The Temple, its courts, the Roman Antonia fortress that overlooked the Temple, and a variety of other religious and government structures occupied a large portion of the city. This left little space for the common people. Houses were built at most only two or three stories high. Entire extended families lived in one or two rooms. The streets were crowded with donkeys, chickens, dogs and other animals.

I preferred the simplicity of my hometown in Bethsaida, a 22-acre fishing harbor on the north end of the beautiful Sea of Galilee. Bethsaida means "house of the fishermen." Most of the fishing families lived in relatively simple homes consisting of one or two rooms with a small yard in front. That was where my friend Andrew and I waited for the Messiah King who, we thought, would restore Israel to a glorious kingdom like King

David's and overthrow the tyrannical Roman rule.

I used to read and discuss the Prophets and what they told us about this glorious king and his kingdom. I yearned to make myself a better person to prepare myself for this kingdom but I didn't know how — until ten years later when I heard another thunderous voice, like my father's voice, over the waters.

John the Baptist

"Repent, for the Kingdom of God is at hand! Bear fruit that befits repentance! Every tree that does not bear good fruit is cut down and thrown into the fire."

It was in the year 29 and I was 23 years old. It was in the fifteenth year of the reign of Tiberius Caesar, when Pontius Pilate was governor of Judea. I stood with my friend Andrew on the bank of the River Jordan, near Jericho, listening to a man standing in the water. He looked to be in his 30's. The river ran about 156 miles from its origins in the north near Mount Hermon all the way south through the Sea of Galilee to its end in the Dead Sea, the salt region of what once was Sodom and Gomorrah, before the Lord destroyed its inhabitants for their sins.

We had walked for three days all the way south from Bethsaida through Galilee to a bend in the river near Jericho to listen to this man whose preaching was drawing the people to himself. Throngs of people were going out to him from Jerusalem, from all Judea and from the whole region around the Jordan. He looked very strange. His clothing was made of camel's hair and he had a leather belt around his waist. He held a long staff in his left hand as he hammered his fisted right hand into the air and his voice boomed over the water. It reminded me of Dad's voice. He thundered for us to change our ways and act accordingly or suffer from unquenchable fire.

I turned in awe to the man next to me and asked him, "What's he talking about?"

"His name is John the Baptist and he's preaching repentance and knowledge of salvation through the forgiveness of sins. He came out of the desert about a year ago and started preaching. I was one of his first disciples."

I knew that only God could forgive sins so I asked more questions.

"What was he doing in the desert?"

"He told us that he lived there eating locusts and wild honey and that he prayed and fasted to prepare himself to fulfill his father's prophecy. When he was a baby, his father prophesied that his son would be the Prophet of the Most High. He was a miracle baby. His father's name was Zechariah and his mother's Elizabeth. They had no children and were beyond childbearing age when God answered their prayers for a child in a miraculous way."

"How was that?" I asked.

He replied, "God sent the angel Gabriel to his father who was a priest. Gabriel told Zechariah while he was at the altar of the Temple that God had heard his prayer and that Elizabeth would bear a son whom he should name John."

"Zechariah doubted the angel and, in punishment, he was struck speechless by God until John was born. Then, on the day of his circumcision, Zechariah wrote on a tablet, 'His name is John.' "

"Immediately, Zechariah was able to speak again and he prophesied about his new son, 'You will be called Prophet of the Most High, for you will go before the Lord to prepare His ways, to give His people knowledge of salvation through the forgiveness of their sins.' "

"And that's what he's doing now—preparing the way of the Lord and helping us through his baptism to acknowledge our sins and to start a new life. The whole countryside and most of Jerusalem are coming out here to receive his baptism."

"What's baptism?" I asked.

"Baptism is the pouring of water on us as a symbol of our turning away from sin. By his baptism we repent, receive cleansing and turn to the Lord to live His ways."

15

"But," I asked, "only God can forgive sins. Who is this 'Lord' that John's father prophesied he'd go before and who would be the one who will forgive our sins?"

"We don't know yet. John hasn't pointed Him out. He just says that he himself is *not* the one."

"He says that he comes to testify, to bear witness to the light, that all might believe through him. He himself is not the light, but comes to bear witness to the light. He says that the true light that enlightens every man is coming into the world. He is in the world, and the world was made through Him, but the world doesn't know Him."

Suddenly, another man cried out to John, "What are we to do?"

John answered him, "Whoever has food or two cloaks should share with those who have none."

Even tax collectors had come to be baptized and they also asked him, "Teacher, what should we do?"

He answered them, "Stop collecting more than what is prescribed."

He said this because many of them collected more than the actual tax and kept the difference for themselves.

Soldiers then joined in and asked him, "And what is it that we should do?"

He told them, "Do not practice extortion, do not falsely accuse anyone, and be satisfied with your wages."

He said this because the soldiers were underpaid and so they made false accusations to extort more money from the citizenry.

I noticed that his exhortations were to perform charitable acts and to practice justice.

The people seemed to be filled with expectation and to be asking in their hearts whether John might be the Messiah. John answered them all, saying, "I am baptizing you with water for repentance, but a mightier one than I is coming."

Then John saw many Pharisees and Sadducees coming toward him. The Sadducees were aristocratic priests and landowners

16

who came from wealthy families, but observed only the Torah, the written Law. They did not keep any of the oral laws or believe in the oral tradition. They accepted the Roman occupation because the Torah did not forbid it and they cooperated with the Roman soldiers. They denied the existence of angels and the resurrection of the dead, in both of which the Pharisees believed.

The Pharisees thought that they were the only true Jews and children of our Patriarch Abraham. They taught that we should practice the Mosaic Law and regulations strictly in daily life and they interpreted them strictly. But they were hypocrites since they didn't follow their own teachings, but expected everyone else to do so. They laid burdens on others that they themselves refused to carry. They were contemptuous of the common people and had no compassion or love for them. They acted from their heads and not from their hearts. Both the Pharisees and the Sadducees were unrepentant.

John yelled out to them, "You brood of vipers! Who warned you to flee from the coming wrath? Produce good fruits as evidence of your repentance; and do not begin to say to yourselves, 'We have Abraham as our father,' for I tell you, God can raise up children to Abraham from these stones. Even now the ax lies at the root of the trees. Therefore, every tree that does not produce good fruit will be cut down and thrown into the fire. His winnowing fan is in His hand to clear His threshing floor and to gather the wheat into His barn, but the chaff He will burn with unquenchable fire."

I saw in my mind's eye the image of the threshing floor where the good wheat is separated from the bad chaff which is burned. I saw this threshing as a metaphor for God's judgment that would separate the good from the bad, who would burn "with unquenchable fire." Exhorting them in many other ways, John the Baptist preached to the people.

Andrew and I were moved by John's preaching and his call to perform charitable acts. We wanted to prepare ourselves for the "mightier one" whom John said was coming. So, we accepted John's invitation to come into the river and receive his baptism.

However, I had an interior struggle. On the one hand, I didn't want to look like a fool by walking into the river and having people laugh at me, like my father did. On the other hand, I wanted to repent, become a better person and turn away from my sins of selfishness, but I was holding myself back.

I struggled to overcome my pride, made a supreme effort and walked down the riverbank. Andrew and I stepped into the water up to our waists. I humbled myself and gave up any fear of how I would appear to others. I no longer held myself back for fear of losing human respect.

John came towards us, dipped his ladle into the water and poured it over our heads. I felt clean inside and thought,

Maybe this is the start of something new – something meaningful – the fulfillment of the prophecies that speak of a cleansing by water before the coming of the Kingdom of God in the messianic times. John speaks with such authority and conviction! And with a severity of selflessness and charity, so opposed to the self-righteousness of the Pharisees and all of their rules, which forbid even good deeds on the Sabbath.

I wonder if he's the Messiah – the Anointed One. He could be him. Who else can speak like this? But he said that he's not the light. He's coming only to bear witness to the light to help us believe in the true light. But who is the true light who will enlighten everyone and give us grace and truth? Who is this unknown man? Who is the "mightier one" who is to come? Well, I'm going to follow John and find out – so long as Dad will let me stay away from the fishing nets.

That was the day that Andrew and I became disciples of John the Baptist and followed him whenever we could get away from our nets.

The Baptism of Jesus

John continued baptizing in the area around the Jordan River near Jericho, where Joshua had led the Israelites across the river into the Promised Land that God had promised to Moses.

Joshua defeated the city of Jericho by humbly following God's directions to walk around the city's walls seven times while giving the victory shout. The city's walls fell on the seventh time around and the Promised Land was delivered to them. As Joshua had delivered the Promised Land, I wondered if John the Baptist could deliver to us the Promised One, since he had said, "The true light that enlightens every man is coming into the world."

One day, a tall, handsome, muscular man approached the riverbank. He looked to be in His 30's, around John's age, wore a seamless garment, and His chestnut brown hair flowed over the top of it. His face was slightly bearded and His penetrating eyes were full of kindness and compassion. His movements were slow and rhythmical. He was totally at peace. The very sight of Him moved me to tears.

Someone said that the man's name was Jesus. The name means "God saves". John seemed shocked that He would present Himself for baptism. He said, "I need to be baptized by you, yet you come to me!"

Jesus said, "Let it be so for now; for through us all righteousness will be fulfilled."

Immediately I thought, *All righteousness will be fulfilled only through the Messiah, the true righteous one. Is Jesus the Messiah? But don't the Scriptures say that before the Messiah comes, Elijah will come? Elijah hasn't come, but John acts and looks like I always imagined Elijah – a lonely Prophet speaking the truth and dressed in camel's hair. How could the Scriptures be fulfilled?*

Jesus then humbly walked down into the river and John baptized Him. When He came out of the water, dripping wet and praying. We were amazed to see the heavens open up and the Spirit of God descend like a dove and rest upon Him.

Then a voice like sweet thunder came from the heavens and said, "This is my beloved Son, with whom I am well pleased."

The scene reminded me of Isaiah's prophecy of the Messiah, "On him the spirit of the Lord rests, a spirit of wisdom and insight, a spirit of counsel and power, a spirit of knowledge and of the fear of the Lord." (Isaiah 11:2).

I thought, *Was that the voice of God, over the head of Jesus, who said that He was His beloved Son? But what does this mean? How can God have a Son? He looks and acts like a man. Can God have a Son? The*

19

Nations worship many gods but we Jews believe in only one God. How can one God have a Son? And if He is God's Son, why did He get baptized?

Is He God who became a man? Both a Son of God and a Son of Man, as prophesied by Daniel? Is He a God-Man? But whoever heard of such a thing? How could this be? So many questions raced through my mind!

Later, we were with John when he was baptizing east of the Jordan in one of its tributaries near Bethany.

As John was baptizing there, a group of priests from Jerusalem appeared. John was also a priest since he was the son of a priest. So they were sent to investigate him. John had previously enraged King Herod Antipas who ruled over Galilee. John had publicly confronted him and told him that it was wrong for him to live in adultery with his brother's wife, Herodias.

Herod probably pressured the priests to question John. But they really didn't want to know his answers. They were just trying to trap him into saying something against their teachings so that they could silence him and prevent him from claiming to be the Messiah, Elijah or the Prophet.

One of the priests asked John the question that I had pondered myself, "Are you the Messiah?"

"No," he answered, "I am not the Messiah."

Then they asked him, "What then? Are you Elijah?"

He said, "I am not."

"Are you the Prophet?"

And he answered, "No."

The Jewish leaders expected the comings of the Prophet, Elijah and the Messiah. God had prophesied to Moses that the Prophet would come. Elijah was taken up in a fiery chariot and was prophesied by Malachi to return to Earth to prepare the way for the Messiah. The Messiah was the expected liberator, the Anointed One, the Christ. John denied that he was any of these. Perhaps he was Elijah in spirit, but not in person.

20

Then they said to him, "Well, who are you then? Let us have an answer for those who sent us. What do you say about yourself?" They needed to give an answer to the leaders to their question as to who was this unknown person starting this new ritual of baptism.

John knew who he was because his father Zechariah had prophesied that John's mission was to be the "Prophet of the Most High" who would "go before the Lord to prepare His ways, to give His people knowledge of salvation through the forgiveness of their sins." But John merely told them, "I am a voice of one crying in the desert, 'Make straight the way of the Lord,' as the Prophet Isaiah said."

"Then why are you baptizing, if you are neither the Messiah, nor Elijah, nor the Prophet?" they asked.

John answered in humility, "I baptize with water, but one mightier than I is coming. He stands among you but you don't know Him. I am not worthy to untie the thongs of His sandals. He will baptize you with the Holy Spirit and fire."

They left for Jerusalem with no understanding of John's true mission or that of his successor, who would baptize with the Holy Spirit and fire. Their hearts were not open to receive an understanding of their missions. They had much knowledge of the Law and the Prophets, but no understanding, because they lacked faith and love.

When John the Baptist described himself as "the voice of one crying in the desert, 'Make straight the way of the Lord,' " every one of us recognized the passage in Isaiah from which he quoted and the circumstances about which it originally spoke. (See Isaiah 40:3).

Isaiah spoke of the restoration of Israel after the Babylonian Captivity of the Israelites and their call to be a witness to the nations. They were conquered and made captive in Babylon from 597 BC to 539 BC. Because of this, John expected us to recognize how he was applying that imagery to our present circumstances when, after being downtrodden for years, we were now to be finally granted the salvation promised by Isaiah.

However, it seemed that our salvation would not merely be like the political return of the Babylonian captives to Jerusalem, nor the mere return of Israel to its own political rule, like that of King David. Rather, John's implication was that all of these past events were foreshadowings of our ultimate liberation from sin and our restoration to holiness by the Messiah.

I thought, *He uses the words of the Prophet Isaiah but what is John really talking about? A new King David? Probably not. It seems to be about a King of our hearts. Maybe there will be a new Kingdom of God. Maybe the prophecy of Ezekiel will be fulfilled and we'll be given a new heart and a new spirit. (See Ezekiel 36:26). There will be a new covenant with God, a new relationship with Him by which hearts of flesh will replace our hearts of stone, with a new spirit within us to obey the law of the Lord. . . . Maybe this is the true time of restoration. Maybe a new King will save us from the captivity of sin – how it holds us and we can't seem to free ourselves from it.*

I came to understand that the "way for the Lord" was my open heart and I resolved to make this way straight by reforming my life and by continuing to follow John in the hopes of finding the Christ and being baptized with the promised Holy Spirit and fire.

I truly believed that John was sent to us from God. He came for testimony, to testify to the Messiah, so that all might believe through him. He was not the Messiah, but came to testify to the Messiah. The true Messiah, the Christ, the light which enlightens everyone, was coming into the world and I wanted to come out of my darkness to follow Him, the true light.

The Messiah and the Call of His Followers

On the next day, around 4 p.m., Jesus came. John looked at Him hard as he saw Jesus coming toward him. He cried out to us all, "Behold the Lamb of God, who takes away the sin of the world! This is He of whom I said, 'The one who is coming after me ranks ahead of me because He existed before me.' He is also the one of whom I said, 'One mightier than I is coming. I myself did not know Him; but for this I came baptizing with water, that He might be revealed to Israel.' "

As he spoke, I imagined a lamb as white as Jesus' tunic and, like Him, pure, docile, gentle and innocent. I was very confused, but as his disciple, I trusted John. Then I began to meditate on his statement that Jesus was the Lamb of God.

It reminds me of Isaiah's sacrificial lamb, the symbol of innocence. Isaiah compared the sufferings and death of the Suffering Servant of the Lord with the sacrifice of a lamb. (See Isaiah 53:7-12).

Also, as our Israelite ancestors made their Exodus from the slavery of Egypt, they smeared the blood of lambs on their doors as God had instructed them. This protected their firstborn children from the deaths that were inflicted on the firstborn of the Egyptian children. The angel of death passed over those doors that had on them what came to be known as the blood of the Passover lambs.

That might have been a prefiguring of the true Lamb of God – the Christ. Is Jesus the Christ? Does John mean that He will be an innocent sacrificial lamb? Will He shed His blood like the Passover lambs and protect us with it in some way, like the lambs' blood that protected the Israelites? Is He really the Lamb of God who takes away the sin of the world? Not just Israel, but the whole world, all nations?

But how can He take away the sin of the world? Will He somehow carry our sin on His shoulders as Isaiah prophesied that the Suffering Servant would do and be pierced for our offences and crushed for our sins? (See Isaiah 53:4-5).

John then testified, "I saw the Spirit come down like a dove from the sky and remain upon Him. I myself did not know Him; but He who sent me to baptize with water said to me, 'On whomever you see the Spirit descend and remain, He is the one who will baptize with the Holy Spirit.' And now I have seen and bear witness that He is the Son of God."

Son of God! I thought, *Son of Man and Son of God. This sounds impossible. How could he be both? Most of our Scriptures used the term Son of Man to mean mankind, generally, in contrast to God. But Daniel used the term to refer to a particular man who was seemingly presented before God. Daniel had a vision of "one like the Son of Man who came upon the clouds of heaven and was presented to the Ancient One. He received authority, glory and sovereign power; all peoples, nations and men of every language worshiped him. His dominion is an everlasting*

23

dominion that will not pass away, and his kingdom is one that will never be destroyed." (Daniel 7:13-14).

Perhaps Daniel's Son of Man was a Prophetic vision of the Messiah. But, John says that Jesus is the Son of God. That term was used by our Scriptures to refer to some of our kings, but never literally to God Himself. No one was called both Son of Man and Son of God. Jesus could be a great man and the Messiah, but could He really be a man and God? I need to follow Him to find out. I need to follow the one who John testifies is the Lamb of God and the Son of God.

Andrew and I trusted John and shyly followed Jesus as He walked away. He turned, saw us following Him and kindly said, "What are you looking for?"

His question is one that everyone must examine his conscience to answer. I thought, *Do I want to follow a worldly king who will liberate us from our Roman occupation? Am I looking for pleasure, fame, fortune, power and glory?*

Or, do I want to know the truth about Him and His teachings and humbly submit to them? Do I want to calculate the cost or do I want to become converted in naked faith and pure love? Do I want to leave my father, his fishing business and my first teacher, John the Baptist? Why not? He's the one who has pointed out Jesus as the Son of God.

I think that I honestly want to get to know Jesus and His teachings. His demeanor and personality attract me, it isn't merely curiosity. I don't just want to have a chat with Him. I want to know Him intimately. I want to spend some time in His company with Him as a friend. So I will follow Him.

The next day, Jesus approached John, who again said, "Behold, the Lamb of God!" I heard him say this and began to follow Jesus with Andrew. He turned, saw us following Him as on the day before and said, "What do you seek?"

I asked, "Rabbi" (which means Teacher), "Where are you staying?"

He gently invited us, "Come and see."

He didn't say, "See and come." I had to take the first step and come without seeing so that I could later see. I didn't understand where I was going or what would become of me, but my heart told me it was the right thing to do.

So I took that first step in blind faith and pure love. Somehow I knew that this would be a life-changing decision for me. But I didn't think of the reasons why I should or should not go with Him. I didn't reason it out. I was moved by the sweetness of His speech and His tender invitation. His demeanor was meek, kind and friendly. I was attracted by some mysterious irresistible magnetism that drew me to Him. I totally surrendered to His love and lost myself, without concern for my personal security, in order to find myself in Him. Once I took that first step, there was no turning back.

I wanted Him to answer my questions about the meaning of life: why we were created and where we were going, the meaning of true love of the heart, the meaning of the Messiah and what kind of a king he would be for Israel. I wanted to have an intimate friendship with Him. His answer was not to give me a lecture, but to allow me to experience His person and presence. I hoped that my experience would answer my questions.

Andrew and I followed the Lamb of God. We were following a person, not a cold and legalistic doctrine, not a philosophy or abstract ideology, but a real person. That's why I asked Him, "Where are you staying?" I didn't ask Him what I should do to follow Him or what His opinions were on different points of the Law or what His ideas were. No, I just asked Him where He was staying so that I could get to know Him.

Jesus' answer was in the same manner. "Come and see." He didn't choose to give us a theological discourse or sermon. He didn't tell us what we would see. He simply asked us to come and stay with Him. So we went and shared His humble lodgings.

The following day, the fruits of our experience had already begun to show forth. Andrew opened his heart and experienced within it the love of Jesus for him. He went to his brother Simon and told him, "We have found the Messiah, the Christ, the Anointed One!" Andrew was the first to recognize Jesus as the Messiah and he was so convincing that Simon followed him back to Jesus and me.

Jesus looked at Simon, with His piercing eyes that read his

heart, and said, "So you are Simon, the son of John? You shall be called Peter."

Peter means "rock". Peter was amazed. Jesus knew his name and his father's name and gave him a new name because He saw what Peter could be, something that Peter did not see in himself. He did not see Peter as a fisherman. He saw someone who could be a fisher of men, a leader. His change of name signified a changed relationship with God. It reminded me of when God changed Jacob's name to Israel, who would become the father of the twelve tribes of Israel. Now Peter would become a rock. His life then radically changed. Like Andrew and me, he left his nets and the fish behind.

The next day, Jesus decided to go to Galilee. On the way there, He came upon Philip, who was from Bethsaida, as were Peter, Andrew, my brother James and I. Jesus said to him, "Follow me." Philip did so.

Philip, in turn, looked for and found his friend Nathaniel. He was eager to tell him about his decision to follow Jesus. He told him, "We have found the one that Moses and the Prophets talked about in the Law, Jesus, son of Joseph, from Nazareth."

Moses talked about a particular Prophet that God would later raise up. God told Moses, "I will raise them up a Prophet from among their brothers, like you, and will put my words in his mouth and he shall speak to them all that I shall command him." (Deuteronomy 18:18).

We had all waited for the raising up of this Prophet and now Philip had identified Jesus as the one.

Nathaniel responded with sarcasm, "Can anything good come from Nazareth?" Nathanial was very skeptical because he didn't think it was possible for the Messiah to come from Nazareth. He held the town and its residents in contempt.

Besides, he probably doubted that the Messiah could come from Nazareth when the Prophets said that he would come from Bethlehem.

Rather than argue with his friend, Philip simply invited him to see for himself. As Jesus had said to us, Philip now said to

Nathaniel, "Come and see!" He meant, as Jesus had meant with us, follow first and then you will see. You must follow in faith before you will see the truth. So Nathaniel went to see for himself.

When Jesus saw Nathaniel coming towards Him, He looked into his heart, as He had with Peter, and said, "This man is a true Israelite. There is no duplicity in him."

Nathaniel was stunned and asked, "How do you know me?"

Jesus answered, "Before Philip called you, when you were under the fig tree, I saw you." Now the fig tree was leafy and its shade provided a peaceful place to meditate. Nathaniel had probably been meditating upon the coming King of Israel.

Nathaniel's jaw dropped in surprise as if Jesus had read the thoughts of his innermost heart. He said, "Teacher, you are the Son of God! You are the King of Israel!"

Instantly, he had relinquished his doubt and believed. He enthusiastically surrendered and opened himself to the person of Jesus. He now publicly recognized Jesus as Son of God and King of Israel. I thought, *This is a confirmation of the revelation at the baptism of Jesus that He is the Son of God. If He's the King of Israel, then He may be the Messiah because the prophecy says that the scepter will never depart from the tribe of Judah, fourth son of Jacob, until the Messiah, the expectation of all nations, comes. (See Genesis 49:10) Now is the time that the scepter has departed from Judah, because the Romans rule over us and now is the time of the expectation of the Messiah.*

Jesus said to Nathaniel, "So, you believe just because I told you that I saw you under the fig tree? You shall see greater things than that! I solemnly assure you, that you will see heaven opened, and the angels of God ascending and descending upon the Son of Man."

I thought, *There it is again! – Son of God, according to Nathaniel, and Son of Man, according to Jesus. Could He be both a man and God? If not, how could He have seen Nathaniel from afar beneath the fig tree, beyond His natural eyesight?*

Nathaniel was also probably meditating on our Patriarch Jacob's dream where he saw the angels ascending and descending on the ladder from heaven to Earth at Bethel. (See Genesis 28:12). That's probably why Jesus assured him that he will see the angels of God ascending and descending upon Himself. Could Jesus Himself be the ladder that unites heaven and Earth as the Son of God and the Son of Man? By His opening of heaven, will He open for us its mysteries? Will heaven be open and accessible to us?

Jesus called Himself the Son of Man, but He can't mean that He is just an ordinary man, as our Scriptures usually meant by that term. He must mean a special Son of Man, like the one prophesied by Daniel, who we understand to be the Messiah. But if He comes straight out and says, "I am the Messiah" or "I am the Son of God," He would probably be crowned by His followers but killed by His enemies. So Jesus is probably being subtle in referring to Himself as the "Son of Man" to keep safe, but to emphasize that He's no ordinary man. He's speaking for those who have ears to hear what He means. I think that I should understand that He is saying, "I'm the man for whom you've been watching and waiting. I'm the one! Don't look for anyone else. Listen to me."

When Nathaniel called Jesus the "Son of God" and the "King of Israel," he may have meant that He was literally both God and the Messiah, God and man. But how could a man be God and transcend and pre-exist creation, the world and humanity?

Now, with Nathaniel included, there were six of us followers of Jesus: Andrew; his brother Simon, whose name Jesus changed to Peter; Philip; Nathaniel; my brother James and me. Five of us were from Bethsaida. The pattern of discipleship seemed to be that the testimony of one witness to Jesus was transmitted from him to another who, in turn, transmitted it to the next. It began with John the Baptist, then to Andrew and finally to Nathaniel.

Eventually, there would be six more of us for a total of 12 followers: Thomas; Matthew, a tax collector; James, the son of Alphaeus; Thaddeus; Simon the Cananean and Judas Iscariot.

Matthew later explained to me how he was called directly by Jesus Himself, without having any witness point Jesus out to him. He told me that he was sitting at his tax table in the street one day collecting taxes. He said that he was an honest tax collector and never collected more than was due to Rome, plus his own commission. He did not gouge the people, like so many other tax collectors, and take more than his due. While he was sitting there, a Pharisee, whom he had seen before in the Temple, came up to him and loudly excoriated him before the crowd of people. The Pharisee said that Matthew was a sinner and that everyone should avoid him, have nothing to do with him and treat him like a leper.

Just then, Jesus stepped out from the crowd and stood before Matthew and the Pharisee. Matthew said that Jesus began to tell a story. Jesus said, "Two men were in the Temple praying, one was a Pharisee and the other one was a tax collector. The Pharisee prayed, 'O God, I thank you that I am not like the rest of humanity — greedy, dishonest, adulterous — or even like this tax collector over there. I fast twice a week and I pay tithes on my whole income.' "

Jesus went on, "While the Pharisee was praying like that, the tax collector stood off at a distance and would not even raise his eyes to heaven. He simply stood there, beating his breast and praying, 'O God, be merciful to me a sinner.' And he kept repeating this prayer. Which one of them, do you think, was justified in the eyes of God? I tell you, the tax collector went home justified, but not the Pharisee. For everyone who exalts himself, like the Pharisee, will be humbled but the one who humbles himself, like the tax collector, will be exalted."

Then Matthew said that Jesus looked at the Pharisee in Matthew's presence and said, "You judge by appearances and think that this man is unjust, like many of the other tax collectors. But God looks for goodness in the heart. He searches all hearts and examines secret motives. He gives all people their due rewards, according to what their actions deserve."

Then Jesus turned to Matthew, looked at him directly in the eyes and said, "Matthew, come and follow me." Matthew then got up, abandoned his table, followed Jesus and joined us as one of His disciples. He told me that he, himself, and the Pharisee were the very same people who prayed in the Temple just like Jesus had told it in the story. Jesus must have seen Matthew at prayer in the Temple, just as He had seen Nathaniel at prayer beneath the fig tree. I marveled at Jesus' gift of clairvoyance.

John the Baptist was a great Prophet who was sent by God to

prepare the way for Jesus, by pointing Him out to the people and declaring that He was the Lamb of God so that they would follow Him. And now we twelve followed Him.

The Temptation in the Desert

After we had followed Jesus for a few days, He told us about His temptation in the desert. After His baptism, the Spirit had led Him into the desert near the city of Jericho. It was a barren wasteland of ravines, cliffs and mountains about a mile directly west of the city. He said that He went up into the desert like John the Baptist had done. He said that He went to pray and fast for 40 days in order to defeat Satan.

So, Peter asked Jesus, "What do you mean 'defeat Satan?' "

Jesus answered, "I mean that he tempted me and I overcame him. He appeared to me as a man and stood before me just like you. He tempted me to break my fast, to be presumptuous and to be an idolater. He offered me food, protection and the power and glory of all of the kingdoms of the world. Each time I overcame him."

"But exactly how?" Peter persisted.

Jesus told us the story. "Satan came and said to me, 'If you are the Son of God, command these stones to become loaves of bread.' "

"But," I answered, "it is written, 'Man shall not live by bread alone, but by every word that proceeds from the mouth of God.' "

"Then Satan took me to the holy city, and set me on the pinnacle of the Temple, and said to me, 'If you are the Son of God, throw yourself down; for it is written, He will give his angels charge of you, and on their hands they will bear you up, lest you strike your foot against a stone.' "

"I said to him again, it is written, 'You shall not tempt the Lord your God.' Again, Satan took me to a very high mountain, and showed me all the kingdoms of the world and the glory of them.

30

He said to me, 'All these I will give you, if you will fall down and worship me.' "

"Then I said to him, 'Be gone, Satan! For it is written, you shall worship the Lord your God and Him only shall you serve.' "

"Then Satan left me, and behold, angels came and ministered to me. I did all of this to show you how to defeat Satan. I will never allow your temptations to be too great. But you have to meet temptations on the threshold of your imagination and not entertain them. Just say 'no' like I did. Say, 'Be gone Satan!' I will always help you to overcome him. If I did it, you can do it too. Soon I'll conquer the last enemy . . . death."

He made this statement with great mystery and seriousness. I wanted to ask Him how He could conquer death, but some force restrained me. He spoke with such majesty that it seemed irreverent to ask for an explanation. He sounded as if He were the Master of Satan and not a mere man like us. I wondered whether He really was the Son of God.

But, if He was the Son of God, how could Satan tempt Him or "take" Him anywhere? Jesus must have been supernaturally "taken" by Satan from the desert across many miles to the Temple in Jerusalem and to its pinnacle located at its southwest corner 450 feet above the Kidron Valley below and then from there on to the very high mountain miles away!

Jesus must have submitted to these temptations and "takings." He must have allowed them, if He was truly the Son of God, in order to show us how to conquer Satan. We should not engage Satan with human dialogue or reasoning like Eve did in the garden. We should confront Satan's temptations, like Jesus did, with the Word of God and the truth and not sacrifice the truth for food and material gain, or for fame through spectacular actions, or for the power and the supposed glory of the world through worshiping false gods. This is the pretentious life. All of these temptations availed Satan nothing and Jesus conquered him thoroughly.

I came to understand that this is why we must not love the world or the things of the world. Because if anyone loves the world, the love of the Father is not in him. For all that is in the world, such as sensual lust, enticement for the eyes, and a pretentious life, is not from the Father but is from the world.

Then Jesus looked off in reflection and said, "Now that I think of that time in the desert, I think it's time for me to go back there for a period of prayer and fasting to prepare for my public ministry to preach the Gospel of Love."

He then spoke like a practical man gently suggesting that He should go alone and that perhaps we should return home to our families until He came for us again. So we did and we reluctantly returned to our regular jobs.

Dad was happy to see us again, but he acted angry, as if we had abandoned him. I couldn't blame him for feeling that way. After all, he had lost to Jesus his partner Peter, Andrew, and his sons James and me. He had managed to carry on the fishing business with some hired men, but it was hard for him without his usual helpers. We took over where we had left off, in Galilee.

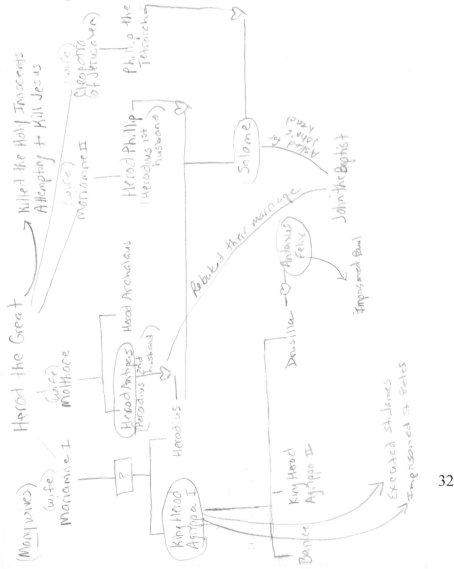

32

King Herod Antipas = "that fox" — eager to meet Jesus, expecting miracles, then returning Jesus to Pilate; unwilling to pass judgment on Jesus

→ tetrach of Galilee & Peracea

Pilate = prefect and procurator (Governor of Judea; serving under Emperor Tiberius)

— presided over Jesus' trial & ordered his crucifixion

Procurator ⇒ an agent representing others in court (lawyer)
⇒ in charge of the financial affairs of a province
Prefect ⇒ a superintendent of law enforcement (Magistrate)

3. The Galilean Ministry

The region of Galilee was located about 50 miles north of Jerusalem and the region of Judea. The region measured about 30 miles wide by 40 miles long. In 722 BC the Assyrian Conquest, that included the Galilee, led to the exile and disappearance of ten of the original twelve tribes of Israel. So Isaiah called it "Galilee of the Nations." (See Isaiah 9:1).

As a result of their long intercourse with Gentiles, adjoining foreigners and Greek immigrants, and their separation from their Jewish brethren in Judea by Samaria on the south, the Galileans spoke a country dialect and had peculiar customs. The city inhabitants of Jerusalem were under the rule of Herod Antipas, a son of King Herod the Great. They had nothing but scorn and contempt for Galileans.

I lived in Bethsaida, in the region of Ituraea and Trachonitis, about four miles northeast of the Galilee region. We were under the rule of King Herod Philip, another son of King Herod the Great.

The Galilee region was the center of roads that crossed from all directions. It had good communications, extreme fertility, beauty and the Sea of Galilee.

The Sea of Galilee is really a lake. It is 13 miles long, 7 miles wide and up to 160 feet deep. The Sea lies on the ancient Via Maris (Sea Route), which linked Egypt with the northern empires. The Sea supported a thriving fishing industry, with over 200 boats regularly working.

Jesus grew up in Nazareth, about 30 miles southwest of Capernaum on the Sea of Galilee. Cana was located in the center of Galilee, about six miles north of Nazareth.

The Transformation of Water to Wine
at the Wedding at Cana

After His time in the desert, Jesus returned to Galilee and came for us. Once again, Peter, Andrew, James and I left our nets to follow Him.

One day we all went with Him to a wedding reception in Cana. We all were invited to the wedding, but even passersby came and joined in the celebration. It was a very large crowd. The wine flowed freely and there was a festive atmosphere with much music and dancing. The celebration lasted for several days.

Jesus introduced us to His mother. Her name was Mary. I was awestruck by her natural beauty, dignity, simplicity and humility. She wore a plain dress, unlike the bold and gaudy dresses of many of the other women.

Mary personally welcomed us and introduced us to the bride and groom. They were very happy and were sharing in their guests' festivities. Mary then excused herself and I watched her as she left us to greet other guests. Her words were soft and lyrical. They seemed more like singing than speech. Everything about her was serenity and majestic beauty. She moved with grace and a regal posture and bearing. An aura of light seemed to glow out from her. All of her movements were rhythmical, pure and dignified. Rather than simply attract me to her, her beauty seemed more to bathe me in its grace.

In contrast with her peace, I then noticed the groom approach her with a stiff face and pursed lips. His face reddened as he

34

spoke to Mary. Then she came back and spoke to Jesus, who was standing next to me. She seemed concerned for the groom and, moved with pity, she said softly, "They don't have any more wine."

Jesus shrugged His shoulders and said, "So what does this have to do with me woman? They'll need gallons of wine to finish this reception. My hour has not yet come." He just seemed to be saying that the time to manifest Himself in His public ministry had not yet come.

He didn't use the term "woman" to signify dishonor or reproach. He spoke it with reverence. It flashed in my mind that His mother might be the "woman" that God referred to in Genesis when He told Satan that He would put enmity between him and the "woman" whose offspring would crush his head. (See Genesis 3:15). Jesus was her offspring and He crushed Satan's head when He was victorious over him during His temptation in the desert.

Mary seemed to accept His statement, as Jesus walked away to talk to some of the guests. However, she exuded an air of confidence and not disappointment. So I joined Mary as she went over to the chief wine steward, pointed to Jesus and simply said, "Do whatever He tells you."

I thought that this sounded strange since Jesus had just said that His time had not yet come. But Mary said this with so much conviction that it was as if she knew something that I didn't. She seemed confident that Jesus would do something to come to the newlyweds' rescue. She trusted Him even though she did not understand Him. She was an intercessor without being asked. She saw the need and sought to fill it by mediating it to her Son. She placed herself in the middle and acted like a caring mother.

As I stood there, somewhat bewildered, I noticed that the steward was standing next to six empty stone jars that were used to hold water for purification rites. Each one held about 20 gallons. The water was used to wash the dirty and dusty sandaled feet of those who entered the home from the dirt roads.

Jesus seemed to come out of nowhere up to the head waiter and said with authority, "Fill the jars with water."

35

The head waiter obeyed Him without question and passed on His order to the servants who got water and filled all six jars to the brim.

Then Jesus said, "Now draw some out and take it to the steward of the feast." So they took it to him and he tasted the water that had miraculously turned into wine.

The steward didn't know where it had come from, so he called the bridegroom and said to him, "Every man serves the good wine first and then, when men have drunk freely, they serve an inferior wine. But you have kept the good wine until last."

This was the first of the miracles of Jesus, the first of His great signs. He changed the very substance of something material. He changed water into wine. It confirmed our faith in Him. He acted out of His compassion in a deed of simple kindness. He acted in response to His mother's simple request to save a wedding couple from humiliation.

Later that night, as I lay down to sleep, I reflected on this great miracle that I had witnessed. Jesus had manifested His glory. He manifested the presence of God! It was His own self-revelation.

I thought, *The steward said, "You have kept the good wine till now." How different than most hosts who serve their best wine first and serve their worst wine last, hoping that the guests who have drunk the best will not later notice the worst.*

But, Jesus surprised them and gave them the best last! It's as if He is the greatest of all the Prophets whom God has saved for last after He gave us Moses, Elijah and John the Baptist. We, like the wedding guests, thought that we had the best first, but now we're surprised to find that the best was saved till now. He is the greatest of the Prophets.

Maybe this wedding and the abundance of wine are a sign of the change from the old times to the best of times, the promised Messianic times. It was prophesied that in the Messianic times "the vats shall overflow with wine and oil." (Psalm 85).

After the wedding at Cana, we returned to our nets. A few weeks later, Jesus came by the Bethsaida shore as James and the hired men were mending the nets and I was caulking the outside of the boat. It had been leaking and Dad didn't like a wet boat. He was watching over my shoulder as I hammered the caulking into the boat's seams. Andrew and Peter were with Jesus. Andrew came over to me and whispered to me. The noise from my hammering covered his words so that Dad could not hear him.

He said, "We've made a clean break with our lives and have given ourselves over to serving Jesus. We've given up everything—home, jobs and family. Peter's wife gave her consent to his joining us. Why don't you ask your father for his consent for you and James?"

"He'd never let us go. He's too dependent on us," I whispered back.

Just then Jesus looked at James and me and said, "Come follow me, and I will make you fishers of men."

Our father heard Jesus and said to us, "If I were younger, I'd go myself. James and John, you may go with Jesus with my blessing. I'll do fine with the fishing with the hired men. Go quickly before I change my mind and may God go with you!" I was happily surprised by my father's change of heart.

So, I didn't even have to ask my father if we could leave him. My decision to go was not a gradual one, but a plunge. In that instant, I decided to totally surrender to Jesus and to lose myself in order to offer myself completely to Him.

We got up, left the boat and the nets, and followed Him. Here we were, just ordinary people with no worldly wealth, education, position or power. Maybe He chose us not for who we were, but for who we could become under His direction.

I asked Peter where we were going. He said to Capernaum. This made no sense to me and I started yelling at Peter, "We should be going to Jerusalem! That's where the Temple is. That's where the important people are. There is nobody important in Capernaum. Jesus needs to bring His message of love to the priests, and the Pharisees, Scribes and Sadducees. They're the ones that need to hear His message so that they can relax the strict regulations that they impose on the people. If Jesus starts with the important people first and they change, then the rest of the people will follow."

Peter said, "Calm down John. You're thinking from a man's point of view and not from God's. Jesus has a good reason to start His public ministry in Capernaum. It's located in the region in which the former Israelite tribes of Zebulun and Napthali lived in the northern kingdom. They were conquered during the first of the Assyrian invasions in 722 BC. This was the first land of the Jews to be permanently conquered. From that time on, the two tribes of Zebulun and Napthali were in the darkness and gloom of foreign domination. This conquest was a chastisement from God because they had sinned against Him and broken their covenant with Him."

"I know my history, Peter!"

"Yes, I'm sorry John, I didn't mean to be patronizing. However, you don't know its significance."

"What do you mean?" I asked.

"Well, the Prophet Isaiah prophesied that one day the people of Zebulun and Napthali would no longer walk in darkness and gloom, but that a light would shine upon them and bring them deliverance." Peter quoted the prophecy to me:

> First the Lord degraded the land of Zebulun and the land of Naphtali; but in the end he has glorified the seaward road, the land west of the Jordan, the District of the Gentiles.
>
> Anguish has taken wing, dispelled is darkness: for there is no gloom where but now there was distress.
>
> The people who walked in darkness have seen a

great light; upon those who dwelt in the land of gloom a light has shone.

You have brought them abundant joy and great rejoicing, as they rejoice before you as at the harvest, as people make merry when dividing spoils.

For the yoke that burdened them, the pole on their shoulder, and the rod of their taskmaster you have smashed, as on the day of Midian.

(Isaiah 8:23; 9:1-3).

Peter explained to me that Jesus would now fulfill Isaiah's prophecy by going to Capernaum which was in the former land of the tribes of Zebulun and Napthali. The place where the physical conquest of Israel and Judah began, would now be the place where its spiritual conquest would begin. The place where oppression and darkness began, would now be the place where Jesus would bring His great light. This light would begin to shine in Capernaum. I accepted his explanation, calmed down, and we left Bethsaida for Capernaum on the northwest coast of the Sea of Galilee, only four miles away.

Capernaum was a busy city because it was situated near one of the main highways connecting Galilee with Damascus. Merchants used to bring silk and spices from Damascus and trade for our dried fish.

Jesus taught in the synagogue at Capernaum and was praised by all. Synagogues were individual local houses of worship, prayer and study. No sacrifices were performed there. Sacrifices were only performed in the Temple in Jerusalem. One Sabbath day, Jesus entered the synagogue and taught. The people were astonished at His teaching, because He taught them as one having real and absolute authority, unlike the supposed authority of the Scribes and Pharisees, who were the so-called expert interpreters of the Law.

There was a man in the synagogue who was possessed by a demon. The demon cried out from the man, "What do you have

39

to do with us, Jesus of Nazareth? Have you come to destroy us? I know who you are. You are the Son of God!"

I was amazed that the demons would say the same thing that John the Baptist had said, that Jesus was the Son of God, but I still struggled with what the title meant. Then Jesus surprised me with His authoritative voice.

He rebuked the demon and said, "Be quiet! Come out of him!"

The demon convulsed the man with a loud cry and came out of him. Everyone was astonished and they asked one another, "What is this? A new teaching with authority. He commands even the demons and they obey Him!"

After we left the synagogue, we went to Peter's house. His mother-in-law lay sick in bed with a fever. Jesus calmly approached her, gently grasped her hand and helped her up. The fever immediately left her and she became well and was able to wait on us.

Later that evening after sunset, people brought to Jesus all those who were ill or possessed by demons. It seemed like the whole town was gathered outside the door. He cured many who were afflicted with different diseases and He drove out many demons.

The next morning, before dawn, Jesus got up, left us and went off to a deserted place where He prayed. We pursued Him. When we found Him, Peter said, "Everyone has been looking for you."

He answered us, "Let us go on to the nearby villages so that I may preach there also."

So from there, we went into many of the nearby synagogues and Jesus preached, healed and drove out demons from many people.

The Proclamation of the Kingdom of God

King Herod Antipas of Galilee had put John the Baptist in jail because he had rebuked him for living with his brother's wife in adultery. Later, he had John killed at the request of his wife, Herodias. John had angered her by his rebuke of Herod. Her daughter, Salome, danced seductively for Herod at a banquet. In his drunken state, he promised her anything that she requested. Her mother had her ask Herod for the head of John on a platter. Herod ordered John beheaded and his head was brought into the banquet to Herodias on a silver platter. It was a public showing of his horrible murderous brutality.

After John's martyrdom, Jesus began preaching the message of the good news of eternal life in the Kingdom of God through repentance. He said, "This is the time of fulfillment. The Kingdom of God is at hand. Repent and believe in the Gospel."

I thought about His words. *I know that repentance requires a life change, turning back to God with a change of mind and heart, with sorrow for my sins and with a firm resolution to avoid them in the future. I can do that with His help. And to believe means to take Jesus at His word. But what will the Kingdom of God be like?*

The kingdom of Herod the Great was great and powerful. How much more would the Kingdom of God be great and powerful? But the Prophets announced that God would establish a kingdom, not just for one nation or people, but for all nations, for the whole world. Daniel told us that this kingdom is given to the Son of Man and that's what Jesus called Himself. Will He be the King? Maybe Jesus will make me His Prime Minister and entrust to me the keys of the Kingdom. Dad would be so proud of me!

We walked all over the region of Galilee. Jesus taught in the synagogues, proclaimed the Gospel of Love, and cured every disease and illness among the people. His fame spread to all of Syria, and the people brought to Him all who were sick with various diseases and racked with pain and those who were possessed with demons, lunatics, and paralytics. He cured them all and cast out demons from all who were possessed. He went about doing good and He did all things well. Great crowds followed Him.

One day, I walked with Jesus, His disciples and a large crowd towards the village of Nain. It was located about 20 miles southwest of Capernaum. I was meditating on how Elijah had raised the dead son of a widow. He was her only child. I wondered if Jesus could perform such a mighty miracle.

Elijah took the dead boy from his mother's lap, carried him to the upper room where he was staying and put him on his bed. He called out to the Lord to let the life breath return to the boy's body. The Lord heard Elijah's prayer and the life breath returned to the boy's body. Elijah returned him to his mother.

As we drew near to the gates of the city, we saw a large crowd and some bearers carrying a coffin, containing the dead body of another only son of a widowed mother.

When Jesus saw the mourning mother, He seemed moved with compassion and said to her, "Do not weep."

He then stepped forward and touched the coffin. The bearers halted, and He said, "Young man, I tell you, arise!"

Amazingly, the dead man sat up and began to speak, and Jesus gave him to his mother, just as Elijah had done.

Everyone was seized with fear and amazement. They glorified God, exclaiming, "A great Prophet has arisen in our midst," and "God has visited His people." This report about Him spread throughout the surrounding region.

What amazed me the most was that Elijah had prayed to the Lord for the life of a child. He did not exercise his own authority. But Jesus didn't pray to the Lord, He simply commanded on His own authority that the child arise. Only God Himself could do such a thing. No one had ever commanded a dead person to rise on his own authority. He acted as if He were God and not a man.

The Sermon on the Mount

A few days later, as we walked near Capernaum with the crowd behind us, we approached a mount close to the shore of the Sea of Galilee. It formed a natural amphitheater in which a voice would be amplified for a crowd to easily hear.

Jesus led us to the mount, where He sat on a rock and began to teach the crowd. He taught us the exact opposite of what the world thought was happiness. The world of the Roman and Jewish leaders thought that happiness came from materialism, money, power and fame. On the contrary, Jesus taught us that the Kingdom of God is spiritual. He taught us that happiness comes from poverty of spirit, meekness and humility. He taught this by making eight statements of Beatitudes. These were the blessings of those who live in the Kingdom of God with true happiness.

He started his Sermon on the Mount with the promise, that He had recently proclaimed, that we could enter the Kingdom of God through repentance. Now He taught us what kind of people could enter that Kingdom. The Kingdom of God is His sovereignty over all nations, the entire world, and heaven that we must recognize on Earth. It is God's answer, as the King of Love, to the evils of a world that rebels against Him. It is His Kingdom of God, which surpasses and transcends all the kingdoms of this world, which come and go, but His Kingdom will never end.

Jesus taught us that the Kingdom of God belongs to eight categories of blessed people: the poor in spirit; those who mourn; the meek; those who hunger and thirst for righteousness; the merciful; the pure of heart; the peacemakers; and to those who have been persecuted for the sake of righteousness. He also said that we are blessed when people insult us and persecute us because of Him. He told us to rejoice and be glad, for they persecuted the Prophets who were before us and our reward would be great in heaven.

Jesus then went on to teach us about the Jewish Law as we were taught it, our misunderstandings of it and the fulfillment of the Law and its extension. We had been taught not to kill, but Jesus taught us not to be angry. We had been taught not to commit adultery, but Jesus taught us not to look upon a person with lust, because that is the commission of adultery in our heart. We had been taught that we could divorce, but Jesus taught us that if we divorced from a lawful marriage and married another that we would be committing adultery and that if we married a divorced person, we would also be committing adultery.

We had been taught to moderate vengeance by only taking an eye for an eye and a tooth for a tooth, so that the punishment should not exceed the injury. But Jesus taught us to offer no resistance to one who is evil and that if someone struck us on our

43

cheek, we should turn the other cheek as well. We had been taught that we should love our neighbor and hate our enemy, but Jesus taught us to love our enemies and to pray for those who persecute us, because God makes His sun rise on the good and the bad and causes the rain to fall on the just and the unjust.

Jesus also taught us to avoid the hypocrisy of some of our leaders in the practice of our good works, almsgiving, prayer and fasting. He taught us that these should be done not for others to see in order to win their praise, but for God to see, and that He will repay us. He taught us to pray to God intimately as our Father, "Our Father who art in heaven, hallowed be thy name, thy kingdom come, thy will be done, on Earth as it is in heaven. Give us this day our daily bread and forgive us our trespasses, as we forgive those who trespass against us, and lead us not into temptation, but deliver us from evil." He told us that if we forgive others their trespasses, our heavenly Father would forgive us. But if we did not forgive others, neither would our Father forgive our trespasses.

Jesus told us not to worry about anything. He said not to worry about our life, our food, our body or what we are to wear, because our heavenly Father takes care of all of that, just like He does the birds of the sky, and we are more important than they are. He told us that God knows all that we need and if we seek first His Kingdom and His righteousness, all of these things will be given to us besides. He said, "Do not worry about tomorrow; tomorrow will take care of itself. Sufficient for a day is its own evil."

He said that we should ask our heavenly Father for all of our needs. He said, "Ask and it will be given to you; seek and you will find; knock and the door will be opened to you. For everyone who asks, receives; and the one who seeks, finds; and to the one who knocks, the door will be opened."

He also told us not to pass judgment in the spirit of arrogance against others, while being forgetful of our own faults, for as we judge so will we be judged. He said, "Why do you notice the splinter in your brother's eye, but do not perceive the wooden beam in your own eye? How can you say to your brother, 'Let me remove the splinter from your eye,' while the wooden beam is in

44

your eye? You hypocrite, remove the wooden beam from your eye first; then you will see clearly to remove the splinter from your brother's eye."

Jesus summed up His teachings, "Do to others whatever you would have them do to you. This is the Law and the Prophets." He concluded, "Everyone who listens to these words of mine and acts on them will be like a wise man who built his house on rock. The rain fell, the floods came, and the winds blew and buffeted the house. But it did not collapse; it had been set solidly on rock. And everyone who listens to these words of mine, but does not act on them will be like a fool who built his house on sand. The rain fell, the floods came, and the winds blew and buffeted the house. And it collapsed and was completely ruined."

When Jesus finished these words, the crowd was astonished at His teaching, for He taught them as one having authority of His own and not just what someone else had taught Him, as the Jewish teachers did. He taught as if He were God and not a man.

The Forgiveness of Sins

We walked back to Peter's house in Capernaum. Many people gathered around the house to hear Jesus preach. There was no room for anymore, even around the door. Then four men brought a paralytic to the house. They carried him on a mat and were not able to get to Jesus because of the crowd. So they actually removed a part of the roof above Him and lowered the paralytic on his mat down to Jesus through the opening.

Jesus saw their incredible faith and said to the paralytic, "Son, your sins are forgiven."

But some of the Scribes just sat there staring at Jesus. The Scribes were Pharisees who thought that they were the expert interpreters of the Law. They must have thought to themselves, "Why does this man speak that way? He is blaspheming! Who can forgive sins but God alone?"

Jesus became aware in His spirit that they thought this way and said to them, "Why are you reasoning about these things in your hearts? Which is easier, to say to the paralytic, 'Your sins are forgiven' or to say, 'Get up, pick up your mat and walk'? But so that you may know that the Son of Man has authority on Earth to forgive sins," He then turned to the paralytic and said, "I say to you, get up, pick up your mat and go home."

The man got up immediately, picked up his mat and went out in the sight of everyone. We were all amazed and glorified God, saying, "We have never seen anything like this!"

Of course, I thought, only God can forgive sins, no man can. But Jesus is the Son of Man and the Son of God, so as Son of God He must have the power to forgive sins. And He proved to the skeptics that He had the power to do this by a sign that only God could provide – the healing of a paralytic. So God, through Jesus, could heal the body and the soul. This was what all people have yearned for – to hear, to believe and to know that their sins are forgiven!

Great crowds continued to follow Him. Finally, He went to His hometown of Nazareth about 30 miles southwest of Capernaum.

Nazareth

Jesus stood in the synagogue in His small hometown of Nazareth. It was a poor town where He had grown up in age, wisdom and obedience.

He read from a scroll, "The Spirit of the Lord is upon me, because He has anointed me to preach good news to the poor. He has sent me to proclaim release to the captives and recovery of sight to the blind, to set at liberty those who are oppressed, to proclaim the acceptable year of the Lord."

As He finished reading the passage from the Prophet Isaiah, Jesus closed the scroll, gave it back to the attendant, and sat down. The eyes of all in the synagogue were fixed on Him. They had heard of His miracles and were curious to see what He would say and do.

He calmly said, "Today this Scripture has been fulfilled in your hearing." He was referring to the prophecy of Isaiah. (See Isaiah 61:1).

But the people began whispering amongst themselves. Jesus had just identified Himself as the Messiah or the Anointed One prophesied by Isaiah. He said that He fulfilled Isaiah's prophecy of the anointed preacher of good news. He had been doing this throughout Galilee and all were attracted to Him. The people of His own hometown had heard about His preaching and His miracles, but they knew that Jesus had no formal learning and they thought that He was just the son of Joseph, a poor carpenter.

Jesus had not been taught by any of the great Rabbis. They wondered how He could be the Anointed One. They admitted His marvelous teaching and miraculous works, but were at a loss to account for them because their extreme familiarity with His humanity made it hard for them to believe that He was a Prophet.

In the early part of His ministry, Jesus had been at Cana, only six miles from Nazareth, and, turning away from it, He had gone up to Capernaum. He had performed miracles in both towns. However, He did not call upon His own townsmen in Nazareth to believe in His divine mission until the evidence was so complete that they could not deny it.

However, now that they had the evidence, they did deny His mission and they murmured, "Is not this Joseph's son?"

Then He said to them, "Doubtless you will quote to me this proverb, 'Physician, heal yourself.' Do here in your own country what we have heard you did at Capernaum. Truly, I say to you, no Prophet is accepted in his own hometown."

When they heard this, they were filled with anger. He had likened Himself to the great Prophets, but they didn't believe Him because of His humble origins in their own town.

Their demeanor changed. Their faces contorted in rage. Their pride revolted against Jesus' rebuke of their lack of faith. I was astonished at their reaction, but Jesus calmly sat there with His fearless, loving eyes piercing their eyes of anger.

A loud voice cried out, "Maybe you can fool the people in Capernaum, but you can't fool us. We know who you are. You're nothing but a carpenter's son!"

Then the angry man led the congregation as they rose up, seized

Jesus, pulled Him out of the synagogue and dragged Him away. I was outraged and determined to defend Jesus. Peter, my brother and I tried to rescue Him, but the mob was too dense and some invisible spiritual force seemed to restrain us. Jesus Himself offered no resistance to them and suffered their brutality. We settled down and tried to imitate His calmness which was so contrary to my fiery temperament. Perhaps this apparent madness was meant to be.

We followed as they led Jesus away to the western end of the town to the brow of a hill on which the town was built. The hill was a perpendicular cliff about forty feet high, with a naked floor of rock at the bottom. Just as they were about to throw Jesus off the cliff, He fearlessly passed unharmed through their midst. We started off back to Capernaum as I wondered what the meaning of this event was.

The Origins of Jesus

As we walked along the dusty road toward Capernaum, I also wondered about the origins of Jesus. *The people of Nazareth think that He's just a poor carpenter's son. I don't blame them for wondering how He got His powers or where He received the sublimity of His teachings – especially since He had no formal education. But, they shouldn't have gone mad and tried to kill Him!*

He said that He was the Anointed One, the Christ. Why didn't they inquire with an open heart to learn more about Him and His origins? For that matter, why don't I?

So I dropped back from the other disciples who were leading the walk and I let the women who were following catch up to me. Mary was leading them. My own mother, Salome, was among them. My father had become a martyr of love. He had given up his own wife and two sons and allowed them to follow Jesus while he worked hard with the hired men to help support Jesus' ministry.

I waited until Mary caught up with me and then I questioned her. "Mother, that was terrible what they tried to do to Jesus. Why didn't they listen to Him and give Him a chance to minister to them? Why would they want to kill Him?"

"You heard Him say that the prophecy of Isaiah was fulfilled in their hearing. Jesus said that He was sent 'to proclaim release to the captives and recovery of sight to the blind, to set at liberty those who are oppressed, to proclaim the acceptable year of the Lord.' These were the attributes of Isaiah's prophecy of the Messiah which Jesus attributed to Himself. He said that the Lord 'anointed me to preach the good news to the poor.' Of course we know that the 'Anointed One' is the Christ, the Messiah."

"John, if He had said directly that He was the Messiah, they would've probably stoned Him on the spot. So, He identified Himself in an indirect manner so that those who have ears, like yourself, would listen. But so that those who did not, like most of them, would not listen and would even try to kill Him."

"He came to His own people in His hometown and they refused to accept or receive Him. But to those who do accept Him, like yourself, He will give the power to become children of God."

"But," I asked, "to those who don't accept Him, Mother, how could they go so far as to try to kill Him? I just don't understand why they would go mad over someone who said He was there to preach good news to the poor, to proclaim release to the captives and recovery of sight to the blind and to free those who are oppressed."

"They don't want to help the poor, the captives or the oppressed, John. They are the ones who are blind and whose sight needs recovery but they are content in their own comfort zone and don't want any changes. Jesus represents a sign of contradiction for them. His person contradicts their culture and ways of self-satisfaction. They don't want to be contradicted. They don't want to hear the message of Jesus to repent, reform and change their lives. They want to stop the voice of the Prophets like their ancestors did to those who went before Jesus. They killed the Prophets and that's why the Nazareans tried to kill my son."

I replied in anger, "I'll never understand the wickedness of the human heart. I hope that Jesus can purify mine. I get so angry with the evildoers. I wanted to cry out to God to let fire and brimstone fall on them like they fell on Sodom and Gomorrah. But somehow, Jesus' peaceful countenance prevented me. Pray that He might purify my heart, Mother."

"I will, John, and I'll pray that you will always be true to Him no matter what pressures come from men."

"My heart is drawn to Him," I said. "I tried to do honest work with my hands as a fisherman. Now I've learned that He did the same. The man from Nazareth said that He was a poor carpenter's son. Was He, Mother?"

"Yes, He was, John. He made beautiful furniture and farming tools with my late husband Joseph. But He was more than just a carpenter's son."

"What do you mean?"

Mary told me that from His beginning, after she and Joseph were married, but before they lived together, Jesus was announced as King and Son of God. She said, "Before He was conceived, the angel Gabriel came to me in Nazareth. He appeared before me just like you are now and said, 'Behold, you will conceive in your womb and bear a son, and you shall call His name Jesus. He will be great, and will be called the Son of the Most High. The Lord God will give to Him the throne of His father David and He will reign over the house of Jacob forever and of His kingdom there will be no end.' "

Mary continued her story. "However, John, I was a virgin. So, I was greatly troubled by Gabriel's words. I said, 'How shall this be, since I have had no relations with a man?' "

"Gabriel said, 'The Holy Spirit will come upon you and the power of the Most High will overshadow you. Therefore, the child to be born will be called holy, the Son of God.' It was to be a miraculous conception."

"Then I understood that the Annunciation fulfilled the prophecy of Isaiah, 'Behold, a virgin shall conceive, and bear a son, and shall call His name Emmanuel.' (Isaiah 7:14). That means 'God is with us.' "

"This Annunciation of Jesus' Kingship in the line of David over a kingdom that would be everlasting also fulfilled the vision of the Prophet Daniel. He said, 'In my vision at night I looked, and there before me was one like a Son of Man, who came upon the clouds of heaven. He was presented to the Ancient One. He received authority, glory and sovereign power; all peoples, nations and men of every language worshiped Him. His dominion is an everlasting dominion that will not pass away, and His kingdom is one that will never be destroyed.' " (Daniel 7:13-14).

"The Annunciation also fulfilled the prophecy of Isaiah, 'For unto us a child is born, unto us a son is given: and the government shall be upon His shoulder: and His name shall be called Wonderful, Counselor, The mighty God, The everlasting Father, The Prince of Peace. Of the increase of His government and peace there shall be no end, upon the throne of David, and upon His kingdom, to order it, and to establish it with judgment and with justice from henceforth even forever. The zeal of the Lord of hosts will perform this.' (Isaiah 9:6-7). I knew that I was of the house of David and so was Joseph and that's how Jesus would inherit the throne of David, His father, over an everlasting kingdom, just as Gabriel had announced to me."

"Gabriel also told me that my elderly cousin Elizabeth, whom everyone thought was barren, was in her sixth month with child. He said that nothing was impossible for God. I totally submitted to God's will for me to be a mother and told Gabriel, 'Behold, I am the handmaid of the Lord, may it be done to me according to your word.' Then he parted from me."

"What did you do then?" I asked.

"I quickly acted on Gabriel's news that Elizabeth was with child and made a long trip to visit and help her at her home in the hill country of Judah. When I entered her house and she heard my greeting, Elizabeth was filled with the Holy Spirit. She cried out in a loud voice and said, 'Most blessed are you among women, and blessed is the fruit of your womb. And how does this happen to me that the mother of my Lord should come to me? For the moment the sound of your greeting reached my ears, the infant

51

in my womb leaped for joy. Blessed are you who believed that what was spoken to you by the Lord would be fulfilled.' "

"I had said nothing to Elizabeth about my being with child, so the Holy Spirit must have given her the knowledge that I was the mother of her Lord. She was proclaiming my child to be our Lord and God."

"What happened next, Mother?"

"I broke into praise and said, 'My soul proclaims the greatness of the Lord and my spirit rejoices in God my Savior. For He has looked upon His handmaid's lowliness. Behold, from now on all ages will call me blessed. The mighty one has done great things for me and holy is His name.' "

"When I returned to Nazareth, three months later, after the birth of Elizabeth's son, John the Baptist, it was obvious that I was with child. This caused Joseph, my husband, much confusion. I did not explain to him how this had happened. I remained silent and trusted that God would work everything out."

"Joseph was a righteous man, yet he didn't want to expose me to public shame, so he decided to divorce me quietly. But God prevented this through His angel who appeared to Joseph in a dream and said, 'Joseph, son of David, do not be afraid to take Mary your wife into your home. For it is through the Holy Spirit that this child has been conceived in her. She will bear a son and you are to name Him Jesus, because He will save His people from their sins.' Jesus means 'God saves!' After Joseph woke up, he did as the angel had commanded him and took me, his wife, into his home."

"When Joseph told me this story, it relieved my anxiety and confirmed what Gabriel had said to me at the Annunciation, that His name would be Jesus."

"So you see, John, He's much more than just a carpenter's son, as the Nazareans think. But because they judge by appearances and not by the heart, they think that He's nothing more than a common worker. If they listened to Him and reflected on His miraculous powers, they would know that He is much more than a carpenter's son. But they don't want to know."

"Was He born in Nazareth?" I asked.

"No, but everyone thinks that He was. That's why they don't believe that He's the Messiah King. They quote the Prophet Micah who said that the Messiah would be born in Bethlehem. Micah said, 'And you, Bethlehem, land of Judah, are by no means least among the rulers of Judah; since from you shall come a ruler, who is to shepherd my people Israel.' " (Micah 5:2).

"So the Nazareans say that Jesus can't be the Messiah because they think that He was born in Nazareth."

"Well, where was He born?"

"In Bethlehem."

"In Bethlehem? How, why?"

"Well, John, Rome ordered a census and Joseph and I had to return to the town of his origin to register. Joseph was born in Bethlehem. So while I was late with child, we returned from Nazareth to Bethlehem. As you know, it was an arduous journey of 90 miles south, down the valley of the River Jordan to Jericho, then west 15 miles through the Judean wasteland and up to Jerusalem, and finally south again about five miles to the tiny town of Bethlehem. Joseph had friends there and was sure that we could find lodgings. But when we arrived, they had all been taken. There was no room for us anywhere."

"So what did you do?"

"Joseph was crestfallen and very concerned for me. When I felt that the time was ready for the birth of Jesus, we took emergency shelter in a cave used as a stable for animals. That's where Jesus was born, at midnight of the winter solstice. On the darkest day of the year, the true light of the world was born in a cold and dark cave in the town of Bethlehem, the city of King David's birth. I wrapped Him in swaddling clothes and laid Him in a manger. The body heat of the animals and Joseph's small fire kept us warm. "

"So, then, did He fulfill the prophecy of Micah?"

"To the letter."

"Well why doesn't He just tell them?"

"They don't want to know and they're not open to believing Him. If they won't believe Him because of the good works that He does, why should they believe Him on His word that He was born in Bethlehem?"

"Yes, Mother, I understand. It's that closed human heart again!"

Mary continued, "He was born during the reign of King Herod the Great, who was not a true Jew and not a descendent of Judah nor a member of the tribe of Judah. The prophecy of Judah's father, Jacob the Patriarch, was that the scepter or kingship of the Jews would not depart from the line of Judah until the advent of the Messiah and true King. (See Genesis 49:10). The scepter departed from the line of Judah with the advent of Roman rule, so Jesus' birth was truly the advent of the Messiah and true King and confirmation that He was the one."

"But," I asked, "did anyone recognize His birth as the advent of the Messiah and true King?"

"Yes, John, those for whom He came recognized Him. They were both the poor and the rich who were openhearted. Local shepherds came and worshiped Him and they recognized Him as the Messiah. Wise Men came from the East bearing gifts and recognized Him as the true King."

"An angel made the announcement to the shepherds. They told me how it happened. They were out in the fields at night keeping watch over their flocks. Suddenly, the glory of the Lord shone around them, and they were filled with fear. An angel appeared to them and said, 'Be not afraid, for behold, I bring you good news of a great joy which will come to all the people. For to you this day is born a Savior in the city of David who is Messiah and Lord. And this will be a sign for you: you will find a babe wrapped in swaddling clothes lying in a manger.' "

"And then a multitude of the heavenly host appeared with the angel. They were praising God and saying, 'Glory to God in the highest and peace on Earth among men with whom He is pleased!' "

"When the angels went away from them back to heaven," Mary

continued, "the shepherds said to one another, 'Let's go over to Bethlehem and see this thing that has happened, which the Lord has made known to us.' "

"They left in haste, and found Joseph and me with the baby Jesus who was wrapped in swaddling clothes and lying in a manger, just like the angel had told them. So they believed that He was the Savior, the Messiah and the Lord as the angel had told them. The angel's message also confirmed for me what the angel told me and later Joseph, that we should name my son Jesus, which means 'God saves', because He would save people from their sins."

"These Wise Men studied the stars and sought the newborn King of the Jews. They followed a brilliant star that guided them to our cave over which it stopped. They entered the cave, recognized Jesus as the true King, bowed before Him, and offered Him gifts of gold, frankincense and myrrh. This fulfilled the prophecy, 'A star shall advance from Jacob and a Scepter shall rise out of Israel.' " (Numbers 24:17).

"To me, John, the gifts of the Wise Men were symbolic. I saw the gold as symbolic of the Messiah King of All Nations, the Son of Man; I saw the frankincense as symbolic of God, the true Son of God; and I saw the myrrh as symbolic of His future burial."

"I remembered the psalm prayer asking for a great king for us and about other kings offering him gifts, especially the prayer, 'May all kings bow before him and all nations serve him.' (Psalm 72:11). In my meditations, I applied this psalm to my own son, the Messiah King and the true King of All Nations. The homage of the Wise Men was the beginning of His recognition as the King of All Nations by Gentiles, the other peoples and nations. I pray that His own people, especially those from our hometown of Nazareth will also recognize Him."

"I'll pray with you Mother. May their hearts, and mine also, be softened and open to His teaching."

Mary continued, "Eight days after His birth, my son was circumcised and named Jesus, the name that Gabriel gave for Him at the Annunciation and the name that the angel later told to Joseph in his dream."

"Well, Mother, if the angel told the shepherds, 'Peace on Earth among men with whom God is pleased,' God must certainly not have been pleased with those Nazareans who tried to kill Jesus. I still can't believe it! It just makes my blood boil — to want to kill Him who is so good."

"Listen, John. It's been that way from the beginning."

"How so?"

"He is a sign of contradiction that causes non-believers to hate Him. When Joseph and I went to the Temple in Jerusalem, 40 days after His birth, to present Him to God in the Temple, an elderly man named Simeon took my baby in his arms. It had been revealed to him by the Holy Spirit that he should not see death before he had seen the Messiah. He blessed God and uttered a prophecy. He said that Jesus would be a light to the nations, and glory for the people of Israel."

"I recognized Simeon's prophecy as the fulfillment of the prophecy of Isaiah that the Messiah would not only restore Israel but that He would be 'a light for the nations that salvation may reach to the ends of the earth.' (Isaiah 49:6). So it was that Simeon recognized Jesus as the Messiah."

"Then Simeon said to me, 'Behold, this child is destined for the fall and rise of many in Israel, and to be a sign that will be contradicted and you yourself a sword will pierce so that the thoughts of many hearts may be revealed.' I shuddered at this prophecy that He would be contradicted and that I would be pierced, but I understood that if the Messiah had to suffer, then so too did His mother. Since then I have pondered this prophecy and kept it in my heart. Each time that my son is badly treated by people like those in Nazareth, the sword pierces me more deeply."

"Then we returned to Bethlehem. When the Wise Men came to King Herod the Great on their way to honor the baby Jesus there they asked, 'Where is the newborn King of the Jews? We saw His star rising in the East and have followed it here to do Him homage.' "

"Now Herod thought that he himself was the true King of the

Jews since he had been appointed as such by the Roman Senate, which gave him that title. However, giving him that title did not make it true. Herod was not even a Jew. He was an Edomite who was now troubled by the Wise Men's story about seeking the King of the Jews. He was afraid of losing his power to a newborn king who was the true King of the Jews."

"Well," I said, "he sure had reason to be afraid of losing his power. What did he do about it?"

"When King Herod heard their story, he was very jealous. So he asked the Chief Priests and the Scribes where the Messiah was to be born. They told him in Bethlehem of Judah to fulfill the prophecy of Micah." (See Micah 5:1).

"Then Herod summoned the Wise Men secretly and learned from them what time the star appeared and he calculated how old this new king might be. To eliminate his perceived threat to his kingship, he ordered all of the male children in Bethlehem who were two years old or younger to be killed."

"His massacre of the innocents fulfilled the prophecy of Jeremiah, 'A voice was heard in Ramah, sobbing and loud lamentation; Rachel weeping for her children, and she would not be consoled, since they were no more.' (Jeremiah 31:15). As you know, Rachel was the wife of the Patriarch Jacob. She had wept for her children who were taken into exile at the time of the Assyrian invasion of the northern kingdom. Now, Rachel wept through the tears of the mothers of these innocent slaughtered children."

"But God's Providence protected us. After the Wise Men left, an angel appeared to Joseph in a dream and said, 'Rise, take the child and His mother, and flee to Egypt. Remain there till I tell you, for Herod is about to search for the child, to destroy Him.' "

"So, Joseph got up in the middle of the night and took us to Egypt. I didn't question why, I trusted that God would protect me and my child through my husband. It was an exhausting journey of over 300 miles to a foreign land."

"What happened when you got there?"

"We found shelter through some kind Egyptians. Joseph

struggled to find work and to try to overcome the language barrier. We didn't know where our next meal would come from or how long we should stay there. We just trusted that God would work things out for us."

"Then what happened?"

"We lived in that strange pagan land until the death of Herod. Then the angel appeared again in a dream to Joseph and said to take Jesus and me back home because His threatened killer was dead. So Joseph took us out of Egypt and we returned to Nazareth. Our return journey was over 400 miles, but we were happy to be going home!"

"This fulfilled the prophecy of Hosea, 'Out of Egypt I called my son.' (Hosea 11:1). Israel, God's son, was called out of Egypt at the time of the Exodus. Now Jesus, the Son of God, was also called out of that land and into a new Exodus to Nazareth. Jesus grew and became strong, filled with wisdom."

"So you see, John, as I started to tell you, the world has hated Jesus from the beginning. But God will protect Him until His plan is accomplished." I didn't ask her what the plan was.

Mary went on, "My first terrible experience of the suffering prophesied by Simeon was when Jesus was a child and we lost Him in the Temple. Every year, Joseph and I had gone with Him to Jerusalem for the Feast of Passover. When He was 12 years old, we went as usual. After the festival, as we were returning to Nazareth, Jesus had remained behind in Jerusalem, but we did not know that. We thought that He was in the caravan. So we journeyed for a day and looked for Him among our relatives and friends. However, when we couldn't find Him, we returned in distress to Jerusalem and looked for Him there."

"After three days, we found Him in the Temple, sitting in the midst of the teachers, listening to them and asking them questions. All who heard Him were astounded at His understanding and His answers. When we saw Him, we were astonished and I said to Him, 'Son, why have you done this to us? Your father and I have been looking for you with great anxiety.' And He said to us, 'Why were you looking for me? Did you not know that I must be in my Father's house?' "

"But we didn't understand what He said to us. Later, I understood that by calling the Temple His Father's house, He meant that God was really His Father. This experience of losing Him then was to prepare me for my separation from Him, which is now beginning with His public ministry."

"After we found Him in the Temple, He came back with us and was obedient to us. Jesus advanced in age, in wisdom and in favor before God and man. As for me, I kept all these things in my heart."

"I considered what the angel Gabriel told me at the Annunciation that my son was the Son of God. When I visited my cousin Elizabeth she called me the mother of her Lord, who, of course, is our God. The angels told the shepherds that my son was the Messiah, the Lord, and when I found my son in the Temple He referred to it as His Father's house, thereby acknowledging that He was the Son of God. However, He can't say that directly because they would kill Him for blasphemy. So He uses veiled language to identify Himself, as He just did in Nazareth by identifying Himself with the Anointed One, the Messiah, prophesied by Isaiah."

"I pondered and reflected in my heart on all of these revelations from the angels, my cousin Elizabeth and my son and concluded that He was indeed not only the prophesied Messiah King, but truly God, Savior and Lord. He is the Son of Man and the Son of God who will forgive the sins of men. I hope that you come to this faith John."

"I'll try to come to believe it, Mother, but I honestly don't understand it. He is not like the Messiah whom I expected. I had expected a great king who would conquer our enemies and gather Israel as a light to all nations. Not someone who would be born in obscurity, suffer and be rejected by his own people. This is very difficult for me. Please pray for my faith."

"Of course I will, John. But this good news is not just for us Jews, the Chosen People. The angels also told the shepherds that their good news was for all the people, for all nations. And Simeon said that my son would be 'a light for the nations.' I understood this when God led the Wise Men to us from the East."

I didn't think that I should ask her what was in my heart. I had already asked too many questions and felt like I was prying. But Mary was very gracious and had explained the origins of Jesus as I had requested her to do. I meditated on what she had already told me and we walked on in silence to Capernaum.

His origins seem almost divine. . . . The angel Gabriel told Mary that He was the Son of the Most High and a King forever over a Kingdom that will never end. Gabriel told Mary and Joseph to name Him Jesus which means 'God saves'. Then the angels told the shepherds that He is our Savior, Messiah and Lord. The Magi recognized Him as a true King and Simeon said that He would be a light to the nations and glory for the people of Israel. Jesus Himself called God His Father and said that He must be in His Father's house. All of this leads me to understand that Jesus is truly the Anointed One that John the Baptist awaited, the Messiah, our Savior and our King of All Nations, who, as the angel Gabriel told Mary, will receive the throne of King David. However, Gabriel also said that He will reign forever and His Kingdom will be without end. How can a king reign forever?

Those who are in power and tied to this world will probably never recognize Him and, more likely, they'll try to kill Him just like King Herod the Great and the people in Nazareth had tried to do. I still can't believe the iniquity of the human heart in the face of such goodness.

Return to Capernaum

When we reached Capernaum, we stayed at Peter's house. Jesus continued to cure many who were sick with various diseases, and He drove out many demons, not permitting them to speak because they knew who He was. By these exorcisms, Jesus demonstrated His dominion and power over Satan and demons.

A demoniac who couldn't speak was brought to Jesus who immediately cast out the demon. The dumb man then spoke and the crowds were amazed, saying, "Never was anything like this seen in Israel." But some of them said, "He casts out demons by the power of Satan, the prince of demons."

Such hardness of hearts, I thought. *Not only to refuse to believe in the Godly works of Jesus, but to attribute the wonders seen by their own eyes to Satan himself. As if Satan could do good and cast out his own demons to help the people to believe in Jesus. It made no sense.*

As if reading my thoughts, Jesus said to them, "Every kingdom divided against itself is laid waste, and a divided household falls. And if Satan also is divided against himself, how will his kingdom stand? For you say that I cast out demons by the power of Satan. But if it is by the finger of God that I cast out demons, then the Kingdom of God has come upon you."

"When a strong man, fully armed, guards his own palace, his goods are in peace. But when one stronger than he assails him and overcomes him, he takes away his armor in which he trusted, and divides his spoil. I am stronger than Satan and I have overcome him. He who is not with me is against me, and he who does not gather with me scatters."

These miracles stupefied me, but seemingly left the townspeople indifferent. Afterwards, they didn't respond to His message any better than had the Nazareans. They didn't change and life went on for them just as before — eating and drinking, working, buying and selling. They were building up their own material world while ignoring the greater world of the spirit of divine love.

Their response was so negligible, that Jesus later called a judgment upon the city for their failure to repent. He said, "You, Capernaum, will you be exalted to heaven? You shall be brought down to Hades! For if the mighty works done in you had been done in Sodom, it would have remained until this day. But I tell you that it shall be more tolerable on the Day of Judgment for the land of Sodom than for you."

Jesus seemed to be exhausted from His labors on behalf of the people of Capernaum and saddened by their failure to repent and believe in Him. We all went to bed, but when we got up we found that Jesus had slipped out of the house before daybreak. We were very anxious when we saw that He was missing, so we went out searching for Him. Peter led the way. We were very relieved when we found Him sitting calmly at the edge of the Sea of Galilee.

"We've been looking all over for you!" Peter exclaimed.

Jesus calmly replied, "Be at peace, Peter, you're too anxious and you worry about too many things. Look at this calm sea — it's like a diamond. See how the light of the sun is reflected by its gentle wavelets and how it sparkles all over like light radiating from a diamond. You should all be as calm as this sea is now — gently reflecting the light of God's love, like so many diamonds in the world. When the sea is tumultuous, it doesn't reflect the light and neither do you when you are in turmoil."

"Now let's leave Capernaum and go out to others. This is why I have come. There are good people out there whose hearts are open to my message. Let's go. Peter, you lead."

And so we moved on and went about to other cities and villages. Jesus appealed to the simple childlike people who believed and who were weren't skeptical and doubtful of His words and works like those who thought they were wise.

He praised these kinds of persons and said, "I thank you, Father, Lord of heaven and Earth, that you have hidden these things from the wise and understanding and revealed them to the child-like. Yes, Father, for you have graciously willed it so. All things have been delivered to me by my Father. No one knows who the Son is except the Father, and who the Father is except the Son and anyone to whom the Son wishes to reveal Him."

He prayed directly to God and called Him His "Father" who delivered everything to Him, the Son, who alone knows the Father who alone knows the Son. I was coming to believe that He was truly the Son of God who came to call us to Himself.

"Come to me," He said, "all who labor and are heavy burdened and I will give you rest. Take my yoke upon you and learn from me, for I am meek and gentle in heart and you will find rest for your souls. For my yoke is easy and my burden is light."

4. The First Passover in Jerusalem

At Passover time, we went up to Jerusalem for the first time together. It was about a four-day journey over the dusty dirt roads from Capernaum. We walked south down the Jordan River valley to Jericho, 900 feet below sea level. From there, we went west through the desert and up to Jerusalem. It was located on top of the Judean hills, 2,500 feet above sea level and higher than most of the inhabited places in Judea. When we reached Jerusalem, we could see the Temple Mount and the Temple gleaming white and gold in the bright sun, surrounded by its mighty walls stretching a quarter mile in length, almost 500 feet above the Kidron Valley.

Over two million Jews from many nations crowded the tiny city. According to the Law of Moses, each male Israelite had to appear in the Temple before the Lord God during the Feast of Passover to make a sacrifice and give alms. The Passover was celebrated in remembrance of the angel of death, who, "passed over" the homes of the Israelites when they were in Egypt, but had killed the firstborn of the Egyptians. The Israelites had marked the doors of their homes with the blood of sacrificial lambs. This happened around 1440 BC, just before Moses led them out of Egypt. This began their Exodus from over 200 years of slavery, across the Red Sea and into the desert for 40 years before they finally entered the Promised Land.

During the Feast, more than 200,000 lambs were sacrificed in the Temple by thousands of priests. I didn't think that it was possible for the blood of even that many lambs to take away sins. To repair for all the sins against God who is all-good, only a perfect sacrifice made by God Himself could do that. But I didn't think that could ever happen.

The Temple was a huge and magnificent complex. It consisted of the main Temple building, a large plaza, courtyards, porticos, columns and staircases. The first Temple was built by King Solomon in 960 BC. It was destroyed in 586 BC by the Babylonians who then led the Jews as prisoners out of Jerusalem and into the years of their Babylonian Captivity. Later, they were released, returned to Jerusalem and rebuilt the Temple in a simple style. It was completed in 516 BC. Then, in 18 BC King Herod the Great began his monumental construction project to turn it into a grandiose structure.

The majority of the complex was the Court of the Gentiles, a large open-air stone courtyard. The Temple itself was located in the center of the complex. The Temple was about 150 feet high with separate courtyards for men and women, rooms for priests to sleep and altars of sacrifice. It was a magnificent sight and the first thing that pilgrims could see as they approached Jerusalem.

The Holy of Holies was the innermost and most sacred area of the Temple. It was a windowless square room. Only the High Priest could enter it and only on one day of the year, the Day of Atonement, to burn incense and sprinkle sacrificial animal blood to atone for sins. The Holy of Holies was separated from the rest of the Temple by the veil, a huge, heavy drape made of fine linen and blue, purple and scarlet yarn and embroidered with gold cherubim.

We climbed the broad southern stone staircase and entered the Court of the Gentiles. When we arrived, there was a lot of commotion. We saw money changers yelling their exchange rates to the foreign Jews who came to worship, since only Temple money was accepted as alms at the Temple and not their foreign currency. The money changers took advantage of the pilgrims and charged them exorbitant exchange rates.

Vendors of animals and doves for sacrifices were hawking them for sale. They too charged exorbitant prices. There was much shouting by men amid the bellowing of animals. The animals left their manure everywhere. It all seemed very exploitive of the people and irreverent of God. They seemed focused more on making money than on praying and worshiping God.

The First Cleansing of the Temple

Jesus seemed very angry. He made a whip of cords of rope and used it to drive out the animal sellers with their sheep and oxen. Then He poured out the coins of the money changers and overturned their tables. He told those who sold the pigeons, "Take these things away; you shall not make my Father's house a marketplace!"

Tables lay upside down, coins were scattered in every direction and lay on the stone courtyard, animals ran amok and doves flew from their opened cages. I recalled the words of the psalm, "Zeal for your house has consumed me." (Psalm 69).

The Prophet Malachi had foretold that the Lord would come unexpectedly to His Temple, just like Jesus had just come. Malachi prophesied that He would "suddenly come to His Temple, the messenger of the covenant in whom you delight" who would "purify the sons of Levi and refine them like gold and silver, till they present right offerings to the Lord." (Malachi 3:1-4). And now it seemed to me that Jesus was fulfilling that prophecy.

I understood that by Jesus' reference to the Temple as His Father's house, Jesus was explicitly referring to Himself as the Messiah and to the God of the Temple as His Father. That's why He used force to cleanse it. By driving out the commercial abusers of the Temple, He clearly acted as if He were the Messiah foretold by the Prophets, the Son of God. By calling God His Father, He implied that He was in fact the Son of God, just as the voice of the Father had announced at His baptism in the River Jordan.

The Jews, recognizing His words and actions as those of the Messiah, angrily demanded of Him, "What sign have you to show us for doing this?"

We called them "the Jews" to distinguish them from us as followers of Jesus. They were the leaders of the Jewish people. Many of them profited from the business of the Temple and saw Jesus as a threat to themselves.

Jesus answered them, "Destroy this Temple, and in three days I will raise it up."

The Jews then said, "It has taken forty-six years to build this Temple, and will you raise it up in three days?"

The Jews were right. I didn't know what Jesus was talking about, but it must've been something spiritual and not material. The Jews had no plans to destroy the Temple and Jesus had no plans to rebuild it.

I thought, *Perhaps He is referring to Himself as the new Temple which, if destroyed by His death, would be resurrected to new life. Now this would be a great sign that should convince everyone that He was truly the Messiah and Son of God. But it seems impossible!*

Jesus continued to work more signs in Jerusalem, and many came to believe in His name when they saw them. However, Jesus did not trust Himself to them, because He knew all men and needed no one to tell Him about man because He Himself knew what was in man. That's why He didn't openly proclaim, "Here I am, Messiah and Son of God." The people would have then taken Him as their earthly king in hopes of lifting the Roman oppression. The Jews would have killed Him for blasphemy.

Most men didn't want to know the truth, they just wanted to see signs and wonders or to justify themselves and not to change. Jesus wanted faith in Him, not in His signs. He worked signs to bring people to faith in Him. But a faith that demands signs is only a superficial faith that will never mature and will always demand more signs.

So He didn't trust them. They were fickle and inconstant, without commitment and closed to His message of repentance, faith and love.

However, to us He fully revealed the meaning of the human person, created with intrinsic dignity in the image of God, with a mortal body and an immortal soul, with an intellect to know the truth, with a will to love and to do good and with emotions to appreciate beauty.

We were destined to live with God eternally in His Kingdom, but we had to repent, change from within and be transformed and reformed in order to come into it. It was like being born again. Our faith had to come from the heart and not just from the head, as Nicodemus was to learn.

Nicodemus

Jesus gave His most dramatic teaching about being born again to a great mind and leader of the Jews. He was a member of the Sanhedrin, the 71-member religious Council of the Jews. He was also a member of the Pharisees, the strict Jewish religious sect. His name was Nicodemus and he came one night to visit Jesus in secret. He didn't come during the day for fear that he would be seen and reported to the Pharisees. They were the teachers of the Law who practiced it literally and strictly in daily life. They practiced more law than love. They were beginning to teach that Jesus was a false Prophet.

The Pharisees believed that they were saved by the Law and therefore that there must be a regulation to govern every possible incident for everyone. So they extracted from the Law hundreds of rules and regulations. For example, the Law said to keep the Sabbath day holy without work. So the Pharisees then had to define what work was. One so-called "work" was to tie a knot on the Sabbath. But then a "knot" had to be defined. They ruled that a woman could tie up the strings of her girdle with a knot but that a man could not tie a knot in a line to a bucket to let it down into a well to get water. So, on the Sabbath it was unlawful for a man to tie a knot in a line to a bucket, but it was lawful for a woman to tie the bucket by a knot to her girdle strings and then let the bucket down. What the Pharisees really did was to tie God's first law of love into knots through their rules and regulations.

Jesus had told us that He had met with Nicodemus. So, just as he had gone to Jesus at night, I went one night to visit Nicodemus to learn of their discussion. He was very hospitable and anxious to tell me of his visit with Jesus. He said that he had no one to share this with and was happy that I had come to visit him.

He said that he knew in his head that Jesus was a teacher from God because no one could do the signs that He did unless God was with Him. But Nicodemus still didn't understand who He really was. He had not yet opened his heart to Jesus. He thought that Jesus would tell him about His mission or some intellectual talk like that, but He had surprised him completely.

"Well what did He say?" I asked him.

Then Nicodemus told me about their conversation. He answered me very solemnly and said that Jesus told him, "Truly, truly, I say to you, unless one is born again from above, he cannot see the Kingdom of God."

"So I said to Jesus, 'How can an old man be born again? Surely he can't reenter his mother's womb and be born again, can he?' "

Jesus answered me, "Truly, truly, I say to you, unless one is born of water and the Spirit, he cannot enter the Kingdom of God. You must have both. What is born of flesh is flesh and what is born of Spirit is spirit. Do not be amazed that I told you, 'You must be born again.' The wind blows where it wills, and you can hear the sound that it makes, but you don't know where it comes from or where it goes. So it is with everyone who is born of the Spirit."

Nicodemus told me, "I wanted to change, but I could not change myself and none of this made any sense to me, so I asked Jesus, 'How can this be?' "

Jesus firmly replied, "Are you a teacher of Israel and yet you do not understand this? Truly, truly, I say to you, we speak of what we know, and bear witness to what we have seen; but you do not receive our testimony. If I have told you earthly things and you do not believe, how can you believe if I tell you heavenly things? No one has ascended into heaven but He who descended from heaven, the Son of Man. And as Moses lifted up the serpent in the wilderness, so must the Son of Man be lifted up so that whoever believes in Him may have eternal life."

"Then I said to Him, 'Jesus, I'm trying to understand, I'm trying to believe. Are you saying that you, a mere man, descended from heaven, that you are the Son of Man? That you have the title that the Prophet Daniel said would be applied to the Messiah? Are you the Messiah? Are you sent by God? Are you going to be lifted up on a pole like Moses lifted the bronze serpent on the pole to heal the people who were being killed by the serpents that God sent them in punishment for their complaining against Him in the wilderness? How will you be lifted up? Why?' "

"Jesus looked me right in the eye and said very slowly, 'God so loved the world that He gave His only-begotten Son, so that whoever believes in Him should not perish but have eternal life. For God did not send the Son into the world to condemn the world, but that the world might be saved through Him. He who believes in Him will not be condemned, but he who does not believe is already condemned, because he has not believed in the name of the only-begotten Son of God.' "

"Then Jesus concluded His teaching to me and said, 'And this is the judgment, that the light has come into the world but men preferred darkness rather than light, because their deeds were evil. For everyone who does evil hates the light, and does not come to the light, so that his works might not be exposed. But he who does what is true comes to the light, so that his works may be clearly seen as done by God.' "

Nicodemus was silent for a moment and then said to me, "So John, since then I've been meditating on His words and the Scriptures and it seems that He claims to be both the Son of Man and the Son of God, a man and God! He says that He was sent by God, comes from heaven and speaks the words of God, and if we believe in Him we have eternal life and if we do not believe in Him we will be condemned. But this condemnation will come through our own free will in refusing to believe in Him. So our reaction to Him is a judgment upon ourselves. We judge ourselves. It is not God who condemns us. God loves all of us. We condemn ourselves by preferring the darkness to the light."

"Can He be claiming to be both man and God?" he continued. "It sounds impossible! But He seems to say it's so. Who else can give eternal life? I've tried to reason this out but it's beyond reason. Not contrary to reason, but certainly beyond it. Despite all of my studies and learning, I'm still really ignorant about the things of God. If I'm to understand this, reason is not enough. I must open my heart and not just my mind. I must become humble and accept it on faith. I have to pray for more faith to believe!"

"I can't simply decide for myself to join the Kingdom of God. It's beyond my power. I must be born again from above, as He said, to enter the Kingdom of God and receive His teachings with simplicity of heart."

"Divine things are great mysteries that really are over our heads, but if we just believe and meditate on them we can come into a greater understanding of them. He said that we must believe in Him or be condemned. But if we do believe, we will not perish but have eternal life. John, we must do good and seek the light and turn away from the darkness of unbelief. We must be born again into the light by faith. But God has to help us to believe. We have to want to believe and He will help us. I think that's how it will work."

"So do I," I replied. "But His words seem to make it very difficult for us. Let's continue to pray for the gift of faith."

"And let's hope that the apparent difficulty is made easier by His grace," Nicodemus concluded.

And with that we bid each other good night.

The Samaritan Woman

After this, we went with Jesus north from Judea to return to the Galilee region. But instead of taking the usual route around Samaria along the River Jordan valley, we took the shorter route directly through Samaria. Now many Jews hated the Samaritans since they were no longer accepted as Jews. After the Assyrian conquest of this land and the deportation of the Jews in 722 BC, those remaining intermarried with foreigners and lost their Jewish identity. They did not believe in our Prophets.

I found the Samaritans to be unrepentant, not open to Jesus' message and totally inhospitable to us. One night, as we sat around a campfire talking about their lack of response to Jesus' message, I was so angry that I came on like the Son of Thunder that Jesus had previously called me. I asked Him to call down fire from heaven to destroy the unrepentant and inhospitable towns. I wanted Him to act like Elijah did on Mount Carmel when he called down fire. But Jesus was merciful. His way was not to condemn and destroy but to save.

He rebuked me, "Destruction is not my way. Reconstruction is my way . . . to rebuild fallen men and women and not to destroy them. You must not discriminate against the Samaritans. You must love all people, even your enemies. There are many good Samaritans and some are even better than some of the self-righteous Jews. I'll tell you a story about one. It's called 'The Good Samaritan'."

"A man was walking down from Jerusalem to Jericho. Some robbers attacked him, stripped him, beat him, and departed, leaving him half dead. Now a Jewish priest was also walking down that road and when he saw the man, he passed by on the other side. Likewise, a Jewish Levite came to the place, saw him and passed by on the other side."

"But a Samaritan came down the same road, saw him and had compassion for him. He went up to him and bound up his wounds, pouring on oil and wine. Then he set him on his own donkey and brought him to an inn and took care of him. The next day, he took out some money and gave it to the innkeeper, saying, 'Take care of him and whatever more you spend, I will repay you when I come back.' "

Then Jesus asked us, "Which of these three, do you think, proved to be a neighbor to the man who was attacked by the robbers?"

I said, "The Samaritan who showed mercy to him."

"That's why they called him the 'Good Samaritan'," Jesus replied. "All of you should do likewise."

So, as we passed through Samaria, we tried to be like the Good Samaritan and "do likewise" as we had been admonished by Jesus. We came upon a city called Sychar about noon and the hot sun was high in the sky overhead. We were near the field that Jacob the Patriarch gave to his son Joseph. Jacob's well was there.

As Jesus reached the well, He sat down. We were all weary, hungry and thirsty from the long and hot morning walk. I sat down with Him as He sent the other disciples into the city to buy some food and water. We were both very thirsty, but we didn't have a container to get some water from the deep well.

Soon, however, a Samaritan woman came to the well to draw some water with her water jar and rope. It was unusual for a woman to come alone and more unusual for a man to talk to her and most unusual for a Jew to talk to her, a Samaritan woman. But Jesus said to her, "Give me a drink." He said it slowly and respectfully with such love and longing that I thought He was more thirsty to bring her to conversion than to satisfy His physical thirst.

She answered, "How is it that you, a Jew, a people who don't even talk to us Samaritans, ask a drink of me, a woman of Samaria?" She was firm and unafraid and seemed to possess a readiness to talk to Jesus. I saw it as a sign of her open-heartedness.

Jesus said, "If you knew the gift of God, and who it is that is saying to you, 'Give me a drink,' you would have asked Him, and He would have given you living water."

I knew that Jesus was not talking about physical water but about His Word which gives His life to the soul. However, she took Him literally and said, "Sir, you don't even have anything to draw any water with, and the well is deep; where do you get that living water? Are you greater than our father Jacob, who gave us this well, and drank from it himself with his sons and his cattle?" She showed her openness to talk of the things of God.

72

Jesus said, "Everyone who drinks of this well water will thirst again, but whoever drinks of the water that I shall give him will never thirst. The water that I shall give him will become in him a spring of water welling up to eternal life."

I saw the image of living, bubbling water that satisfies the thirst of a human heart, unlike the dormant water of the well that could only satisfy the human body temporarily. It seemed to me that Jesus was making a comparison between the old revelation to the Jews, represented by Jacob's well with its dormant earthly water, and the new revelation of His Word, represented by His new living water that brings us to eternal life.

She said, "Sir, give me this water, so that I won't be thirsty and won't have to come to this well to draw it anymore." She addressed Him with respect and her heart seemed predisposed to accept Jesus as some kind of a Prophet. But Jesus knew that her sinful life was an obstacle to her conversion.

He said, "Go, call your husband, and come here."

She answered, "I have no husband."

Jesus, all-knowing said, "You are right in saying, 'I have no husband,' for you have had five husbands, and the man whom you're living with now is not your husband. So you are speaking truly."

Yes, she spoke the literal truth, but, in moral truth, she was an adulteress. Maybe that was why she came to the well alone in the middle of the day. Most village women come to draw their water together early in the cool morning and share their news. Perhaps this woman had been ostracized by them.

She winced as Jesus had read her heart, penetrated the intimacy of her conscience, and exposed her own sins to her. "Sir, I can see that you are a Prophet. Our fathers worshiped on this mountain, but you Jews say that Jerusalem is the place where men ought to worship."

I was amazed that she called Jesus a Prophet since the Samaritans didn't believe in the Prophets or any of the Scriptures, except for the Patriarchs. Her acceptance of Jesus as a Prophet and her questioning Him as to the location of true worship showed the openness of her heart to the truth. It was the beginning of her conversion.

Jesus said, "Woman, believe me, the hour is coming when you will worship the Father neither on this mountain nor in Jerusalem. You worship what you do not know. We worship what we know, for salvation is from the Jews. But the hour is coming, and now is here, when true worshipers will worship the Father in spirit and truth, for those are the kind of people the Father seeks to worship Him. God is spirit, and those who worship Him must worship in spirit and truth."

Jesus meant that the physical place of worship is not important anymore. God wanted all peoples, Jews, Samaritans and all nations, to worship Him from their hearts, to be moved by His spirit and truth as He now moved the Samaritan woman.

She said, "I know that the Messiah, the Christ, is coming. When He comes, He will show us all things."

Jesus solemnly said, "I who speak to you am He."

I was amazed that Jesus revealed Himself as the Messiah to her, a Samaritan stranger, since He had not revealed Himself in this way to the Jews. It must have been in honor of her openheartedness. She had humbly and truthfully acknowledged her sins to Him and sought Him in spirit and truth.

Just then the rest of the disciples came. They marveled that Jesus was talking with a woman, and moreover that she was a Samaritan. But none of them said, "What do you wish?" or, "Why are you talking with her?"

The Samaritan woman dropped her water jar and ran back to the city. She forgot her original mission to fetch water and went to fetch people with her newfound faith in Jesus. She later came back and told us with great enthusiasm that she told everyone that she met, "Come and see a man who told me all that I ever did. Can this be the Christ? He Himself said, 'I am He.' "

Meanwhile the disciples kept telling Jesus, "Rabbi, eat."

But He said to them, "I have food to eat of which you do not know." Like the water that He spoke of to the Samaritan woman,

Jesus was not talking about earthly food, but they still didn't understand. So they said to one another, "What's He talking about? Has anyone brought Him food?"

Jesus said, "My food is to do the will of Him who sent me, and to accomplish His work. "

I noticed in Jesus' dialogues with Nicodemus and the Samaritan woman that He was speaking more in metaphors. He spoke to them on the earthly plane in order to raise their minds and hearts to the heavenly plane.

He had told Nicodemus on the earthly plane that he was born of the flesh but that he needed to be born again on the heavenly plane from above of the Spirit. He likened the heavenly Spirit to the earthly wind that blows where it wills, but we don't know where it comes from.

He told the Samaritan woman that He would give her living water. He raised her mind and heart from the earthly water in the well, which gives life to the body, to the heavenly water of His Word, which gives eternal life to the soul. Likewise, He told the other disciples that His food was not earthly food for His body, but heavenly food that was to do the will of His Father who sent Him to accomplish His work.

Then Jesus said, "Don't you say, 'In four months the harvest will be here?' I tell you, look up and see the fields ripe for the harvest. The reaper is already receiving payment and gathering crops for eternal life, so that the sower and reaper can rejoice together. For here the saying is verified that 'One sows and another reaps.' I sent you to reap what you have not worked for. Others have done the work and you are sharing the fruits of their work."

He was telling us that the Patriarchs and Prophets had prepared the Jews for eternal salvation — they were the sowers. But now the spiritual harvest is ready for all nations, all souls, not just the Jews, and we were sent to reap the fruits of the work of the Patriarchs and Prophets. The first fruits of our work in the Samaritan city were those who believed because of the woman's testimony.

In response to the Samaritan woman's call, many Samaritans came out from of the city to meet Jesus at the well. Many of them believed in Him because of the woman's testimony when she said, "He told me all that I ever did." When they came to Him, they asked Him to stay with them. So we went into the city and stayed for two days amongst the Samaritan people whom we had formerly scorned and avoided.

Jesus didn't perform any signs or wonders for them as so many other people had demanded. The Samaritans believed simply because of His Word.

The people said to the woman, "It is no longer because of your words that we believe, for we have heard for ourselves, and we know that this is indeed the savior of the world."

The world, I thought, not just the savior of the Jews, but the savior of all nations, the entire world! And it was the Samaritans and not the Jews, God's Chosen People, who recognized this. In a very subtle way Jesus had revealed this to them only through His Word and without miracles. However, they had received the grace to believe and proclaim it, unlike His own people who had both His Word and many miracles, but still did not recognize Him as their savior.

5. The Galilean Ministry Continues

The Healing of the Royal Official's Son

After two days in Samaria, we departed to Galilee. Jesus Himself had testified that a Prophet has no honor in his own country. So when He came to Galilee, we were surprised that the Galileans welcomed Him. This was because they had seen all that He had done in Jerusalem at the Passover Feast, for they too had gone to the Feast.

We came again to Cana in Galilee, where He had transformed the water into wine. While we were there, a royal official from Capernaum heard that Jesus was in Cana. So he went there and begged Jesus to come and heal his son, for he was at the point of death. I was amazed that such a high official would humble himself to come to Jesus to ask for help.

Jesus said to him, "Unless you see signs and wonders you will not believe." It seemed as if Jesus was calling him to believe without seeing.

Without receiving any sign, the official persisted in faith and said, "Sir, please come to my home before my child dies."

But Jesus didn't go to Capernaum, which was 24 miles away from Cana. Jesus simply spoke His word and said to him, "Go. Your son will live." He didn't perform any sign or wonder.

The man believed what Jesus said to him and, in trust, turned around and started on his way home to Capernaum. As he was going, his servants met him and told him that his son was alive. When he heard this incredible news, he asked them when he began to get better, and they said to him, "Yesterday at one in the afternoon the fever left him."

The father knew that was the hour when Jesus had said to him, "Your son will live." Not only the official himself, but his whole household came to believe. This was the second of the great signs of Jesus that manifested His glory by the healing of the Royal official's son.

The Healing of the Paralytic

After this, there was another feast so we went back up to Jerusalem to the north of the Temple area. By the Sheep Gate there is a pool which has five porticoes or corridors, one at each corner and one across the middle. In Hebrew it is called Bethesda, meaning House of Mercy. Near the pool lay a multitude of invalids, blind, lame and paralyzed. One man was a paralytic who had been ill for 38 years.

When Jesus saw him and knew that he had been lying there a long time, He asked him, "Do you want to be healed?" *Well, I thought, who wouldn't want to be healed? But, maybe he doesn't.*

The sick man answered Him, "Sir, I have no one to put me into the pool when the water moves, and while I am going another steps down before me." He didn't say that he wanted to be healed. Perhaps he had lain there so long that he had given up hope. But it seemed to me that he was just offering an excuse. Maybe he was attached to his suffering and just looking for pity. Some people enjoy their invalidism because it not only relieves them of personal responsibility, but it also brings attention to themselves.

Jesus seemed to be moved with compassion. He said to him, "Rise, take up your mat and walk."

To my amazement, the man immediately moved his legs, stood up, picked up his mat and started walking. He was healed. However, that day was the Sabbath, so the Jewish leaders said to the cured man, "It is the Sabbath, it is not lawful for you to carry your mat," because to them that was work. In fact, if work were done intentionally on the Sabbath it carried the penalty of death by stoning.

So, he quickly blamed Jesus and answered them, "The man who healed me said to me, 'Rise, take up your mat and walk.' "

So they asked him, "Who is the man who said this to you?" The healed man didn't even know who it was and Jesus had withdrawn because of the crowd in the place. The man never even thanked Jesus, he just blamed Him!

Afterward, Jesus found the man in the Temple, and said to him, "See, you are well! Sin no more, that nothing worse will happen to you."

Then the man went away and told the leaders that it was Jesus who had healed him. This was why they persecuted Jesus, because He did this so-called "work" on the Sabbath. This was the third of His great signs that manifested His glory by His healing of the paralytic.

Now the Sabbath rest was originally meant to be a time to remember and celebrate God's goodness and the goodness of His creation. It was a day set apart for the praise of God and His work of creation. Of course, God rested from His work of creation on the seventh day, but He didn't rest from love and mercy nor from His providence in maintaining life in existence. The Sabbath rest was intended to bring everyday work to a halt and to provide needed rest and refreshment, not to prevent merciful healing.

Jesus acted as if God gave the Sabbath for our benefit, to refresh and renew us in living for God. It was intended for good and not for evil. Withholding mercy and kindness in response to human need was not part of God's intention when He commanded that we keep the Lord's Day holy. But the Scribes and Pharisees were filled with fury and contempt for Jesus because they put their own thoughts of right and wrong above God's. They were ensnared in their own legalism because they did not want to see God's purpose for rest on the Sabbath.

Jesus did not apologize when they confronted Him for what they thought was work on the Sabbath. Rather, He courageously answered them, "My Father is working still, and I am working."

This was why they sought all the more to kill Him, because they thought that He had not only broken the Sabbath, but also because He called God His Father, making Himself equal with God. To me this was total blindness on their part since He only did good and for that they wanted to do evil — just like those that had tried at Nazareth — they wanted to kill Him!

Because of their misinterpretation of the Law, Jesus mercifully told them the truth — for those who were open to it — even though most of them wanted to kill Him.

Jesus said to them:

> Truly, truly, I say to you, the Son can do nothing of His own accord, but only what He sees the Father doing; for whatever He does, that the Son does likewise. For the Father loves the Son, and shows Him all that He Himself is doing; and He will show them greater works than these so that you may be amazed.

> For just as the Father raises the dead and gives them life, so also does the Son give life to whom He will. The Father judges no one, but has given all judgment to the Son, that all may honor the Son, just as they honor the Father. He who does not honor the Son does not honor the Father who sent Him. Truly, truly, I say to you, he who hears my word and believes in Him who sent me, has eternal life. He does not come into condemnation, but has passed from death to life.

Truly, truly, I say to you, the hour is coming, and now is, when the dead will hear the voice of the Son of God, and those who hear will live. For just as the Father has life in Himself, so He has granted the Son also to have life in Himself, and has given Him authority to execute judgment, because He is the Son of Man.

Do not be amazed at this because the hour is coming when all who are in the tombs will hear His voice and come forth, those who have done good, to the resurrection of life, and those who have done evil, to the resurrection of condemnation.

I can do nothing on my own authority. As I hear, I judge. And my judgment is just, because I seek not my own will, but the will of Him who sent me.

I thought, *Only God can give eternal life and render an eternal judgment of acquittal or condemnation. He must be not only the Son of Man, as He just said, but also the Son of God, as He also has just said.*

He promised that whoever hears His word and believes in the Father who sent Him, has eternal life and does not come into condemnation. All who have done good will have the resurrection of life, and those who have done evil, the resurrection of condemnation. But the Scribes and Pharisees must not really love God since they have rejected His Son. They love human glory, and attempt to justify themselves with their prejudiced interpretation of the Scriptures, and so they condemn themselves.

Jesus did not merely bear witness to Himself, but He also reminded the Scribes and Pharisees of His witnesses, all of whom testified to Him as the Son of God. His witnesses were John the Baptist, His Father, the Scriptures and His own works. He told them:

If I bear witness to myself, my testimony cannot be verified. But there is another who bears witness

81

to me, and I know that the testimony which he bears to me is true. You sent emissaries to inquire of John the Baptist and he testified to me. I do not accept testimony from a human being, but I say this so that you may be saved.

John was a burning and shining lamp, and you were willing to rejoice for a while in his light. But the testimony which I have is greater than John's. The works which the Father has granted me to accomplish, these very works that I perform, bear witness to me that the Father has sent me.

Moreover, the Father who sent me has Himself borne witness to me. But you have never heard His voice nor seen His form, and you do not have His word abiding in you, because you do not believe in Him whom He has sent.

You search the Scriptures, because you think that you have eternal life through them. Yet it is the Scriptures that bear witness to me. But you refuse to come to me that you may have life.

I do not receive glory from men. But I know that you do not have the love of God within you. I have come in my Father's name, and you do not receive me. If another comes in his own name, him you will receive. How can you believe, when you accept praise from one another but do not seek the glory that comes from the only God?

Do not think that I shall accuse you to the Father. Moses will be the one who accuses you, on whom you set your hope. If you had believed Moses, you would believe me, because he wrote about me. But if you do not believe his writings, how will you believe my words?

Jesus spoke with the authority of God, whom He called His Father, and implicitly proved His own divinity. But His opponents refused to accept His divine authority. They demanded evidence for His claim. Jesus answered their charges by saying that His own testimony could not be sufficient under their Law, so He supported it with the evidence of His witnesses. The Law of Moses had laid down the principle that the unsupported evidence of one person could not prevail against a man for any crime or wrong in connection with any offense he committed. (See Deuteronomy 17:6). At least two or three witnesses were needed.

Jesus began His defense by citing John the Baptist as a witness, since John publicly pointed to Jesus as the Messiah and had repeatedly borne witness to Him. Jesus also asserted that greater proofs of His identity are the signs and miracles that He performed. He cites His works not to point to Himself, but to point to the power of God working in and through Him. He cites God the Father as His supreme witness.

The Scribes and Pharisees thought that they had eternal life through the Scriptures. But Jesus asserted that the Scriptures themselves point to Him as the Messiah. Eternal life is through Him and not through the Scriptures.

In spite of all of these witnesses, in their pride they still refused to come to Jesus for eternal life. The problem with the Scribes and Pharisees was that they really did not believe what Moses had written. Jesus reminded us that His Father gives all judgment to Him and He assured us that he who believes in the Father has eternal life.

The Multiplication of the Bread and Fish

A few months later, we went with Jesus across the Sea of Galilee. A large crowd followed Him, because they had seen the signs He performed by healing the sick. He went up on the mountain and sat down with us. It was near the Jewish Feast of Passover. At Passover we ate unleavened bread in memory of the unleavened bread that the Israelites ate in their hasty Exodus under God's protection from the slavery of the Egyptian Pharaoh.

When Jesus raised His eyes and saw that a large crowd was coming to Him, He said to Philip, "Where can we buy enough bread for them to eat?"

He said this to test him, because He Himself knew what He was going to do.

Philip answered Him, "Two hundred days' wages would not buy enough bread for each of them to have a little."

Andrew, Simon Peter's brother, said, "There is a boy here who has five barley loaves and two fish; but what good are these for so many?"

Jesus said, "Have the people recline." Now there was a great deal of grass in that place. So the men reclined, about five thousand in number. They sat in small circular groups and looked almost like flower-beds on the grass.

Then Jesus took the boy's loaves, gave thanks, and had them distributed in baskets to those who were reclining, and also as much of the fish as they wanted. As they were distributed, the quantity did not diminish at all. When they had had their fill, He said to us, "Gather up the fragments left over, so that nothing will be wasted."

So we gathered them up and filled twelve wicker baskets with fragments from the five barley loaves that had been multiplied into more than they could eat. This was the fourth of the great signs of Jesus that manifested His glory by multiplying the bread.

This was an astounding miracle revealing both the sympathy of Jesus for the hungry people and God's bountiful blessings. Jesus was sensitive to both the peoples' spiritual and material needs. He used the resources that were available, the clearly inadequate loaves and fishes, supplied what was lacking, and exceeded their needs.

This reminded me of the story of the multiplication of the barley bread by the Prophet Elisha. He had also said that his skeptical servant should give the many people the few barley loaves that he had. Elisha insisted, "Give it to the people to eat. For thus says the Lord, 'They shall eat and there shall be some left over.' " (2

Kings 4:42-44). And there was, just as there was after the multiplication by Jesus.

When the people saw the sign that Jesus had done, they said, "This is truly the Prophet, the one who is to come into the world."

They referred to the Prophet whom Moses prophesied God would raise up after his lifetime. The people of Israel had been waiting for the Prophet. Moses had promised, "The Lord your God will raise up for you a Prophet like me from among you, from your brethren—him shall you heed." (Deuteronomy 18:15). I thought that the signs which Jesus did, including this miraculous feeding of the five thousand, signified that God had indeed sent Him as anointed Prophet and King, the Messiah.

However, most of the Jews expected the Prophet to be an earthly savior who would bring material prosperity, like this multiplication, and save them from Roman domination. They just wanted to renew the political government and the external disorder. They did not want to renew their own personal government and their own internal disorder. They did not heed the preaching of Jesus to repent and reform their lives. Since Jesus knew that they were going to come and carry Him off to make Him an earthly king, He withdrew again to the mountain, alone.

Jesus Walks on the Water

When evening came, we went down to the Sea of Galilee. Jesus told us to go to the other side of the Sea while He dismissed the crowds and went off to the mountain to pray. So we got into the boat and started rowing towards Capernaum, about seven miles away. It got dark and the sea rose because a strong wind was blowing and the sea was against us. The boat was being tossed about by the waves and we were frightened.

Soon the waves were coming over the sides into our boat. We started bailing the water out, but it came in too fast and we couldn't keep up with it. The boat was filling up and on the verge of sinking. We feared for our lives.

Just then, we saw Jesus miraculously walking on the water, approaching the boat. We were terrified, but Jesus said to us, "It is I. Do not be afraid."

Then He got into the boat with us and the wind died down immediately. We were completely astounded and said, "Truly, you are the Son of God."

The Bread of Life Discourse

The next day, the crowd of people who had remained across the Sea saw that there had been only one boat there, and that Jesus had not entered it with us, and that we had gone away alone.

But there were other boats there that came from Tiberius near the place where they had eaten the bread when the Lord gave thanks. So when the crowd saw that neither Jesus nor we were there, they got into the other boats and went to Capernaum looking for Jesus.

They found Him teaching in the synagogue and asked Him, "Rabbi, when did you get here?"

Jesus answered, "Truly, truly, I say to you, you seek me, not because you saw signs, but because you ate your fill of the loaves."

Then, in the manner that He spoke to the Samaritan woman at the well, He said, "Do not work for food which perishes, but for the food that endures for eternal life, which the Son of Man will give to you. For on Him, God the Father has set His seal."

I thought, *If God the Father has placed His seal on the Son of Man, then He is also truly authenticated by the Father as the Son of God! That's what the Father's voice over the waters called Him when John baptized Him. He called Him "my beloved Son." And as the seal impresses its form on wax, so has the Father impressed His form in some mysterious way on His Son as God's truth in the flesh of the Son of Man. He is the image of God in the flesh. But what is this "food" that He says He'll give us? Will it be like the manna God gave to the Israelites in the desert?*

Then they said to Him, "What must we do, to accomplish the works of God?"

Jesus answered, "This is the work of God, that you believe in the one whom He has sent." They thought that works were actions that you did and not beliefs that you held. They wanted Jesus to tell them what actions they should do. But He told them that the one basic work was to believe in Him as the one sent by God the Father as His Son.

So the crowd asked Him, "Then what sign can you do, that we may see and believe you? What can you do? Our ancestors ate the manna in the desert." They quoted the psalm and said, "As it is written, 'He gave them bread from heaven to eat.' " (Psalm 77).

Jesus said to them, "Truly, truly, I say to you, it was not Moses who gave the bread from heaven; my Father gives you the true bread from heaven. For the bread of God is that which comes down from heaven and gives life to the world."

They said to Him, "Sir, give us this bread always."

Jesus said to them, "I am the bread of life; he who comes to me shall not hunger, and he who believes in me shall never thirst."

Our teachers had always regarded the manna in the desert as the bread of God. (See Psalm 78:24; Exodus 16:15). They also taught that when the Messiah came he would give manna from heaven just as Moses had done. So the Jewish leaders were demanding that Jesus produce manna from heaven as proof that He was the Messiah. He responded by telling them that it was not Moses who gave the manna in the desert, but God. So the manna given to Moses and the people was not the real bread from heaven, but only a symbol of Jesus, the bread to come.

I thought, *Jesus Himself is the bread of life and He gives Himself so that we will not have supernatural hunger. He satisfies our supernatural hunger, unlike Moses through whom God gave manna and satisfied the natural hunger of our ancestors.*

Jesus makes a claim which only God can make, "I am the bread of life." But how can He be bread and what is this life that He gives? The manna in the wilderness sustained the Israelites on their journey to the

87

Promised Land. Will Jesus sustain us on our journey to the eternal Promised Land? How?

Jesus continued His discourse, "But I told you that although you have seen me, yet you still do not believe. All that the Father gives me will come to me and him who comes to me I will not reject. For I have come down from heaven, not to do my own will, but to do the will of Him who sent me."

"And this is the will of Him who sent me, that I should lose nothing of all that He has given me, but raise it up at the last day. For this is the will of my Father, that everyone who sees the Son and believes in Him should have eternal life and I will raise him up at the last day."

Jesus now clearly revealed that He is the one sent by the Father, as Jesus Himself had previously told Nicodemus in private. Jesus had told him that He was sent from heaven by the Father as the Son of God to give eternal life to those who believe in Him. Now He clearly revealed Himself in public to the crowd as the Son of God who came down from His Father in heaven as the Bread of Life for all who believe in Him. He would never reject them, as earthly family and friends might reject them.

On the contrary, He would raise them up to eternal life on the last day. Only the true, divine Son of God could say that He was sent by His Father in heaven and could then make such a great promise to raise those who believe in Him on the last day!

The Jews then murmured at Him, because He had said, "I am the bread which came down from heaven." They said, just like His Nazarean neighbors had said of Him in their synagogue, "Is not this Jesus, the son of Joseph, whose father and mother we know? How does He now say, 'I have come down from heaven'?"

Jesus answered them, "Do not murmur among yourselves. No one can come to me unless the Father who sent me draws him and I will raise him up at the last day. It is written in the Prophets, 'And they shall all be taught by God.' Everyone who has heard and learned from the Father comes to me. Not that anyone has seen the Father except Him who is from God. He has seen the Father. Truly, truly, I say to you, he who believes has eternal life."

"I am the bread of life. Your ancestors ate the manna in the desert and they died." Then He pointed to His heart and confirmed my belief in plain language, "This is the bread which comes down from heaven, that a man may eat of it and not die. I am the living bread which came down from heaven. If anyone eats of this bread, he will live forever and the bread which I shall give is my flesh for the life of the world."

Yes, I thought, bread is the staple of life and He is the true living bread of life because He gives us a share in the very life of God through which we will live forever – eternal life!

He said that He is from God and is the only one who has seen God and implied that He fulfills the prophecy that we would be taught by God through Himself! It's as if God spoke through Him, that He was the Word of God and that Word became flesh and was right here among us. And He will give us the bread of His flesh. His Father draws us, but we must come to Jesus voluntarily and accept His word as the truth. I believe this even though I don't understand this mystery.

He's not just the son of Joseph and Mary. He really came down from heaven – from God – to be with us. The bread analogy is clear to me. Natural bread starts with wheat sown and grown in good soil. Then it sprouts, is ground into flour, rises, is baked and becomes bread which we eat for our life.

In the same way, Jesus is the supernatural Bread of Life, He was the wheat sown by God, grown in the good soil of His mother's womb and sprouted in birth. But how will His life fulfill the analogy? How will He be ground and rise? How will His flesh be bread for the life of the world? How will He give it to us and how will we eat His flesh and live forever? How will we rise on the last day?

The Jews then disputed among themselves, asking the same question, "How can this man give us His flesh to eat?"

So Jesus said to them plainly, "Truly, truly, I say to you, unless you eat the flesh of the Son of Man and drink His blood, you do not have life within you. He who eats my flesh and drinks my blood has eternal life and I will raise him up at the last day. For my flesh is real food, and my blood is real drink."

"Whoever eats my flesh and drinks my blood lives in me, and I in him. As the living Father sent me, and I live because of the

89

Father, so he who eats me will live because of me. This is the bread which came down from heaven. Unlike your ancestors who ate manna and still died, whoever eats this bread will live forever." He said all of this while teaching in the synagogue in Capernaum.

When they heard this, many of His disciples were shocked because He said that we had to drink His blood to have life within us. The Law forbade the drinking of blood because the blood of every creature is its life. Even so, I thought that Jesus is the true supernatural life who gives us eternal life. But they said, "This is a hard saying; who can listen to it?"

The words of Jesus did not leave any middle ground for us. We had to either accept His word as divine or reject it as the claim of an impostor. It certainly was a "hard saying." It wasn't just hard to understand, but hard to accept. But Jesus pressed us because He wanted to test our faith and loyalty.

Jesus, knowing in Himself that His disciples were murmuring and were wondering how He could have come down from heaven, asked them, "Do you take offense at this? Then what if you were to see the Son of Man ascending to where He was before? It is the spirit that gives life, the flesh is of no avail, the words that I spoke to you are spirit and life. But there are some of you that do not believe."

For Jesus knew that they would interpret His mysteries in a fleshly, natural sense rather than in a spiritual, supernatural sense. He also knew from the beginning those who would not believe Him and the one who would betray Him. He said, "This is why I told you that no one can come to me unless it is granted him by the Father."

After this, many of His disciples drew back and no longer went about with Him. They knew that Jesus had not spoken symbolically, but literally when He said that His flesh was real food and His blood real drink and that unless they eat and drink it they would have no life within them. But they found this completely incomprehensible. They did not believe the truth of His revelation that He spoke on His own authority as the Son of God.

So Jesus said to us, "Do you also wish to go away?"

Simon Peter answered Him, "Lord, to whom shall we go? You have the words of eternal life. We have believed, and have come to know that you are the Holy One of God." He was confessing his belief in Jesus as the Messiah.

Jesus answered them, "Did I not choose you, the twelve, and one of you is a devil?"

I was shocked that Jesus said this. However, later events proved the truth of His prophecy. He spoke of Judas, the son of Simon Iscariot, for he was the one of the twelve who would later betray Him.

Jesus might have said this to prick the conscience of Judas because He knew that he would plot to betray Him. When He said, "One of you is a devil," Jesus probably saw the seeds of this plot planted in Judas because of His discourse on the bread of life. Yet, He gave Judas an opportunity to examine his conscience to see if he would become a true follower of His.

Unlike Judas, the rest of us believed. Since we had just recently witnessed the miracles of Jesus in the multiplication of the bread and fish and His walking on the water, our faith was strengthened enough to believe His statement that if we ate His flesh and drank His blood, we would remain in Him and He in us. We did not understand this at all, but we believed it. We did not leave Him like so many other disciples did. Like Peter, we believed that we had nowhere else to go. Jesus had the words of eternal life and if we believed and waited, perhaps we would come to understand.

The Son of the Living God

Next, we went by boat to Magdala on the west side of the Sea of Galilee and from there sailed east across the Sea to my village of Bethsaida where Jesus cured a blind man. After that, He took us north to Caesarea Philippi in the extreme north of Israel where the headwaters of the Jordan begin their flow south. This is the place where the Greeks worshiped Pan, their false god. There

Jesus asked us, "Who do people say the Son of Man is?" This is a question that every person should ask himself. Is He just another teacher or someone much greater?

Peter replied, "You are the Christ, the Son of the living God." As he had confessed at the Bread of Life discourse, this was Peter's second confession of his faith that Jesus was the Messiah.

Jesus answered him, "Blessed are you, Simon Bar-Jona! For flesh and blood has not revealed this to you, but my Father who is in heaven. And I tell you, you are Peter, (which means rock) and on this rock I will build my Church, and the powers of death shall not prevail against it. I will give you the keys of the kingdom of heaven, and whatever you bind on Earth shall be bound in heaven, and whatever you loose on Earth shall be loosed in heaven." Then He strictly charged us to tell no one that He was the Christ.

Peter appeared dumbfounded at this revelation that he, a simple fisherman, was the rock upon which Christ would build His Church and that He would give him the keys of the kingdom of heaven! Jesus confirmed Peter's confession of faith that He was the Messiah by acknowledging that it came not from Peter, but from the Father.

From that time on, Jesus began to show us that He must go to Jerusalem and suffer many things from the elders and Chief Priests and Scribes, and be killed, and on the third day be raised. Peter took Him aside and began to rebuke Him, saying, "God forbid, Lord! This shall never happen to you."

But Jesus turned and said to Peter, "Get behind me, Satan! You are not judging by God's standards but by men's."

Poor Peter, I thought. *Jesus just finishes telling him that His Father spoke through him and now He tells him that Satan spoke through him! The thought of Jesus' prophecy of His own death saddens me greatly but, I wonder, what does He mean by being raised on the third day?*

Then Jesus admonished us, "If any man would come after me, let him deny himself and take up his cross and follow me. For whoever would save his life will lose it, and whoever loses his life for my sake will find it. For what will it profit a man, if he gains the whole world and forfeits his life? Or what shall a man give in return for his life? For the Son of Man is to come with His angels in the glory of His Father, and then He will repay every man for what he has done. Truly, I say to you, there are some standing here who will not taste death before they see the Son of Man coming in His Kingdom."

Yes, I thought, *we can gain all the pleasures of this world and lose eternal life, but we can't gain eternal life on our own. It can be gained only as a reward for our faith, self-denial and works of mercy by following in the footsteps of Jesus. And to think that this Kingdom will begin with some of us seeing Jesus coming into it! But how?*

The Transfiguration

Six days later, Jesus took Peter, James and me and led us up Mount Tabor, a 1000-foot-high mountain located southeast of Nazareth. He went to pray. While Jesus was praying, He was suddenly transfigured before us. His face shone like the sun and His garments became white as light. It was as if the light came from inside of Him. I felt a reverent awe come over me as I squinted to see His face.

Jesus' face reflected as Moses' face probably had when he came down from Mount Sinai with the two tablets of the Ten Commandments in his hands. Moses did not know that the skin of his face had become radiant while he conversed with the Lord. When Aaron and the other children of Israel saw Moses and noticed how radiant his face had become, they were afraid to come near him. So he had to put a veil over his face.

To my utter surprise, in the middle of my reflection, Moses, the lawgiver, and Elijah, the Prophet, appeared in glory and were talking with Jesus on Mount Tabor. They spoke of His own Exodus that He would accomplish in Jerusalem. I thought that Jesus must be the fulfillment of the Law and the Prophets — the fulfillment of God's revelation to humanity.

As Moses had led the Israelites on their Exodus from Egypt to the Promised Land, so would Jesus lead us in our Exodus from this world to His Kingdom, the Promised Land of the next world.

Suddenly, we were overcome by sleep. When we came fully awake, Peter apparently thought that the Kingdom was going to begin then and there. He impulsively said to Jesus, "Lord, it is well that we are here. If you wish, I will make three tents here, one for you, one for Moses and one for Elijah."

He was still speaking when a bright cloud overshadowed us and a voice from the cloud said, "This is my beloved Son, with whom I am well pleased. Listen to Him."

It was that voice again! The voice that I had heard after Jesus was baptized in the River Jordan. Again God had called Jesus "His Son." We had encountered God on Mount Tabor just as Moses and Elijah had encountered Him on Mount Sinai.

The appearance of Jesus reminded me of the psalm, "Bless the Lord, O my soul! O Lord my God, you are very great! You are covered with majesty and glory, robed in light as with a garment." (Psalm 104:1-2). This confirmed for me that He was indeed the Son of God since He had revealed His Father's light to us and was identified by the Father's voice as His Son to whom we should listen. He received honor and glory from His Father when that unique declaration came to Him. This confirmed His Father's identification of Jesus in almost the same words as at the beginning of His ministry when He was baptized by John in the River Jordan. Only this time the Father told us to listen to Him, which I began to do even more attentively than before.

In this discovery of the identity of Jesus, we could do nothing but fall on our faces in awe and reverence. But then Jesus came and touched us, saying, "Rise, and have no fear." So we got up. When we lifted up our eyes, we saw that Jesus was now alone and in His normal appearance.

As we were coming down the mountain, Jesus commanded us, "Tell no one the vision, until the Son of Man is raised from the dead."

Again, I wondered what it meant to be raised from the dead and why Elijah appeared and disappeared on the mountain.

We asked him, "Why do the Scribes say that first Elijah must come?"

He replied, "Elijah does come, and he is to restore all things; but I tell you that Elijah has already come, and they did not know him, but did to him whatever they pleased. So also the Son of Man will suffer at their hands."

Then I understood that He was speaking to us of John the Baptist. He meant that the spirit of Elijah had already come in the person of John the Baptist. The Kingdom had come in the person of Jesus, with His precursor John the Baptist in the spirit of Elijah.

The next day, after we came down from the mountain, a large crowd met us. There was a man in the crowd who cried out, "Teacher, I beg you, look at my son. He is my only child. A demon is in him and he suddenly screams and it convulses him until he foams at the mouth. It releases him only with difficulty and wears him out. I begged your disciples to cast it out but they could not."

Jesus said in reply, "O faithless and perverse generation, how long will I be with you and endure you? Bring your son here." As the child was coming forward, the demon threw him to the ground in a convulsion. But then Jesus rebuked the demon, healed the boy and returned him to his father. We were astonished by the majesty and power of Jesus.

After that, on another day, my "Son of Thunder" fiery temperament got the best of me. I was angry because Jesus' own disciples could not cast out that demon from that boy, but I saw that another man, who wasn't one of us, was driving out demons in the name of Jesus.

I complained to Jesus, "Teacher, we saw someone driving out demons in your name and I tried to prevent him because he does not follow us."

But Jesus said, "Do not prevent him; for no one who does a mighty work in my name will speak evil of me. Anyone who is not against us is for us. Truly I tell you, whoever gives one of you a cup of water to drink because you are one of my followers, will by no means lose his reward."

We had thought that Jesus had come just to save us Jews, the Chosen People. But, He seemed to be saying that He came to save all peoples and all nations, truly a King of All Nations and that all those who do good might have their eternal reward whether or not they were one of our followers.

The End of the Galilean Ministry

Then we went back to Capernaum for the last time. This was the end of our Galilean ministry and Jesus instructed us on the Kingdom. We asked Him, "Who is the greatest in the Kingdom of God?"

He called a child to Himself, put him in the midst of us and said, "Truly, I say to you, unless you turn and become like children, you will never enter the Kingdom of God. Whoever humbles himself like this child, he is the greatest in the Kingdom of God. Whoever receives one such child in my name receives me; but whoever causes one of these little ones who believe in me to sin, it would be better for him to have a great millstone fastened round his neck and to be drowned in the depth of the sea."

"See that you do not despise one of these little ones," He continued, "for I tell you that in heaven their angels always behold the face of my Father who is in heaven."

Then Peter came up and asked Him about forgiveness, "Lord, how often shall my brother sin against me and I forgive him? As many as seven times?" Jesus said to him, "I do not say to you seven times, but seventy times seven."

"Therefore, the Kingdom of God may be compared to a king who wished to settle accounts with his servants. When he began the reckoning, one was brought to him who owed him ten thousand talents. Since he could not pay it, his lord ordered him to be sold, with his wife and children and all that he had, and to make the payment. So the servant fell on his knees and implored him, 'Lord, have patience with me, and I will pay you everything.' So, out of pity for him, his lord released him and forgave him the debt."

"But that same servant, as he went out, came upon one of his fellow servants who owed him only a hundred denarii. He seized him by the throat and said, 'Pay what you owe.' His fellow servant fell down and besought him, as he had besought his lord, 'Have patience with me, and I will pay you.' But he refused and went and put him in prison till he should pay the debt. When his fellow servants saw what he had done, they were greatly distressed, and they went and reported to their lord all that had taken place."

"Then his lord summoned him and said, 'You wicked servant! I forgave you all that debt because you besought me. Now, shouldn't you have had mercy on your fellow servant, as I had mercy on you?' And in anger his lord delivered him to the jailers, till he should pay all his debt. So also my heavenly Father will do to every one of you, if you do not forgive your brother from your heart."

I resolved to follow this teaching of Jesus on forgiveness.

6. The Feast of Booths in Jerusalem

In autumn, we usually celebrated the Feast of Booths (or Tabernacles) in Jerusalem. This was the joyful Jewish harvest feast that lasted for eight days in thanksgiving for the yearly harvest. During the feast, we lived in temporary improvised huts with leafy branches. This was to remind us of the 40 years that our ancestors lived in booths, or tents, with Moses in the desert, to give thanks for the permanent home that God gave to us in the Promised Land, and for His home in the Temple, which succeeded His Tabernacle in the desert.

The images of light and water were associated with the Feast of Booths. Light reminded us of the pillar of fire that accompanied and guided our ancestors in the desert. Water reminded us of how God quenched the thirst of our ancestors in the desert when Moses struck the rock and water flowed from it.

The feast was coming up, so Jesus' relatives tried to give Him some worldly advice in order for Him to become more popular. They said to Him, "Let's leave here and go up to Judea, so that your disciples may see the works that you're doing. Nobody works in secret if he wants to be known openly. If you're going to do these things, show yourself publicly."

Sadly, even His relatives didn't understand that His mission was not to save us from Roman domination but to save us from our sins. They were worldly and just wanted to show Him off and bask in His glory in the great city of Jerusalem.

So Jesus said to them, "My time hasn't come to show myself publicly, but your time is always here. The world can't hate you, but it hates me because I say that its works are evil. You can go to the feast yourselves. I'm not going because my time hasn't fully come."

Jesus stayed in Galilee. When He said that the world "hates me because I say that its works are evil," it reminded me of the time that His cousin John the Baptist said that its works were evil. He told King Herod Antipas, "It's not right for you to live with your brother's wife." Her name was Herodias. She always hated John for what he had said and later had Herod order his beheading and had his head delivered to her on a silver platter. I feared for the life of Jesus due to the hatred of the world.

A Sign of Contradiction

So Jesus stayed behind while His relatives went up to the feast in a caravan. Then a few days later, Jesus also went up, but He traveled alone so that the leaders wouldn't know that He was coming and have time to make plans to kill Him. They were looking for Him at the feast and asking everyone, "Where is He?"

There was much muttering about Him among the people. While some said, "He's a good man," others said, "No, He's leading the people astray." Yet no one spoke openly of Him. They were all afraid of the leaders. It seemed to me that Jesus was truly a sign of contradiction as Simeon had prophesied to His mother when He was presented in the Temple as a baby.

Four days later, in the middle of the feast, when the time was right, Jesus suddenly appeared in the Temple and taught the people. He taught just as if He were one of the leaders of the Jews. The leaders were amazed.

They said, "How is it that this man has learning when He has never even studied in any of our schools? He's just teaching His own inventions." They misjudged Him to be a simple ignorant son of a carpenter from rural Galilee.

So Jesus humbly and truly answered them, "My teaching is not mine, but His who sent me. If any man's will is to do His will, he shall know whether the teaching is from God or whether I am speaking on my own authority. He who speaks on his own authority seeks his own glory. But he who seeks the glory of Him who sent Him is true, and in Him there is no falsehood. I have no interest in my own glory, but only in that of the one who sent me."

He said it very plainly to them. His teaching was not His own, He had not invented anything. In fact, His teaching was divine. It was revealed to Him by His Father.

"Didn't Moses give you the Law?" Jesus continued, "Yet none of you keeps the Law. But you are angry at me because you think that I don't keep the same Law that you don't keep?"

Then He asked them straight out, "Why do you seek to kill me?"

The crowd answered, "You have a demon! Who is seeking to kill you?"

Jesus answered them, "I did one good deed at Bethesda on the Sabbath. I cured a paralyzed man and you are all disturbed. Now Moses gave you the law of circumcision on the eighth day from a baby's birth. Of course, that law is not from Moses, but from the Patriarchs before him. You follow this law and you circumcise a baby upon the Sabbath if it falls on the eighth day from his birth."

"So if a baby receives a beneficial circumcision that affects only a small part of his body on the Sabbath, to fulfill the law of Moses, why are you angry with me because on the Sabbath I made a man's whole body well by curing his paralysis? Don't judge by appearances, but judge with right judgment."

Some of the people of Jerusalem then said, "Is not this the man whom they seek to kill? And here He is, speaking openly, and they say nothing to Him! Can it be that the authorities really know that this is the Christ? Yet we know where this man comes from; and when the Christ appears, no one will know where he comes from."

Then Jesus proclaimed, "You think that you know me, and that you know where I come from? But I have not come of my own accord. He who sent me is true, and Him you do not know. I know Him, for I come from Him, and He sent me."

They didn't know that He was referring to God, His Father in heaven. They sought to arrest Him, but no one laid hands on Him because His hour had not yet come. Yet many of the people believed in Him. They asked with the belief that He was the Messiah, the Christ, "When the Christ appears, will he do more signs than this man has done?"

The Pharisees heard the crowd muttering like this about Him, so they and the Chief Priests sent their Temple police officers to arrest Him. Jesus then said, "I shall be with you a little longer, and then I go to Him who sent me. You will seek me and you will not find me, for where I am you cannot come."

The leaders said to one another, "Where does this man intend to go that we shall not find him? Does He intend to go to the Dispersion into Alexandria and Rome and even teach the Greeks? What does He mean by saying, 'You will seek me and you will not find me' and, 'Where I am you cannot come'? "

Unknown to them, Jesus was referring to heaven to which He was going and from which they were excluding themselves by their unbelief and hardness of heart.

Each morning of the feast the High Priest went down to the Pool of Siloam and brought back a gold pitcher of water to the Temple. He poured the water on the altar of holocausts, in remembrance of the water which had sprung up miraculously through Moses in the desert as the people prayed for rain. The people also listened to readings from Isaiah of the joy to come in messianic times and the prophecy from Ezekiel about the torrents of water which would flow from the Temple. They chanted the psalm in remembrance of Moses who "cleft the rock and the water gushed forth and flowed in the dry lands like a river." (Psalm 105).

Just then, as the High Priest poured out the water on the last and greatest day of the feast, Jesus, with reference to the flowing water, stood up, publicly revealed Himself in the presence of the multitude and spoke in a loud voice which attracted everyone's attention. He proclaimed, "If anyone thirsts, let him come to me and drink. He who believes in me, as the Scripture has said, 'Out of his heart shall flow rivers of living water.' "

Jesus was referring to the Prophet Ezekiel who had a vision of rivers of water flowing out of the Temple. But He was talking about living water, whom those who believed in Him would receive from Him who was the true Temple in whom God dwelled. I was thirsty for this living water.

When they heard these words, some of the people said, "This is really the Prophet," referring again to the Prophet whom God prophesied to Moses would arise in the future.

Others said, "This is the Christ." But some said, "Is the Christ to come from Galilee? Has not the Scripture said that the Christ is descended from David and comes from Bethlehem, the village where David was?"

They thought that they knew everything, but they didn't know that in fact Jesus really was descended from David, as was His mother. They didn't know what His mother had told me on the walk to Capernaum, that Jesus actually was born in Bethlehem, the city of David, in fulfillment of the prophecy of Micah. They didn't know that King Herod the Great had tried to kill Him when He was a baby in Bethlehem in response to the Wise Men's pilgrimage there, and they also didn't know of the information that Herod had received from the Chief Priests that the Christ was to be born there. There was a division among the people over Him. Some of them wanted to arrest Him, but no one laid hands on Him.

Jesus impressed the Temple guards so much that they saw no cause to arrest Him. They returned to the Chief Priests and Pharisees who said to them, "Why didn't you bring Him?"

They answered, "No man ever spoke like this man!" They had not even seen a miracle, but they had been convinced by a single teaching from Jesus.

103

The Pharisees answered them, "Are you led astray, you also? Have any of the authorities or any of the Pharisees believed in Him?" (They said this in great anger as if they were the only ones who knew anything and the ignorant people were subject to their contempt.) They concluded in great snobbery, "These people, who do not know the Law, are accursed."

But then Nicodemus, who was one of them, supported the Temple guards and appealed for a fair hearing. Nicodemus was the one who had previously gone to Jesus at night. He said to the Pharisees, "Does our Law judge a man without first giving him a hearing and learning what he does?"

They replied in contempt to him who was one of their own, "Are you from Galilee too? Search the Scriptures and you will see that no prophet is to rise from Galilee."

They thought they knew everything, but they were ignorant of Jesus' true origins and of His birth in Bethlehem. They all went home in their ignorance.

The Woman Caught in Adultery

After teaching in the Temple, Jesus went up to the Mount of Olives that overlooked Jerusalem. He often spent the night there in prayer. Early in the morning, He came back down to the Temple. All the people came to Him and He sat down and taught them.

Then the Scribes and the Pharisees brought to Jesus a woman whom they had caught in the act of adultery and placed her in their midst. Her eyes were swollen red and tears streamed down her cheeks.

They said to Jesus, "Teacher, we caught this woman in the act of adultery. Now the Law of Moses commanded us to stone her for such. What do you say about her?"

They said this to test Him so that they'd have a pretext for some charge to bring against Him if He said something contrary to the Law of Moses or if He exhibited forgiveness instead of saying, "Stone her!"

Jesus bent down and wrote with His finger on the ground. He acted as if He was absorbed in something else. He didn't seem perturbed by their cunning and malice. As they continued to ask Him, He stood up and said to them, "Let him who is without sin among you be the first to throw a stone at her."

Jesus struck their consciences with His statement and made them aware of their own hypocrisy. Once more He bent down and wrote with His finger on the ground. Then, looking shameful, they began to leave, one after the other, beginning with the oldest. Jesus was left alone with the frightened woman standing before Him.

He looked up at her and said, "Woman, where are they? Has no one condemned you?"

She respectfully replied, "No one, Lord." She acted as if she had found a Savior and not a Judge.

And Jesus said, "Neither do I condemn you. Go and do not sin again." The woman left in peace.

He just let her go! He condemned sin, but not the sinner. Her accusers had probably set this poor woman up in the act of adultery just to test Jesus. They used her as a tool and not as a person. Of course, they didn't bring the man whom they also supposedly caught with her in the act and who was probably one of them!

Jesus did not abrogate the Jewish Law that demanded the woman's stoning. He simply shamed them from executing it, because they were all guilty of sins themselves. Jesus did not release her from the Jewish Law, but He had released her from the punishment, letting mercy triumph over justice.

The Light of the World

During the Feast of Booths, the Women's Court of the Temple was lit up at the end of the first day by huge lamps. There were golden candlesticks 75 feet high at the top of which were golden bowls filled with oil by men who had climbed ladders to fill them.

The light reminded us of the pillar of fire by which God had led our ancestors at night during their 40 years in the desert. We had always associated light with God. The Prophet Isaiah said, "The Lord will be our everlasting light" (Isaiah 60:19) and "The people who walked in darkness have seen a great light." (Isaiah 9:1).

Jesus stood before us near the burning candles. Alluding to this light and darkness, He said, "I am the light of the world; he who follows me will not walk in darkness, but will have the light of life."

Jesus had identified Himself with the Lord! I remembered the psalm, "The Lord is my light and my salvation." (Psalm 27). Now He said that He is light, so He must be the Lord. Life cannot exist without light. Just as natural light enables seeds to sprout and grow, God's supernatural light enables us to grow in the life that He offers us.

Like natural light, Jesus wanted to expose the darkness and reveal what is hidden, to enable those with eyes of faith to perceive the hidden truths of God's Kingdom. He wanted us to walk in the light and avoid the darkness of unbelief and rejection.

Yes, I thought, *but Jesus is not just the light of Israel, but of the whole world, for all nations, not just one. He is our new guide through the wilderness and darkness of this world.*

God is light and there is no darkness in Him at all. If we say that we share in God's life while we are living in darkness, we are lying, because we are not living in the truth. But if we live in light, as He is light, we have a share in His life.

Whoever claims to be in light but hates his brother is still in darkness. Anyone who loves his brother remains in light and there is in him nothing to make him fall away. But whoever hates his brother is in darkness and is walking about like the Jews in the wilderness, not knowing where he is going because darkness has blinded him.

And so are the Pharisees blinded by the darkness of their disbelief. Their hearts are closed. They do not listen to Jesus, they just ignore what He says and they argue back against Him.

The Pharisees interrupted my thoughts and yelled out at Jesus, "You are bearing witness to yourself; you have no other witnesses. Your testimony is not true."

Jesus had previously explained to them that He had four witnesses to support Him: John the Baptist pointed to Him; His own miracles supported Him; the words that His Father spoke when He was baptized by John saying, "This is my beloved Son" supported Him and so did the words of Sacred Scripture.

Now Jesus simply pointed to Himself and to His Father as His two witnesses. He calmly answered them, "Even if I do bear witness to myself, my testimony is true, for I know from where I have come and where I am going, but you don't know from where I come or where I'm going. You judge according to the flesh, I judge no one. Yet even if I do judge, my judgment is true, for it is not I alone that judge, but I and He who sent me. In your Law it is written that the testimony of two men is true. I bear witness to myself, and the Father who sent me bears witness to me."

So they said with contempt, "Where is your Father?"

Jesus answered, "You know neither me nor my Father. If you knew me, you would know my Father also."

He spoke these words as He taught in the Temple. But no one arrested Him, because His hour had not yet come.

Jesus, Ambassador of the Father

Jesus continued to teach and said to the Pharisees, "I am going away, and you will seek me and die in your sin. Where I am going, you cannot come." He meant that they would die in their sin of unbelief and therefore could not come to heaven. They knew that He was talking about His heavenly afterlife, but they turned His teaching on its head to imply that He was going to hell and therefore they would not come there.

They replied with odious mockery, "Will He kill Himself, since He says, 'Where I am going, you cannot come'?" It was the height of hypocrisy. They thought that the only place that He could go, that they couldn't go was hell! They saw themselves as destined for heaven and Jesus as destined for hell, where they couldn't go. For Jesus to go to hell, He would have to commit suicide, and that's why they asked, "Will He kill Himself?" What evil worldly thinking!

So Jesus rebuked them and said, "You are from below, I am from above. You are of this world, I am not of this world. I told you that you would die in your sins, for you will die in your sins unless you believe that I AM."

"Who are you?" they said.

Jesus answered, "I am just who I say I am, as I have told you from the beginning. I have much to say about you in condemnation. But He who sent me is true, and I declare to the world what I have heard from Him." They still did not understand that He spoke to them of His Father.

So Jesus said, "When you have lifted up the Son of Man, then you will know that I AM, and that I do nothing on my own authority but speak only as the Father taught me. He who sent me is with me. He has not left me alone, for I always do what is pleasing to Him."

Because He spoke this way, many came to believe in Him. When He spoke of being "lifted up", He used the same language that He did when He spoke to Nicodemus. He had told him, "And just as Moses lifted up the serpent in the desert, so also must the Son of Man be lifted up, so that whoever believes in Him may not perish, but may have eternal life." Now He said that "when *you* have lifted up the Son of Man, then you will know that I AM." I wondered what He meant by being lifted up.

Jesus and Abraham

Then Jesus said to the Jews, "If you remain in my word, you are truly my disciples, and you will know the truth, and the truth will set you free."

They thought that He was talking about human slavery instead of slavery to sin. So they answered Him, "We are descendants of

Abraham, and have never been in bondage to anyone. How is it that you say, 'You will be made free'?" What they said was not true, because our people had been ruled in the past by Egypt, Babylon and Persia and now by Rome. True freedom is not freedom from political domination or of being children of Abraham, because we are still subject to sin. True freedom is freedom from being slaves to sin.

Jesus answered them, "Truly, truly, I say to you, everyone who commits sin is a slave to sin. The slave does not remain in the house forever, but the son remains forever. So if the son makes you free, you will be truly free. I know that you are descendants of Abraham, but you seek to kill me, because my word finds no place in you. I speak of what I have seen with my Father, and you do what you have heard from your father." He was referring to the devil as their father and they did not deny that they sought to kill Him.

They answered him, "Abraham is our father."

Jesus said to them, "If you were Abraham's children, you would do what Abraham did, but now you seek to kill me, a man who has told you the truth which I heard from God. This is not what Abraham did. He believed the truth that he heard from God!"

Yes, I thought, *murderous intentions and obstinate disbelief and resistance to heavenly truth were certainly not the marks of Abraham who was our father in the faith. He believed the truth of God who had promised him when he was old and childless that he would be the father of many nations.*

Jesus, continued, "You do what your father did."

They mocked Him and said, "We were not born of fornication. We have one Father, God."

Jesus responded to them with tenderness and great love, "If God were your Father, you would love me, for I proceeded and came forth from God. I came not of my own accord, but He sent me. Why do you not understand what I say? It is because you cannot bear to hear my word."

Then He forcefully said, "You are of your father, the devil, and your will is to do your father's desires. He was a murderer from the beginning and has nothing to do with the truth because there is no truth in him. When he lies, he speaks according to his own nature, for he is a liar and the father of lies. But, because I tell the truth, you do not believe me. Who among you convicts me of sin? If I tell the truth, why don't you believe me? He who is of God hears the words of God. The reason why you don't hear them is that you are not of God."

Jesus accused them of being liars and murderers, like their father, the devil, who lied to Eve when he said that she would not die if she ate the forbidden fruit and who later led Cain to kill his brother Abel.

Who is the liar, I thought, if not the one who claims that Jesus is not the Christ? This is the Antichrist who denies both the Father and the Son. Whoever denies the Son cannot have the Father either. Whoever acknowledges the Son has the Father too. Whoever lives sinfully belongs to the devil, since the devil has been a sinner from the beginning. This was the purpose of the coming of Jesus, the Son of God, to undo the work of the devil. No one who is a child of God sins because God's seed remains in him. Nor can he sin, because he is a child of God. This is what distinguishes the child of God from the child of the devil: whoever does not live uprightly and does not love his brother is not of God. That's why Jesus now said that these people "are not of God."

But we see what love the Father has bestowed on us that we may be called the children of God. And so we are. The reason that these Jews do not know us is that they don't know Jesus. Whoever believes that Jesus is the Christ is a child of God, and whoever loves the Father loves the Son and would not accuse Him as these Jews have.

Since they couldn't convict Jesus of any sin and they were exasperated by His truth, they resorted to malicious name-calling and insults.

They answered Him, "Are we not right in saying that you are a Samaritan and have a demon?"

Jesus ignored the Samaritan slur and simply answered, "I don't have a demon; but I honor my Father, and you dishonor me. Yet I don't seek my own glory; there is One who seeks it and He will be the judge. Truly, truly, I say to you, if anyone keeps my word, he will never see death." Of course, He meant that His believers would not see spiritual death. But the minds of His enemies thought only in earthly terms and they understood Him to be speaking about bodily death.

So they said, "Now we know that you have a demon. Abraham died, as did the Prophets. But you say, 'If anyone keeps my word, he will never taste death.' Are you greater than our father Abraham, who died? And the Prophets died! Who do you claim to be?"

Jesus answered, "If I glorify myself, my glory is nothing; it is my Father who glorifies me, of whom you say that He is your God. But you have not known Him. I know Him. If I said, I do not know Him, I should be a liar just like you. But I do know Him and I keep His word."

The faces of the leaders flushed with anger. Jesus had essentially told them that they didn't even know the God whom they said they did, but that He Himself knew Him as His Father. The so-called experts were willfully ignorant of the truth about Jesus. His teaching was incomprehensible to them because they disbelieved Him and had closed themselves to faith.

Then Jesus said, "Your father Abraham rejoiced that he was to see my day. He saw it and was glad."

They said in amazement, "You aren't even fifty years old, how could you have seen Abraham?"

Jesus replied, "Truly, truly, I say to you, before Abraham ever existed, I AM."

These were the same words that Jesus had used with reference to His being lifted up. They were also the same words that God had used to identify Himself to Moses in the burning bush before He liberated the Israelites from Egypt, "I AM who am."

In these words, God told Moses that He is the eternal supreme being in a full, complete and absolute sense and that He is dependent on no other being, but that all other things and people depend upon Him for their being and existence. So now when Jesus said of Himself, "I AM," He used the optimal expression of the absolute certainty of the fact that God was in our midst in His person. He identified Himself with the God of Moses.

To the Jews, this was horrible blasphemy. So they took up stones to throw at Him. But Jesus hid Himself in the crowd and left the Temple.

The Healing of the Man Born Blind

Later, Jesus saw a man who had been blind from his birth. He was sitting on his mat on the ground begging. The disciples of Jesus asked Him, "Rabbi, who sinned, this man or his parents, since he was born blind?"

They asked this question because some of His disciples believed that sickness or a physical defect such as blindness was a punishment from God for the sins of the person or of his parents.

But Jesus answered, "It was not that this man sinned, or his parents, but that the works of God might be made manifest in him. As long as day lasts we must carry out the work of the one who sent me. Soon the night will be here when no one can work. As long as I am in the world, I am the light of the world."

I understood that by saying night, Jesus was referring to His death and He meant that He had to do God's work while He could and like we all should, for soon the night will be here for all of us.

As He said this, He knelt on the ground, spat on it, made clay of the spittle (which many believed was a curative), anointed the man's eyes with the clay and said to him, "Go and wash in the pool of Siloam." So, without questions or argument, the man simply did as he was told in faith. He took Jesus at His word.

The blind man started stumbling towards the pool with his clay-caked eyes. I took his hand and guided him there. When we arrived at the pool, he descended the steps to the water basin, next to where the water spilled out of the conduit, bent down and washed his eyes. Suddenly, he shouted that he could see! It was an awesome moment for someone who had never seen the pool before.

The cured man ran off in joy because he could see. The Curer had used the curative of water to cure him. The curative was merely the medium of the Curer who likewise was the mediator for God His Father.

Now the name Siloam means "sent" because water was sent through conduits to the pool as a reservoir for Jerusalem's water supply. Jesus was also sent by the Father to do His works. The sign for this was that the blind man, who also was sent, could now see. As the Father sent Jesus, Jesus sent the blind man to the "sent" pool and the works of God were manifested in him, just as Jesus had said, for that was the reason that he was born blind. Jesus, the light of the world, had brought him out of his night of blindness to the light of sight.

Later, when they saw that the blind man could see, his neighbors and those who had seen him before when he was a beggar said, "Isn't this the man who used to sit and beg?"

Some said, "Yes, it's him." Others said, "No, but he looks like him." But he himself cleared up any doubts and said, "Yes, I am him!"

So they said to him, "Then how were your eyes opened?"

He answered, "The man called Jesus made clay and anointed my eyes and said to me, 'Go to Siloam and wash.' So I did as I was told. I went and washed and received my sight." He was very straightforward.

They said to him, "Where is He?"

He said, "I don't know."

When Jesus had made the clay and opened the blind man's eyes it was on the Sabbath, a day when work was forbidden by the Law. But the Pharisees seldom applied the essence of the Law, which is the love of God and neighbor. They brought the man before the Pharisees who sat at a long table. They also asked the man how he had received his sight. He answered, "He put clay on my eyes, and I washed, and I see."

Some of the Pharisees thought that this healing was work that violated the Law. So they said, "This Jesus is not from God, for

He does not keep the Sabbath." But others said, "If He's a sinner, how can a sinner do such signs?"

There was a division among them. So they asked the blind man again, "What do you say about Him, since He has opened your eyes?"

He answered simply, honestly and courageously, "He is a Prophet!"

However, the Jews didn't believe that the man had been born blind and had now really received his sight. So they called his parents and asked them, "Is this your son, whom you say was born blind? Then how can he see now?"

His parents evasively answered, "We know that this is our son and that he was born blind. But how he can see now, we don't know, nor do we know who opened his eyes. Why don't you ask him? He's of age, let him speak for himself."

His parents said this because they were afraid of the Jews, for the Jews had already agreed that if anyone should say that Jesus was the Christ, he was to be excommunicated from the synagogue. That's why his parents said, "He is of age, let him speak for himself."

So, for the second time, the Pharisees called the man who had been born blind and said to him, "Tell us the truth! We know that this Jesus is a sinner."

But they didn't want the truth. They were just trying to intimidate the man into denying the reality of the end of his blindness through the restoration of his sight by Jesus.

He answered, "Whether He is a sinner, I don't know; but one thing I do know is that I was blind but now I see."

He spoke from his own personal experience and not from some theological understanding. He spoke common sense. I wondered how they could argue against his experience.

They said to him, "What did He do to you? How did He open your eyes?"

He answered them, "I already told you but you would not listen. Why do you want to hear it again? Do you want to become His disciples also?"

They really didn't want to know the truth. They just wanted to continue in their denial by their questioning. Then they reviled Him, saying, "You are His disciple, but we are disciples of Moses. We know that God spoke to Moses, but as for this man, we do not know where He comes from."

The man answered, "Why, that's just amazing! You don't know where He comes from, yet He opened my eyes. We know that God does not listen to sinners, but if anyone is a worshiper of God and does His will, God listens to him. Never since the world began has it been heard that anyone opened the eyes of a man born blind. If this man were not from God, He could do nothing."

They answered him, "Are you trying to teach us? You who were born in utter sin!"

The Pharisees had abandoned any reasonable dialogue and reduced themselves to insulting the healed man. Then they unjustly cast him out for being miraculously cured on the Sabbath.

The Pharisees had condemned the healed man as a sinner. They thought that they were perfect followers of God, but they condemned as sinners those who did not follow their teachings and those like the former blind man whose blindness they attributed to his sinfulness. They were self-righteous and judged themselves as perfect. They would have no association with those whom they judged as sinners. It reminded me of the day when Matthew, who was a follower of Jesus with us, hosted a banquet for Him in his house. Matthew was a former tax collector who had converted from his occupation to follow Jesus. In recognition of his conversion, Jesus changed his name from Levi to Matthew.

The Pharisees hated the tax collectors because they collected more than the actual tax due and lined their own pockets with the excess. However, there were some good tax collectors like Matthew. He had invited other tax collectors to his banquet and they had joined him at his table.

When the Pharisees saw the tax collectors there they complained to Jesus, "Why do you eat and drink with tax collectors and sinners?"

Jesus said to them in reply, "Those who are healthy do not need a physician, but the sick do. I have not come to call the righteous to repentance but sinners." The Pharisees glared at Him. They thought that they were "healthy" and righteous, but they really were not. They needed a spiritual physician as much as did the sinners. Jesus did not judge people by their appearances, but by their hearts. Everyone needed His love and no one could declare himself self-sufficient and righteous, like the Pharisees did for themselves. Only God could judge the human heart. This is a lesson that the Pharisees had never learned and now they had condemned the healed former blind man as just another sinner.

Later, Jesus heard that the Pharisees had cast the healed man out. When He found him, He welcomed him and said, "Do you believe in the Son of Man?" This was the title from the Prophet Daniel who saw in a vision the Son of Man receiving universal dominion over all nations. The healed man respectfully answered, "And who is he, sir, that I may believe in him?"

Jesus said to him, "You have seen Him, and it is He who speaks to you."

The healed man fell to his knees before Jesus and said, "Lord, I believe." Then he worshipped Him.

The healed man now acknowledged his belief in Jesus as the Son of Man with absolute trust and total acceptance of Him as the Christ, the Messiah. He saw not just with his eyes but with his understanding of who Jesus was. His understanding had progressed and increased from his first understanding of Him as a mere man, to that of a Prophet, to that of the Son of Man and, finally, to Lord.

Jesus said, "For judgment I came into this world, that those who do not see may see, and that those who see may become blind."

The very person of Jesus involves a judgment, because each person has to decide his ultimate end, depending on his or her

116

decision to accept Him, as the healed man did, or to reject Him, as the Pharisees did.

Some of the Pharisees near Him had heard what Jesus said. So, they said to Him, "So, are we also blind?"

Jesus said to them, "If you were blind, you would have no guilt. But now that you say, 'We see,' your guilt remains."

Ironically, the simple people, with no pretense to being learned, came to see the truth of Jesus, while those who had all the learning became blind to it. The Pharisees were blind to the truth about Jesus that He really was sent by God to do His works and they, unlike the healed blind man, were guilty because they thought they saw the truth. They who thought that they could see all truth were really blind.

The once-blind man was really the one who saw the truth. He saw on his own that Jesus was a Prophet sent by God. Then he saw that Jesus was the Son of Man when Jesus revealed Himself to him. Then he worshipped Jesus as Lord.

The Pharisees were blind to all of this. They were without any excuse and were guilty because they knew the Law and the Prophets, but refused to believe their fulfillment in Jesus. They refused to see the truth of the witnesses to the blind man's sight— the healed man, his neighbors and his parents. They who were so legal refused to believe many witnesses when the Law only required two. There are none more blind than those who will not see.

The Good Shepherd

Jesus then stood up and said, "Truly, truly, I say to you, he who does not enter the sheepfold by the gate, but climbs in by another way, is a thief and a robber. But he who enters by the gate is the shepherd of the sheep. To him the gatekeeper opens. The sheep hear his voice, and he calls his own sheep by name and leads them out. When he has brought out all his own, he goes before them and the sheep follow him, for they know his voice. A stranger they will not follow, but they will flee from him for they do not know the voice of strangers."

We did not understand this as He continued, "Truly, truly, I say to you, I am the gate of the sheepfold. All who came before me are thieves and robbers, but the sheep did not heed them. I am the gate. If anyone enters by me, he will be saved, and will go in and out and find pasture. The thief comes only to steal and kill and destroy. I came that they may have life, and have it to the full."

Many times our Scriptures had used the metaphor of God as a shepherd of His people, Israel: "The Lord is my shepherd, I shall not want." (Psalm 23:1); "Give ear, O Shepherd of Israel, you who lead Joseph like a flock!" (Psalm 80:1); and "We are His people, and the sheep of His pasture." (Psalm 100:3). The Messiah is also pictured as the shepherd of God's people: "He will feed his flock like a shepherd. He will gather the lambs in his arms." (Isaiah 40:11). But Jesus now said that He was not only the shepherd, but the gate as well.

In Israel, the shepherd tended herds of sheep. He led them to eat in pastures by day and into fenced sheepfolds at night where he brought them for shelter. They lived together and he protected them against wild animals by day and wild thieves by night, when he would lie down on the ground as a gate through the fence to the sheepfold.

The shepherd literally was the gate through which the sheep had to pass to enter the sheepfold. He was close to them and they knew the sound of his voice and they'd follow him when he called them by name. He was so familiar with his sheep that he called each by a distinct name.

Now Jesus applied this metaphor to Himself. He gave us the image of Himself as the gate through which we, the sheep, enter the sheepfold of the Kingdom of God to be saved. Like a shepherd, He also knew each of us by name, meaning our heart, our innermost essence. He loved us with a personal love that treated each of us as if we were the only one who existed for Him. The Jewish leaders, however, were the thieves and robbers who did not recognize His voice or follow Him.

Jesus went on to extend the metaphor. "I am the good shepherd," He said. "The good shepherd lays down his life for the sheep. The hired man, since he is not the shepherd and the sheep do not belong to him, abandons the sheep as soon as he sees the wolf coming. He abandons the flock and runs away and the wolf attacks and scatters the sheep. He runs away because he is a hired man and doesn't care about the sheep. I am the good shepherd. I know my own and my own know me, just as the Father knows me and I know the Father, and I lay down my life for the sheep."

The Scriptures also describe God as a shepherd who brings security and peace to His people: "The Lord will keep your going out and your coming in from this time forth and for evermore." (Psalm 120:8). Even the leaders of God's people are called shepherds: "They shall lead them out and bring them in; that the congregation of the Lord may not be as sheep which have no shepherd." (Numbers 27:17).

Jesus continued, "And I have other sheep that are not of this fold. I must lead them also and they will listen to my voice. So there shall be one flock and one shepherd." It sounded like He was talking as the Messiah. The Scriptures told us that the Messiah would be the King and ruler of all nations and now Jesus said that the nations are also His sheep and that all will eventually be united under Him, the Good Shepherd, the King of All Nations.

"For this reason," He went on, "the Father loves me, because I lay down my life, in order that I may take it up again. No one takes it from me, but I lay it down of my own free will. I have power to lay it down, and I have power to take it up again. This is the command that I have received from my Father."

He's talking about dying again! I thought, *laying down His life like a good shepherd, not only just dying, but taking His life up again, whatever that means. Could He mean that He will rise from the dead? I can understand the shepherd analogy. He's the Good Shepherd, His Father is the gatekeeper and we are the sheep. He calls us each by name, leads us and we follow His voice.*

He's also the gate through which we enter the sheepfold, the Kingdom of God. He's a shepherd who protects His flock like Moses and King David who protected their flocks from wild predators. But He'll protect us from the spiritual predators of demons and false teachers who come against His Kingdom like thieves who come only to steal and kill and destroy. He's referring to these Pharisees!

But He has come to bring us life and not just us, but all nations so that we will be one with Him and there will be one flock of us with Him, the one shepherd — even with the Jews here who think that He is mad.

Oh, do we need the Good Shepherd! We are like sheep who go astray on our own paths and get lost so easily. We need to be led into the sheepfold by the Good Shepherd and not by false shepherds.

I remembered how the Prophet Ezekiel had prophesied against false shepherds like these Pharisees who sought only their own good rather than the good of the flock. He said:

> Woe, shepherds of Israel who have been feeding yourselves! Should not shepherds feed the sheep? You eat the fat, you clothe yourselves with the wool, you slaughter the fatlings; but you do not feed the sheep. So they were scattered, because there was no shepherd; and they became food for all the wild beasts.
>
> For thus says the Lord God: Behold, I myself will search for my sheep, and will seek them out. I will feed them with good pasture, and upon the mountain heights of Israel shall be their pasture; there they shall lie down in good grazing land, and on fat pasture they shall feed on the mountains of Israel. I myself will be the shepherd of my sheep, and I will make them lie down, says the Lord God.
>
> And I will set up over them one shepherd, my servant David, and he shall feed them: he shall feed them and be their shepherd. And I, the Lord, will be their God. (Ezekiel 34:2-5; 11; 14; 23-24).

I hoped that perhaps Jesus would shepherd us as the new David, the Promised One, the Messiah. His self-identification as the Good Shepherd seemed to be a fulfillment of the prophecy of Isaiah concerning the Messiah, "He will feed his flock like a shepherd; he will gather the lambs in his arms and will carry them in his bosom, and gently lead those that are with young." (Isaiah 40:11).

Jesus' metaphor of the Good Shepherd caused a fresh division among the Jews. Many of them said, "He is possessed by a demon, and He is mad. Why do you listen to Him?" Others said, "These are not the words of one who has a demon. Can a demon open the eyes of the blind like He did with the man born blind?"

The answer should have been, "Of course not!" But many persisted that He was possessed and mad. But to me His words and actions were very evidently completely sane. He always loved us, did good for others, performed miracles and obeyed His Father by His willingness to lay down His life for us.

But the Jewish leaders remained stubborn and blind to all of this. They opposed Jesus on every front and could not see themselves as the thieves, robbers, and hired men that he had just excoriated.

7. The Feast of Hanukkah in Jerusalem

The Son of God

After the Feast of Booths, we went back across the Jordan for a few months. Then we returned with Jesus to Jerusalem in the winter for the Feast of Hanukkah, or the Dedication.

Judas Maccabeus led the Maccabean revolt against the Seleucid Empire. He instituted Hanukkah as an eight-day feast in 165 BC to celebrate the re-dedication of the Temple after the Syrian king, Antiochus Epiphanes, had desecrated it. Antiochus had tried to destroy the Jewish religion and culture and replace it with the Greek religion and culture.

Antiochus conquered Jerusalem, killed tens of thousands of Jews, invaded the Temple, carried off the golden altar and sacrificed a pig there to the false god Zeus. He outlawed circumcision and the celebration of the Sabbath and commanded that only pigs be sacrificed in the Temple. Pigs were unclean animals to us and their sacrifice in the Temple was a horrible sacrilege.

Then Judas Maccabaeus rebelled against the rule of Antiochus, freed Jerusalem and cleansed and rededicated the Temple.

Jesus was walking up and down in the portico of Solomon, on the eastern side of the Temple. The Jews gathered around Him and said, "How long will you keep us in suspense? If you are the Christ, tell us plainly."

Jesus had already told the Samaritan woman and the man born blind very plainly that He was the Messiah and the Jews must have known this. However, they weren't really seeking the truth about Jesus but only a reason to accuse Him of blasphemy.

Jesus answered them, "I told you, but you do not believe. The works that I do in my Father's name, they bear witness to me. But you do not believe, because you are not my sheep. My sheep listen to my voice. I know them and they follow me. I give them eternal life, and they shall never perish. No one shall snatch them out of my hand."

"My Father, who has given them to me, is greater than all, and no one can snatch them out of the Father's hand. The Father and I are one."

He had said it very plainly. He was the Christ, the Anointed One, the expected Messiah. But they did not believe Him, even though His mighty works bore witness to Him. His works of healing, deliverance from demons, forgiveness of sins and raising of the dead were works that only God could perform. These works proved His claim. And He, the Good Shepherd, claimed to give eternal life to us, His sheep, a gift that only God can give. Finally, He said that God was His Father and that He and His Father were one. How could He have said it more plainly?

But these Jews believed that Jesus blasphemed because He, supposedly a mere human, claimed to be God. They thought that God could not be a human being. So they limited the power of God. Although they taught that God is Almighty, they didn't believe that He could become a man and be both true God and true man.

The Jews understood the greatness of Jesus' claim, but they did not believe it because they thought that it was blasphemous. Once again, they took up stones to stone Him to death. But this time, Jesus did not leave.

He calmly answered them, "I have shown you many good works from the Father; for which of these do you want to stone me?"

The Jews answered Him, "It is not for any good work that we stone you, but for blasphemy. Because you, who are only a man, claim to be God."

Jesus did not deny the charge or mitigate His claim, but tried to help them to understand it by lifting up their minds and referring them to Scripture in the manner of the lesser to the greater. He referred them to the Scripture where God addressed the Judges of Israel.

Jesus quoted the psalm and said, "Is it not written in your Law, 'I said, you are gods'? (Psalm 82). If he called the Judges gods to whom the word of God came (and Scripture cannot be broken), do you say of me whom the Father consecrated and sent into the world, 'You are blaspheming,' because I said, 'I am the Son of God'?"

He continued, "If I am not doing the works of my Father, then do not believe me. But if I do them, even though you do not believe me, at least believe the works so that you may know for certain and understand that the Father is in me and I am in the Father."

I later understood from Jesus that, essentially, there is a mutual unity of nature in the divine nature of His Father and Himself, but a distinction of persons, one a Father and the other a Son, who shares a human nature with His divine nature – one person with two natures. He is truly the Son of Man and the Son of God, as He had referred to Himself.

Jesus presented His words and His works (His miracles) as His claim to be the Son of God. They couldn't deny His miracles, so they should have believed His words as I finally came to do.

Once again, they tried to arrest Him, but once again He escaped from their hands.

8. Ministry in Betanea and Bethany

In order to avoid the increasing hostility to Jesus, we left Jerusalem again and journeyed to Betanea, east of the Sea of Galilee. This was the place where John the Baptist had first baptized and also the place to which the Prophet Elijah had withdrawn when King Ahab wanted to kill him. It was a four-day journey through the Judean desert and across the Jordan River.

While we remained in Betanea, many came to Jesus and said, "John did no sign, but everything that John said about this man was true." And many there came to believe in Him.

They finally recognized that Jesus was the one about whom John had spoken when he said, "There is one among you whom you do not recognize." And they believed that Jesus was the one whom John had called, "The Lamb of God who takes away the sin of the world and God's chosen One."

The Raising of Lazarus

While we were in Betanea, we received a messenger from Martha and Mary, the sisters of Lazarus of Bethany, a town about two miles east of Jerusalem. The sisters' message was, "Lord, the man you love is ill."

When Jesus heard this message, He calmly said, "This illness is not unto death, but it is for the glory of God, so that the Son of God may be glorified by means of it." He seemed to be speaking a prophecy that the reason that Lazarus was ill was so that God could work a miracle through Jesus and thereby glorify His Son so that others would believe that He was truly the Son of God.

Jesus loved Martha, Mary and Lazarus, but when He heard that Lazarus was ill, He didn't rush off to visit him. He stayed on where He was for another two days. Then He said to us, "Let us go into Judea again."

We said to Him in alarm, "Rabbi, you know that the Jews are seeking to stone you, and yet now you want to go back there?"

Jesus answered, "Aren't there twelve hours in the day? If anyone walks in the day, he does not stumble, because he sees the light of this world. But if anyone walks in the night, he stumbles, because the light is not in him." He seemed to be saying that the time was ripe to go.

Then Jesus said, "Our friend Lazarus has fallen asleep, but I will go to wake him up."

We thought that He meant that Lazarus was really sleeping. So we said, "Lord, if he has fallen asleep, he will recover."

Then He told us plainly, "Lazarus is dead. For your sake I am glad that I was not there, so that you may believe. But let us go to him."

Thomas, whom we called the Twin, boldly said to us, "Let us also go, that we may die with Him." So we started on our four-day journey to Bethany.

When Jesus was near Bethany, He learned that Lazarus had already been buried in the tomb for four days, the time it took us to walk there. Because Bethany was only about two miles from Jerusalem, many of the Jews had come to Martha and Mary to console them concerning their brother. When Martha heard that

Jesus was coming, she went and met Him, while Mary remained behind in the house.

Martha said to Jesus, "Lord, if you had been here, my brother would not have died. And even now I know that whatever you ask from God, God will give you."

Jesus said to her, "Your brother will rise again."

Martha said to Him, "I know that he will rise again in the resurrection at the last day."

Jesus said to her, "I am the resurrection and the life. He who believes in me, even though he die, he shall live, and whoever lives and believes in me shall never die. Do you believe this?"

Martha said to Him, "Yes, Lord. I believe that you are the Christ, the Son of God, He who is coming into the world." She was the third person to publicly confess Jesus as the Christ, the Messiah, after Nathaniel and Peter.

When she had said this, she went back and called her sister Mary. She told her very quietly, "The Teacher is here and is calling for you."

When Mary heard this, she rose quickly and went to Jesus. Unlike the impulsive Martha, who had run to meet Jesus when she heard that He was coming, Mary had calmly remained behind in the house. She did not go to meet Him until He called her. I identified more with Mary's contemplative spirit than with the active spirit of Martha. Martha acted more like Peter than she did like me.

Now Jesus had not yet come into the village, but was still in the place where Martha had met Him. When the Jews who were consoling Mary in the house saw her rise quickly and go out, they followed her. They thought that she was going to the tomb to mourn there.

But Mary went to where Jesus was. When she saw Him, she threw herself at His feet and said the same as Martha had said, in sad disappointment, "Lord, if you had been here, my brother would not have died."

When Jesus saw her weeping, and the Jews who had come with her also weeping, He was deeply moved in spirit and distressed. He said with a profound sigh, "Where have you laid him?"

They said to Him, "Lord, come and see."

Jesus wept. So the Jews said, "See how He loved him!"

But some of them said, "He opened the eyes of the blind man. Couldn't He have kept this man from dying?" *Of course He could have,* I thought, *but He must have something greater in mind for the glory of God.*

Then Jesus, sighing again, walked along the field path down to the tomb. It was in a cave and there was a round five-foot-high stone covering the rectangular opening.

Jesus said, "Take away the stone."

Martha said, "Lord, by this time he will smell! He's been dead four days."

Jesus said to her, "Didn't I tell you that if you would believe you would see the glory of God?"

So they rolled away the stone. Jesus lifted up His eyes and said, "Father, I thank you for hearing my prayer. I know that you always hear me, but I said this for the sake of all of these people standing around me, so that they may believe that you sent me."

Jesus called upon His Father in heaven and thanked Him for granting a great miracle just before it occurred. This was a clear proof of His divinity.

When He had said this, He cried in a loud voice, "Lazarus, come out."

Lazarus, the man who was dead, came stumbling out into our midst. His hands and feet were still bound with his burial wrappings. He struggled to see as his face was wrapped with a cloth.

Jesus simply said to them, "Unbind him, and let him go."

I marveled at the power of Jesus over death itself and I thought, *Here He stands as a Son of Man who weeps at His friend's death and as a Son of God who raises him from the dead. If He has such power over*

130

death as to be able to raise the dead to life, then what have I to fear from death?

The raising of Lazarus from the dead was the seventh and last of the great signs, miracles and wondrous deeds of Jesus. It showed His power over life and death. It gave me hope that I too might rise from the dead. Then I remembered all of the other great signs that Jesus had performed. These signs were types or prefigurements of Jesus' glorification of His Father. They manifested Jesus as the revelation of the Father.

The first sign was the transformation of water into wine at Cana by which He showed the transformation from the Jewish Law to the new law of love symbolized by the replacement of the water of the Jewish ceremonial washing jars with the new wine.

The second sign was the healing of the royal official's son simply by the word of Jesus from a distance. This signified the power of Jesus' life-giving word.

The third sign was the cure of the paralytic at the pool of Siloam. This water symbolized the newness of life that Jesus offered.

The fourth and fifth signs were the multiplication of bread and fish and the walking on the water of the Sea of Galilee. These signs are connected, similar to the manna that God provided the Israelites in the desert and their Exodus before that by the miraculous crossing of the Red Sea. In His discourse, Jesus used the bread of life as a figure for the revelation of God in Himself.

The sixth sign was the healing of the man born blind. This symbolized the triumph of light over darkness, as Jesus revealed Himself as the light of the world who also cures spiritual blindness.

The seventh sign was the raising of Lazarus from the dead for the glory of God, showing Jesus' power over death itself.

As Jesus had said, "This sickness will end not in death, but in God's glory and through it the Son of God will be glorified."

Jesus was glorified not only by all of these great signs, but also by all of the others that He had performed. One day, some disciples of John the Baptist had asked Jesus if He were the

Messiah. Jesus told them, "The blind regain their sight, the lame walk, lepers are cleansed, the deaf hear, the dead are raised, and the poor have the good news proclaimed to them. And blessed is the one who takes no offense at me."

Jesus performed many other signs in my presence but His seven great signs help many to believe that Jesus is the Messiah, the Son of Man and the Son of God, and through this belief they may have life in His name.

Because of the amazing miracle of raising Lazarus from the dead, many of the Jews who had come with Mary and had seen what Jesus did, now believed in Him. It caused a sensation in Bethany and in Jerusalem, from where most of the mourners present had come. They had no excuse to remain in their unbelief.

However, some of them went to the Pharisees and told them what Jesus had done. The Pharisees knew that they could not remain inactive in the face of such a dramatic event. So the Chief Priests and the Pharisees gathered the Council of the Sanhedrin and said, "What are we to do? For this man performs many signs. If we let Him go on like this, everyone will believe in Him and the Romans will come and destroy both our holy place and our nation."

They said that He had healed a blind man on the Sabbath; He had blasphemed about Himself at the Feast of Hanukkah and now He had raised a man from the dead. They were afraid that so many people would run after Jesus that the Romans would suspect His followers of trying to overthrow their power.

Of course it was no crime to do good or to perform miracles, such as raising Lazarus from the dead. But the leaders were envious, jealous and fearful of losing their power, their Temple and their nation.

In the middle of their debate, Caiaphas, who was the High Priest that year, cut it short, and with malice in his voice, said to them, "You know nothing at all. You do not understand that it is to your advantage that one man should die for the people rather than that the whole nation should perish." This was the Council's plan for the death of Jesus revealed by its High Priest.

He did not say this of his own accord, but being High Priest that year, God allowed that his utterance be a prophecy that Jesus, as King of All Nations, should die for the nation, and not only for the Jewish nation, but to gather into one Kingdom of God all of the nations and the scattered children of God. This would be a fulfillment of the prophecy of Jeremiah, "Hear the word of the LORD, O nations. Proclaim it to distant coasts and say, 'He who scattered Israel now gathers them together, he guards them as a shepherd his flock.' " (Jeremiah 31:10).

This would also be the fulfillment of the prophecies of Isaiah and Simeon. Isaiah had said that the Messiah would not only restore Israel, but that he would be "a light for the nations that salvation may reach to the ends of the earth." (Isaiah 49:6). Simeon had told Joseph and Mary at the Presentation of Jesus that He would be "a light to the nations and glory for the people of Israel." Because of Caiaphas' heartless exhortation that it was better for one man to die rather than the whole nation, from that day on they tried to figure out how to kill Jesus.

Since the Passover Feast was near at hand, many went up from the country to Jerusalem to purify themselves before the feast. They were on the lookout for Jesus since the Chief Priests and the Pharisees had given orders that if anyone knew where He was, he should let them know, so that they could arrest Him. They said to one another as they stood in the Temple, "What do you think? Will He come to the feast or not?"

Because of the danger, Jesus no longer walked about in public among the Jews. We left their hostility and went near the desert to a town called Ephraim, about 12 miles northeast of Jerusalem. Eventually, we went to Perea and Jericho.

Jesus' Prophecy of His Death

While making our way from Perea towards Jericho, Jesus took the twelve of us aside and said, "Behold, we are going up to Jerusalem. The Son of Man will be delivered to the Chief Priests and Scribes, and they will condemn Him to death, and deliver

Him to the Gentiles to be mocked and scourged and crucified, and He will be raised on the third day."

Another prophecy of His death, I thought, *by the horror of crucifixion on a cross! Maybe this is what He meant when He said that when He was "lifted up" He would draw all men to Himself. A man who is totally good and innocent is to suffer the worst of Roman tortures, reserved for the worst of criminals – to be mocked, scourged and crucified. And then to be raised on the third day, whatever He may mean by that.*

This time we were all silent, except for my mother. She brought her two sons, James and me, up to Jesus and knelt before Him. Jesus asked her, "What do you want?"

She said, "Command that these two sons of mine may sit, one at your right hand and one at your left, in your kingdom." Mother was always looking out for our best interests but she often embarrassed us in front of the others seeking special honors for us.

Jesus answered, "You don't know what you are asking. Are you able to drink the cup that I am to drink?"

I said, "We are able." I didn't say this with presumption and bravado, but with real faith and love. But of course I didn't know what kind of a cup He was talking about. I thought that it was the cup of His destiny and ours, to rule at His side over the Kingdom of Israel.

Jesus said, "You will drink my cup, but to sit at my right hand and at my left is not mine to grant, but it is for those for whom it has been prepared by my Father."

I still didn't know what He was talking about, but I hoped that His Father had prepared a place for me.

Now when the other ten heard this, they were indignant at us. Jesus called them to Him and said, "You know that the rulers of the nations lord it over them, and their great men exercise authority over them. But it shall not be so among you. Whoever would be great among you must be your servant, and whoever would be first among you must be your slave. Because the Son of Man came not to be served but to serve, and to give His life as a ransom for many."

134

So this is my destiny, I thought, *to become a servant and to give my life for others like He will? What kind of a kingdom is this? And He'll die to buy us back? Like one who pays a ransom to free a slave? But buy us back from what? Who owns us? . . . Satan! That's it! We're slaves to Satan through sin so that He must die as the price to be paid to free us for eternal life with Him through the forgiveness of our sins.*

We continued on, passing through Jericho. This was the beautiful town of gardens architecturally adorned by King Herod the Great. It was the same city that had blocked the entrance of our ancestors into the Promised Land as they left the desert. Joshua and his army had destroyed it when the walls tumbled down after they had faithfully processed around the city carrying the Ark of the Covenant for seven days at the Lord's command.

As we left Jericho, a great crowd followed us. We passed by two blind men sitting by the roadside. When they heard that Jesus was passing by they cried out, "Have mercy on us, Son of David!" Even the blind recognized Him as the Messiah, with this messianic title.

The crowd rebuked them, telling them to be silent; but they cried out the more, "Lord, have mercy on us, Son of David!"

Jesus stopped, called them and said, "What do you want me to do for you?" They said, "Lord, let our eyes be opened."

Jesus touched their eyes with pity and immediately they received their sight and followed Him.

The Anointing of Jesus

On Saturday, one week before the Passover Feast, we returned to Bethany, the town of Lazarus, the man whom Jesus had raised from the dead. Martha and Mary, the sisters of Lazarus, were there and they made us supper. Martha served it and the risen Lazarus was reclining at table with us.

Then Mary approached Jesus, knelt at His bare feet and placed them in a bowl. She then took a pound of costly ointment of pure nard and anointed the feet of Jesus. It was a common courtesy to anoint the head of a distinguished guest, but it was extraordinary

135

to anoint the feet. Mary's humble, gentle and delicate expression of her love for Jesus brought tears to my eyes. The house was filled with the fragrance of the ointment as she bent down in reverence and actually dried the feet of Jesus with her own hair.

Suddenly, Judas Iscariot interrupted the atmosphere of awe and said, "Why wasn't this ointment sold for its great worth of a laborer's yearly wages? Then the money could have been given to the poor!"

He didn't say this because he cared about the poor, but because he was a thief and wanted the money for himself. He took care of the money purse and would steal from it.

Jesus spoke up and defended Mary, "Leave her alone, and let her keep it for the day of my burial. The poor you always have with you, but you won't always have me."

Jesus exposed Judas' hypocrisy of supposedly giving more honor to the poor than to Jesus Himself whom he should have recognized as the Messiah. Wasn't Jesus, the Messiah, entitled to more honor than the poor? Judas hid his evil under a cloak of righteousness.

Jesus hinted at His death and burial. It sounded like it might be soon. This disturbed me. It seemed that if Jesus wanted Mary to keep the ointment for that day, then the day of His burial was not far off. It saddened me to think about it.

When the great crowd learned that Jesus was in Bethany, they came out to Him. But they didn't come out of reverence for Jesus like Mary did. They were merely curious and wanted to see not only Jesus, but also Lazarus, because Jesus had raised him from the dead. That was the reason that the Chief Priests planned to put Lazarus to death, as well as Jesus.

Of course, Lazarus was totally innocent of any wrongdoing but, because of his rising, many of the Jews had come to believe in Jesus. The Chief Priests were jealous of their power and fearful of its loss. What fools the Chief Priests were! As if Jesus, who had already raised Lazarus from a natural death, could not raise him from a death by their murderous hands.

Because Jesus gave life and Lazarus received it, they wanted to give death. Why would they want to kill someone who did nothing but good? It didn't make any sense unless they were the evil ones and not Jesus. They wanted to kill Him and Lazarus because of their envy and their fear of losing control of the people.

That was the crux of it. They wanted to control the people for their own self-interest. Many of them had amassed their wealth and power from the Temple taxes and from the Temple businesses of money changing and the selling of animals.

The raising of Lazarus from the dead after four days in his tomb was an extraordinary miracle that the Chief Priests and Pharisees could not ignore. They thought that the people would now flock to Jesus and they would lose their religious authority and that the Romans would suspect the followers of Jesus of trying to overthrow them. So their answer was to kill Jesus. That's why Caiaphas, the High Priest, said that it was better that "one man should die for the people rather than that the whole nation should perish."

9. The Last Passover in Jerusalem

The Entry into Jerusalem

On Sunday, the next day, we drew near to Jerusalem from the east and entered Bethpage at the Mount of Olives. We came to celebrate the upcoming Feast of Passover. Jesus said to Peter and me, "Go into the village straight ahead of you, and as soon as you enter it you will find a colt tethered there on which no one has ever ridden. Untie the colt and lead it back to me. If anyone says to you, 'Why are you doing this?' say, 'The Master needs it but He will send it back here at once.' "

So we went away on this strange mission and found a colt tied at a door, out in the open street. It was just as Jesus had said it would be. So we untied it, but it must've looked like we were stealing it. Those who were standing around there said to us, "What are you doing, untying the colt?"

We told them just what Jesus had told us to say. They accepted our explanation and let us take it. We brought the colt to Jesus and threw our garments on it. He got up and sat on it. Our King on a colt! He didn't ride triumphantly on a war stallion, but humbly on an animal of service.

This reminded me of the prophecy of Zechariah who had said, "Your king comes to you without display astride an ass, astride a colt, the foal of a beast of burden." (Zechariah 9:9). He described that king as establishing a dominion "from sea to sea, from the River to the ends of the earth." I wondered if Jesus would establish a kingdom for all nations.

He had entered Jerusalem in a manner that identified Himself as Solomon, the Son of King David. King David's enemy, Adonijah, had made an attempt to take David's throne by entering the city in a triumphal procession seated on a war horse with military pomp. On that same day, David had told Solomon that he would be crowned as his successor. He instructed Solomon to ride into Jerusalem on a donkey. Now Jesus was about to do the same thing in order to reveal the humble nature of His Kingdom and to demonstrate that He too was coming, like Solomon, as a true King in the line of King David.

A crowd had followed us from Jericho where they had witnessed the miraculous healing of the blind men. They heard that Jesus was about to enter Jerusalem. So, they cut palm branches from the fields and came out waving them to meet Him as He came down the western slope of the Mount of Olives, across the Kedron Valley and up the opposite slope to the Temple.

The rays of the sun were reflecting from the golden Temple as Jesus began His majestic descent down the Mount of Olives. Tents in which the poor slept during Passover covered the Mount. Jesus rode the colt past them and the throngs of pilgrims that lined His path.

The Pharisees, in their envy and frustration, then said to one another, "See, there is nothing that you can do! The world has run after Him!"

Many others spread their garments and palm branches on the road, in honor of Jesus. Those who went before Him and those who followed acclaimed Him with shouts of jubilation in the words of the psalm, "Hosanna! Blessed is He who comes in the name of the Lord! Blessed is the kingdom of our father David that is coming! Blessed is the King of Israel! Hosanna in the highest!" (Psalm 118:26). By their acclamation, they recognized

Him as the one who comes in the name of the Lord, the long-awaited Messiah. They attributed to Jesus the title of true King and heir of King David.

Yes, I thought, *this confirms what the angel Gabriel had told Mary when he announced that she would give birth to a son who would inherit the throne of His father, David. He is a King, but not merely a King of Israel. He is more. He is the King of All Nations. He is not a King of this world to overthrow the yoke of Roman occupation as they suppose. He wants to be recognized as a King over the minds and hearts of all peoples. He wants to open hearts, forgive sinfulness, heal brokenness and renew all hearts in the peace and joy of His new Kingdom – the Kingdom of God. He wants to bring them to eternal life in His Kingdom. However, many of the people expected the same kind of king that we originally expected – a king of this world who will save them from the Roman occupation and bring them material blessings and prosperity, saving them from the yoke of Roman taxation. But He's riding a colt to show that He is not a king of this world.*

Sadly, they don't recognize this. They'll probably turn on Jesus in anger, just like the Pharisees, if their expectations are not realized.

As we came within sight of the city, Jesus wept over it and said, "If only you had known the path to peace this day; but you have completely lost it from view! Days will come upon you when your enemies encircle you with a rampart, hem you in and press you hard from every side. They will wipe you out, you and your children within your walls, and leave not a stone on a stone within you, because you failed to recognize the time of your visitation."

This seemed like a prophecy of the destruction of the city, but I didn't believe then that God would ever allow that.

When Jesus entered Jerusalem, the whole city was stirred to its depths, saying, "Who is this?"

And the crowds said, "This is the Prophet Jesus from Nazareth of Galilee." When evening came we returned to Bethany.

On Monday, the next day, we returned to Jerusalem. Jesus entered the Temple of God. It had been almost three years since He had driven out the merchants, but nothing had changed. So, once again, He drove out all who sold and bought in the Temple and He overturned the tables of the money changers and the seats of those who sold pigeons.

He said to them, "It is written, 'My house shall be called a house of prayer,' but you make it a den of robbers." They had profaned His Father's Temple by making it into a commercial marketplace. In their greed, they took advantage of the poor by money changing for their own profit.

Then Jesus taught the people in the Temple area and He healed the blind and the lame who came to Him there. However, when the Chief Priests and the Scribes saw the wonderful things that He had done and heard the children crying out in the Temple, "Hosanna to the Son of David!", they were indignant. They said to Him, "Do you hear what they are saying?"

Jesus said, "Yes. Have you never read, 'Out of the mouths of babes you have brought perfect praise'?" He accepted the praise of the children, which was the truth. He didn't defend Himself from the Chief Priests' implied charge of accepting blasphemy from the children.

The Chief Priests did not arrest Jesus, even though they mistakenly believed that He was guilty of blasphemy. They were afraid that the people would riot and defend Him. The people were happy to see Jesus protect the holiness of the Temple and defend it against the abuses of the Chief Priests. If they were ever going to arrest Him, it would have to be in the dark when there would be very few people around.

On Tuesday, the next day, Jesus returned to the Temple. He spoke to the crowds and to us disciples about the Scribes and the Pharisees. He told us to do everything that they told us to do, but not to follow their example. He said this because they did not practice what they preached.

Jesus explained to us that they laid heavy burdens for the people to carry on their shoulders, but that they wouldn't lift a finger to help them. He said that everything they did was meant to be seen, in order for them to gain the respect and esteem of the people.

For example, they loved to sit in places of honor at banquets, to exalt themselves and to be greeted by respectful titles such as Rabbi. However, Jesus said, "Whoever exalts himself will be humbled, but whoever humbles himself will be exalted."

I thought, *Pride is the predominant sin of the Scribes and the Pharisees. I hope that I will be able to humble myself and to maintain a contempt for the type of respect and esteem that they seek from the people.* I silently prayed to receive this grace.

Then Jesus began to excoriate them in a thunderous voice that reminded me of my father's voice. Jesus addressed them as a Prophet, expressing His horror at their sin and warning them of punishment.

Jesus said, "Woe to you, Scribes and Pharisees, you hypocrites! You lock up the Kingdom of God to the people. You don't enter it yourselves, nor do you allow entrance to those who are trying to enter it. You are blind guides who mislead the people. You pay tithes on tiny spices, but neglect the more important things of the Law such as justice, mercy and fidelity. You clean the outside of cups and dishes, but your own insides are full of plunder and self-indulgence. You should clean the inside of the cup first, so that the outside will also be clean. You are like whitewashed tombs. They appear beautiful on the outside, but inside they are full of dead men's bones. Just so, you appear to be righteous on the outside, but in reality your insides are filled with hypocrisy and evildoing."

Then He summed up His prophecy against them and Jerusalem. He said, "You are the children of those who murdered the Prophets and now you will imitate them and do the same. You serpents, you brood of vipers, how can you flee from the coming judgment?"

"I will send you Prophets, some of whom you will scourge and some of whom you will crucify. Because of that, there will come upon you all of the righteous blood ever shed upon Earth. I say to you, all of these things will come upon this generation. Jerusalem, Jerusalem, you who kill the Prophets, how many times I yearned to gather your children together, as a mother hen gathers her young under her wings. But you would not recognize me for who I am! I say to you, your house will be abandoned, desolate. I tell you, you will not see me again until you say, 'Blessed is He who comes in the name of the Lord.' "

Jesus gave the Scribes and Pharisees this severe message, not to condemn them, but to bring them to repentance. He still expressed the tenderness of His heart and His desire to care for them as a mother hen for her brood. But, in their utter perversity, they would not have it.

I was in awe of the majesty of Jesus as He confronted these supposedly great religious men. He was fearless, strong, firm and truthful. He held up their hypocritical teachings and practices before their very eyes so that they could see them in the light of the truth. However, there are none so blind as those who do not want to see. They stood before Him, stone-faced, their eyes blazing with hatred. But they said nothing. Jesus had reduced them to silence. They could say nothing in their own defense because they had no defense.

Among those who had come to the Temple were some Greeks who came from outside of Israel. They were more open to the love of God than many of the Jewish leaders. They came to Philip, who spoke Greek, and said to him, "Sir, we wish to see Jesus." This was the beginning of the acceptance of Jesus by the Gentiles, by all nations, symbolized by these Greeks.

Philip went and told Andrew who went with him and they told Jesus that the Greeks wanted to see Him. But Jesus sensed that they had been only caught up in the excitement of the procession of Jesus into Jerusalem. The procession was not the real triumph of Jesus.

He answered them, "The hour has come for the Son of Man to be glorified in which the Father will manifest to the greatest His presence in His Son. Truly, truly, I say to you, unless a grain of wheat falls into earth and dies, it remains alone; but if it dies, it

144

bears much fruit. He who loves his life loses it, and he who hates his life in this world will keep it for eternal life. If anyone serves me he must follow me; and where I am, there shall my servant be also. If anyone serves me, the Father will honor him."

There it is again, I thought, His death theme. I cringe at the thought. I understand that somehow He is to be glorified in His death. It's as if His burial will be like a seed of wheat that is planted in the ground, dies, sprouts and rises from the ground into a living blade of wheat. In order to have eternal life, we will have to figuratively die to ourselves and natural life by self-denial.

Jesus continued, "Now is my soul troubled. And what shall I say? 'Father, save me from this hour'? No, for this purpose I have come to this hour. Father, glorify your name."

Then a voice came from heaven, "I have glorified it, and I will glorify it again."

The voice was awesome, loud, majestic and authoritative. It was just like the time that I heard the Father speak from the cloud when Jesus was transfigured on Mount Tabor, and also when He publicly spoke from the cloud at Jesus' baptism.

The crowd standing by also heard the voice, but they said that it was only thunder. Others said, "An angel has spoken to Him."

Jesus answered, "This voice has come for your sake, not for mine. Now is the judgment of this world, now shall the ruler of this world be cast out. And when I am lifted up from Earth, I will draw all men to myself."

All men to Himself? I wondered. Weren't the Jews the Chosen People? But now He said that He'd draw all men to Himself. So salvation must be possible even for these Greeks who came to see Him, as well as the whole human race! Perhaps these Greeks are the first fruits of what Jesus had said were "other sheep, that are not of this fold" – the beginning of the conversion of all nations.

I also wondered, Who was "the ruler of this world to be cast out"? And how was Jesus to be "lifted from Earth"? Was this like the lifting that He talked about before when He said that only then would He be recognized? Was His Father going to lift Him up into the clouds? How would He "draw all men to Himself"?

Then I remembered how Moses was in the wilderness with his bronze serpent. When he lifted it up, all those who had been bitten by the serpents were healed. So now we, who were bitten by the serpent of original sin, might be healed by the lifting up of Christ on the Cross that He had prophesied to us. This serpent is Satan, the ruler of this world, who Jesus will cast out.

The crowd had the same questions that I did. They asked Him, "We have heard from the Law that the Christ remains forever. So how can you say that the Son of Man must be lifted up? Who is this Son of Man?"

Jesus answered them indirectly, "The light is with you for a little longer. Walk while you have the light, lest the darkness overtake you. He who walks in the darkness does not know where he's going. While you have the light, believe in the light, so that you may become sons of light."

Then Jesus cried out and summarized His doctrine in His last public teaching:

> Whoever believes in me, believes not in me but in Him who sent me. And whoever sees me, sees Him who sent me. I have come as light into the world, so that whoever believes in me may not remain in darkness. If anyone hears my words and does not keep them, I do not condemn him, for I did not come to condemn the world but to save the world. Whoever rejects me and does not accept my words has a judge — the word that I spoke will be his judge on the last day. For I did not speak on my own authority, but the Father who sent me commanded me what to say and what to speak. And I know that His commandment is eternal life. So what I say, I say as the Father told me.

He had recapitulated His entire doctrine as the Son of God who obeyed His Father and came into the world as the Son of Man and

Savior to execute His Father's command to give eternal life to those who believe in His words and act upon them.

As we left the Temple area, we were talking to Jesus about its buildings. He said, "You see all these buildings, do you not? Truly I tell you, there will not be left here a stone upon another stone that will not be thrown down."

This prophecy was fulfilled to the letter when the Roman General Titus destroyed the city and the Temple 37 years later. This destruction was the result of the failure of so many to recognize the time of the visitation of Jesus and their failure to repent and to accept Him as their Messiah, Savior and Lord.

We left Jerusalem and hid from the crowds in Bethany. Though He had done so many signs in their very presence, they refused to believe in Him. He had healed the sick and disabled, multiplied food, delivered evil demons, forgave sins and even raised the dead back to life — the last of whom was Lazarus who had been dead for four days but now stood living among them.

Jesus did the things that only God could do through Him and these signs should have been enough for them to believe that He was who He said He was — the Son of Man and the Son of God. But still they didn't believe. It reminded me of the Prophet Isaiah who said, "Lord, who has believed our report, and to whom has the might of the Lord been revealed?" (Isaiah 53:1).

It was as if they were totally blind and couldn't see what we saw so clearly. Perhaps this was a judgment or penance that God inflicted on them because of their obdurate refusal to believe in His Son.

The Pharisees were filled with pride. They thought that they had everything figured out. They denied that Jesus was the Messiah because He didn't meet their expectations of an earthly king. While many others did believe that Jesus was the Messiah, they refused to admit it because they were afraid that the Pharisees might eject them from the synagogue. They loved the praise of men more than the glory of God. They would rather look good before men than to show their belief and to look good before God.

On Wednesday, near to the Feast of Passover we spent the day in Bethany. Jesus said, "You know that the Passover Feast is coming and the Son of Man will be handed over to be crucified."

I later learned that, at that same time, the Chief Priests and the elders of the people had gathered in the palace of Caiaphas, the High Priest, and had plotted together in order to arrest Jesus by stealth. But they didn't want to do it during the Feast, because it would stir up the people.

However, Judas Iscariot then went to the Chief Priests and offered to deliver Jesus to them. They paid Judas thirty pieces of silver, which were the wages of a rejected good shepherd in the Prophet Zechariah's allegory. (See Zechariah 11:12). From that moment on, they sought an opportunity to arrest Him without stirring up the people.

Apparently, Jesus didn't meet Judas's standards for the Messiah. Judas was interested in helping an earthly king in order to help himself to money, glory and honor. Jesus' message of repentance, mercy, love, service and sacrifice never reached the heart of Judas.

Judas' actions reminded me of Joseph's brothers who had betrayed him into slavery in Egypt. They also did it for a handful of silver pieces. But if God in His Providence had used the betrayal of Joseph for the good of his father Jacob's family through Joseph's later saving them during a famine in Egypt, God could surely use Judas' betrayal to save us.

The Last Supper

On Thursday, we returned to Jerusalem. There were hundreds of thousands of pilgrims who had come from all over the world to celebrate the Passover Feast. Jesus told Peter and me, "Go and prepare our Passover supper for us." I wondered where we could possibly find a room to celebrate the Passover meal at a time when the city was so crowded.

We asked Him, "Where do you want us to prepare it?"

He explained to us, "Just as you enter the city, you'll meet a man carrying a water jar. Follow him into the house that he enters and say to the owner, 'The Teacher asks you, Do you have a guest room where I can eat the Passover with my disciples?' He'll show you a large, furnished upper room that you are to make ready."

We went in faith on this strange mission. It was just like when we had entered Jerusalem and Jesus had said that we'd find the colt for Him to ride. It happened again just like He said it would happen and we prepared for the Passover supper in the upper room of a house located in the southwest quarter of the city near Mount Zion.

The Passover supper memorialized the original special meal that the Jews in Egypt ate around 1440 BC according to God's command. A lamb was sacrificed and its blood was sprinkled on the door posts of the Jews so that God's angel of death would pass over them and protect their firstborn children. However, the firstborn of the Egyptians would be killed. This was God's chastisement upon the Egyptians in order to free the Israelites, His Chosen People, from slavery.

On that night of the first Passover, the Jews ate the sacrificed lamb. The lamb died as a ransom, in place of the firstborn of the Jewish households who were saved from death. So we would celebrate the Passover supper every year and remember the Exodus under Moses and God's liberation of the Israelites from the Egyptian Pharaoh.

Jesus knew that His hour had come to depart out of this world to go to His Father. His hour of death was always in God's control and He had been saved from it and from those who wanted to kill Him. But now His hour had come.

Jesus led us to celebrate a new and different Passover supper before the actual Feast of Passover, which would fall this year on Saturday, the Sabbath day. During supper, when the devil had already put it into the heart of Judas Iscariot to betray Him, Jesus, knowing that the Father had given all things into His hands, and that He had come from God and was going to God, rose from the supper.

We watched in suspense as He laid aside His cloak, picked up a towel and tied it around His waist. We were all lying on the floor around the low supper table with our feet sticking out from it.

Jesus poured water into a basin, knelt at our feet and began to wash our feet and to wipe them with the towel. It was an act of humble charity.

He came to Peter who said, "Lord, are you going to wash my feet?"

Jesus answered, "You might not realize what I am doing now, but later you will understand."

Peter said, "You shall never wash my feet!" In his great love for Jesus, Peter was obstinate that Jesus, whom Peter had once acknowledged as the Messiah, the Son of the living God, should not stoop so low as to wash the feet of a simple, sinful fisherman.

"If I do not wash you," Jesus answered him, "you will have no share in my heritage."

This threat of separation from Jesus vanquished Peter's obstinacy. He may have remembered Jesus' previous command to him, "Get behind me Satan! You are not judging by God's standards but by man's."

So, Peter went to the other extreme and said to Him, "Lord, then not only my feet, but my hands and my head as well!"

Jesus told him, "He who has bathed doesn't need to wash, except for his feet. He is entirely clean, just as you are, but not every one of you." He knew that Judas was going to betray Him. That's why He said, "But not every one of you."

The exterior cleansing of our feet by Jesus showed me my need for His entire interior cleansing by His forgiveness of my sins so that I could receive the fullness of His love.

After He washed our feet, He put His cloak back on and reclined again at the table with us. He said, "Do you understand what I have just done to you? You call me Teacher and Lord; and you are right, for that is who I am. But if I, your Lord and Teacher, have washed your feet, you also must wash one another's feet.

150

For I have given you an example, so that you must do as I have done to you."

"I solemnly assure you, no slave is greater than his master, nor is any messenger greater than he who sent him. If you understand this, blessed are you if you do it."

"I am not speaking of all of you. I know those whom I have chosen. My purpose is to fulfill the Scripture: 'He who ate bread with me has lifted his heel against me.' "

Jesus alluded to the psalm that related the brutal treason of Achitophel, table companion and friend of King David, who, like Judas, betrayed his King and figuratively lifted his heel against him like the backward kick of a horse's heel against its master. (See Psalm 41:10).

He continued, "I tell you this now, before it takes place, so that when it does take place you may believe that I AM. I solemnly assure you, he who receives anyone whom I send receives me, and he who receives me receives Him who sent me."

Jesus had now identified Himself with God by using the same words that God had used when He addressed Himself to Moses saying, "Tell them I AM sent you."

After He said that, Jesus seemed more disturbed in spirit. Then He directly and forcefully said, "I solemnly tell you that one of you will betray me."

We looked at one another in great surprise, unsure of whom He was speaking. I was reclining close to Jesus, so Peter whispered to me, "Ask Him who is the one."

So, since my head was lying close to Jesus' chest, I looked up at Him and quietly asked, "Lord, who is he?"

Jesus whispered, "The one to whom I'll give this piece of bread that I'll dip in the sauce dish."

At this meal we reclined on our sides and ate from dishes that served all of us. In memory of the trials of our Israelite ancestors in their Exodus, we ate unleavened bread, bitter herbs, wine and the sauce to which Jesus referred. It was made from fruits, nuts, spices and vinegar.

Then Jesus dipped the bread in the sauce dish and gave it to Judas. It seemed as if Satan entered into him and he hardened his heart.

Jesus said to him, "Be quick about what you're going to do."

We didn't know why He said this or what Judas was supposed to do. I thought that, since Judas had the money purse, Jesus was telling him to buy something for the meal or that he should give something to the poor. As soon as he received the piece of food from Jesus, Judas immediately went outside. It was night. He had left the light of the world for the darkness.

After Judas left, Jesus said, "Now is the Son of Man glorified, and God is glorified in Him. If God is glorified in Him, God will, in turn, glorify Him in Himself, and He will glorify Him very soon."

Then, as He sat at the table with us, He said, "I have earnestly desired to eat this Passover meal with you before I suffer. I tell you that I shall not eat it again until it is fulfilled in the Kingdom of God." I didn't understand what He meant.

Then He took bread, gave thanks, broke it and gave it to us saying, "Take this, all of you, and eat of it, for this is my body which will be given up for you."

He meant this literally. Somehow, by God's almighty power, this ordinary unleavened bread was now changed into the real body of Jesus. But I wondered how His body would be given up for us, as He had said.

It was customary to drink four cups of wine at the Passover meal. It was time for the third cup of wine. So, after our supper, Jesus took the third cup, gave thanks and passed it to us to drink. He said, "Take this, all of you, and drink from it, for this is the cup of my blood, the blood of the new and eternal covenant, which will be poured out for you and for many for the forgiveness of sins. Do this in memory of me."

Again, He meant this literally. Somehow, by God's almighty power, this ordinary wine was now changed into the real blood of Jesus. He was offering His very self for our salvation and He wanted us to do what He was now doing in memory of Him.

152

Surely, if He could change ordinary water into wine, as He had done with His first miracle at the wedding in Cana, He could now change this ordinary wine into His own blood.

But we had always been prohibited from drinking blood because it contained life. I remembered that Jesus had spoken to us before about His blood at His Bread of Life discourse. That was in the synagogue in Capernaum after the miracle of the multiplication of the bread and the fish.

He had said then that unless we drank His blood we would have no eternal life in us. When He said that, most of His followers walked away from Him because this teaching seemed so contrary to the prohibition against drinking blood. But Jesus meant it literally both then and now, when the substance of the wine really changed at His word into His blood. This contained His own life, which is eternal.

After He gave us His body and blood, He said, "I solemnly tell you that I will never again drink of the fruit of the vine until the day that I drink it new in the Kingdom of God." I didn't understand this either, as I did not when He said that He wouldn't eat a Passover meal again.

Now I realized that this was not an ordinary Passover meal, but a sacrificial farewell banquet and that at some time in the future we would celebrate some kind of a new banquet with Him.

Later, I reflected on what Jesus did and said at this meal. As a result, His discourse on the Bread of Life now made sense to me. I understood that when we apostles would do what He had done at the meal, in memory of Him, by offering what appeared to be bread and wine, He would really and truly change them into His body and blood.

I understood that when we received His body and blood under the appearances of bread and wine, we received His very self, real food and real drink, His flesh for the life of the world and by His grace we would live in Him and He in us and we would live forever, just as He had promised us in His discourse. He is truly the living Bread of Life which comes down from heaven in His flesh for the life of the world and He will raise us up at the last day.

153

At this new sacrificial meal, Jesus gave us His real flesh and blood under the appearances of bread and wine so that we would have eternal life in and with Him.

His words reminded me of the time when Moses sprinkled sacrificial blood on the Israelites. Moses said, "This is the blood of the covenant which the Lord has made with you in accordance with all of these words of His." Now Jesus gave us His own blood in a new covenant, ratified in His blood, in which we were united to Him by sharing His own body and blood.

I recalled the covenant that God made with Moses and the Israelites at Mount Sinai. He promised to be their God and they would be His people. God gave His commandments to the Israelites through Moses and the Israelites promised to obey them. This covenant was ratified by the shedding of the blood of sacrificial lambs, half of which was sprinkled on an altar and half on the Israelites. The blood represented the life of the victim so the blood on the altar was a sacrifice to God of the victim and the sprinkling of the blood on the people represented the special union between God and His people effected by the covenant. The ratification ceremony ended with the banquet meal of the flesh of the sacrificed lambs that strengthened the bond between God and the Israelites.

In the original Passover meal in Egypt, the lamb was sacrificed and its blood sprinkled on the Israelites' door posts so that the angel of death passed over them. Now I understood that Jesus was a priest who offered Himself as a lamb-like victim. He was both the priest and the victim. He offered God His own blood as the new sacrificial lamb at His new Passover meal so that eternal death in fire would pass over us and we would have eternal life with Him in the Kingdom of God. He gave us His blood in a new sacrificial banquet meal of His own body to ratify His new covenant, to represent our special union and to strengthen the bond between us.

Jesus celebrated this new Passover outside of the Temple because He was the true lamb and the true Temple. He was the living Temple, the one in which God lives, in which we can find ourselves with God and adore Him. He was the awaited lamb, the one that John the Baptist had foretold at the beginning of Jesus' public ministry when he proclaimed, "Behold the Lamb of God, who takes away the sin of the world." He is the new Passover Lamb of God who protects us by His blood from eternal damnation and grants us the forgiveness of our repented sins and eternal life with Him.

However, as I was at the table, I still wondered how He would give us His body and pour out His blood, since He was still before us very much alive. Was He going somewhere else? And what exactly was His new covenant?

Later, I meditated on Jesus' words about His new covenant. The old covenant was a relationship first made with Abraham when God promised him that He would be his God and that Abraham and his progeny would be His people. The old covenant was renewed with Moses when God promised the Israelites that He would be their God and they would be His people, if they obeyed His Law.

Later, Jeremiah prophesied a new covenant whereby God would write His law in our hearts and forgive our sins. Speaking the words of God, Jeremiah prophesied, "I will put my law within them, and I will write it upon their hearts; and I will be their God, and they shall be my people. And no longer shall each man teach his neighbor and each his brother, saying, 'Know the Lord,' for they shall all know me, from the least of them to the greatest, says the Lord; for I will forgive their iniquity, and I will remember their sin no more." (Jeremiah 31:33-34).

I thought, *What is this new covenant? The old covenant was that God would be our God and we would be His people.*

This new covenant must be some kind of relationship like the old, but what is different? Did He ever say anything about His relationship with us? Then it came to me in a flash. I remembered that when He was preaching His Bread of Life discourse, He had said, "He who eats my flesh and drinks my blood has eternal life and I will raise him up at the last day. For my flesh is real food, and my blood is real drink. Whoever eats my flesh and drinks my blood lives in me, and I in him." So, He really would live in us and we in Him.

What an intimate new relationship! It's not like before when He seemed to be a God who was outside of us and we were His people who were outside of Him. Now He is a God who forgives our sins, who lives in us and we in Him, a relationship through which we have eternal life and His promise to raise us up at the last day. This is the new covenant!

This covenant was made not only with the Israelites, as before, but with all humanity, all nations, by the true King of All Nations. And it was ratified by His gift of His own blood for our eternal life through the forgiveness of our sins.

So, I continued to wonder, what is eternal life? Is it simply time forever? Is it only everlasting time? Time without end? Living forever? No! Surely it must be something more than that. It must be a person! Jesus had told Martha, "I am the resurrection and the life." So, He Himself is the life and eternal life must be Him. And we can have that eternal life, His person, now in this new relationship with Him in the new covenant whereby He lives in us and we in Him. It's an intimate and personal relationship with Jesus in which we really come to know the one true God and Jesus Christ whom He sent. We share in His divine nature. We are divinized by the indwelling presence of Jesus Christ within us.

In the old covenant, God had also promised to give the Israelites the Promised Land for their heritage. I wondered what the Promised Land of Jesus would be. Was it His Kingdom of God, a kingdom of eternal life through the forgiveness of our sins? The eternal life that He had promised when He said, "The hour is coming when all who are in the tombs will hear His voice and come forth, those who have done good, to the resurrection of life, and those who have done evil, to the resurrection of judgment." I also wondered whether Jesus had a new commandment for us, as God had given the commandments to Moses.

As I wondered at the table, Jesus answered my question and said, "Little children, I'll be with you for only a little while longer. You'll look for me, but as I once said to the Jews, 'Where I am going you cannot come.' "

Then He spoke like God had spoken to Moses, "So now I give you a new commandment: love one another. As I have loved you, so you must love one another. This is how everyone will know that you are my disciples, by your love for one another."

God had told the Israelites to love God and to love their neighbors as themselves. Jesus went beyond that and told us to love even our enemies. Now He gave us His new commandment to love one another as He had loved us by giving us everything, even His body and blood.

Simon Peter said to Him, "Lord, where are you going?"

Jesus answered, "Where I am going you cannot follow me now, but you will follow me later."

Peter boldly said to Him, "Lord, why can't I follow you now? I will lay down my life for you."

"Simon, Simon," Jesus answered. "Behold, Satan demanded to have you, so that he might shake you up, sift you and separate you from your brothers like chaff is separated from the wheat. But I've prayed for you so that your faith may not fail. When you have returned to me again, strengthen your brothers." I wondered where Peter was going since Jesus said that he would return to Him.

Then Peter spoke up and said, "I'm not going anywhere! I'll stay at your side and I'm ready to go to prison or even to die for you!"

Jesus answered this presumptuous bravado, "You'll die for me? I tell you, Peter, the cock won't crow today before you deny that you know me three times."

Then a dispute arose among us about who should be the greatest in His Kingdom. Jesus ended the dispute and said, "Earthly kings lord it over their people and are called their benefactors. But it can't be that way with you. Rather, the greatest should be like the youngest and the leader like the servant. For who is the greater, the one who sits at table or the one who serves the meal? Isn't it the one who sits at table? But I sit among you as one who serves you."

"You are the ones who have stayed loyally by my side in my trials—in my poverty and in my rejection. So now I assign to you, as my Father assigned to me, a Kingdom. In my Kingdom, you will eat and drink at my table, and you will sit on thrones judging the twelve tribes of Israel." I thought, *This must be the new and*

157

eternal Kingdom of God, not the earthly kingdom that we had always thought of where we would have choice seats and could lord it over the people. It is a kingdom of love, faith, peace and joy where all will be one in Him, Jesus, King of All Nations.

The Farewell Discourses of Jesus

Then Jesus proceeded to teach us in a series of discourses. He explained that by His death, He would go to His Father with whom He is one; that He is the Way to the Father; that if we loved Him, we should keep His commandments and the Father would send us the Spirit of truth who would live in us and that Jesus and His Father would make their home with us.

He announced that He would not leave us orphans but would come back to us; that His Father would send us the Holy Spirit who would teach us everything and would remind us of all that He had said to us.

He repeated His new commandment to love one another as He had loved us.

At the beginning of the discourses, He reassured us and said, "Don't let your hearts be troubled. Believe in God and also believe in me. In my Father's house there are many dwelling places. If that weren't so, would I have told you that I go to prepare a place for you? I'm really going to prepare a place for you and when I come back again I'll take you to myself so that where I am, you may also be. You know the way to where I'm going."

I imagined that His "Father's house" of which He spoke was His Church, the mystical Kingdom of God that He told Peter that He would build upon the rock of Peter. But He also seemed to speak in riddles again. Where was this house? Thomas spoke my thoughts and said to Him, "Lord, we really don't know where you're going, so how could we possibly know the way?"

Jesus answered, "I am the way, and the truth, and the life. No one comes to the Father, except through me. If you really knew me, you would also know my Father. From now on you do know Him and you have seen Him."

I thought, *He speaks like God and says that He is the way and the truth and the life. It's a statement that only God could make.*

He knows that we can't find the way to the Father on our own, without His help. That's why the Father sent Him, the Son, into the world – to rescue us, to lead us in truth and to restore our lives in the Kingdom of God.

Later, I realized that God had promised, through Moses and the Prophets, to guide us in a Holy Way so that we could walk and live His peace and blessing. Isaiah prophesied, "A highway shall be there, and it shall be called the Holy Way; the unclean shall not pass over it, and fools shall not err therein." (Isaiah 35:8). Now Jesus tells us that He is the Holy Way. He did not simply give us advice and direction. He Himself is the way. He leads and guides us personally every day. He Himself is the truth and the life. He Himself is the kind of life that only God can give – eternal life.

Moses led our forefathers to the Promised Land. Now Jesus leads us to the Kingdom of God where we can live with Him and one another in perfect peace, unity and love. He does not simply teach us the way, He is the way. He is also the truth, not merely by His words, but by His example of embodying all truth in His person. He is also the life, not only by showing us the way of life, but by giving us the fullness of life, eternal happiness with Him in the Kingdom of God.

Then Philip spoke up and expressed what would satisfy him. He said, "Lord, show us the Father and that will be enough for us."

Jesus upbraided him for not yet knowing Him, even though His works could have been done only by God – such as walking on the water, controlling the wind, healing the sick, casting out demons, forgiving sins and raising the dead.

He said, "Philip, after all of this time that I have been with you, you still don't know me? Whoever has seen me has seen the Father. How can you say, 'Show us the Father'? Don't you believe that I am in the Father and the Father is in me? The words that I say to you I do not say on my own authority. It is the Father who lives in me who does His works. Believe me that I am in the Father and the Father is in me. Or else believe me because of the works that I do."

He spoke to Philip as He had to the Jews in the Temple at the Feast of Hanukkah when He said that He is in the Father and the Father is in Him. He had also spoken like this to the Pharisees in His last public teaching when He said that He and the Father were one and when He appealed to them to believe His words or else to believe Him because of His works. Jesus continued:

> Truly, truly, I say to you, whoever believes in me will do the works that I do, and will do greater ones than these, because I am going to the Father. And whatever you ask in my name, I will do, so that the Father may be glorified in the Son. If you ask anything of me in my name, I will do it.
>
> If you love me, you will keep my commandments. And I will ask the Father, and He will give you another Counselor to be with you always. He is the Spirit of Truth, whom the world cannot accept, because it neither sees Him nor recognizes Him. But you recognize Him because He remains with you and He will live in you.
>
> I will not leave you orphans, but I will come back to you. In a little while, the world will see me no more. But you will see me because I live and you will have life also. On that day you will know that I am in my Father, and that you are in me and I am in you. Whoever obeys my commandments is the one who loves me. Whoever loves me will be loved by my Father and I will love him and reveal myself to him.

Another of the disciples, Jude (not Judas Iscariot), then said to Him, "Lord, how is it that you will reveal yourself to us and not to the world?"

Jesus answered, "If anyone loves me, he will keep my word and my Father will love him, and we will come to him and make our dwelling with him. Whoever does not love me does not keep my word. But the word that you hear is not mine, but that of the Father who sent me."

I thought, How will He make His dwelling with us if we keep His word? He just told us at our supper that He gave us His body and blood in the form of the bread and wine. That's the word that He just gave us and if we keep it and eat His body and drink His blood we will have His life in us. He'll make His home in us! It's a divine indwelling. He and His Father will come back to us within our very selves. He commanded us to take and eat His body and blood. This is His word.

I later realized that we keep His word by keeping His commandments. This is how we know that we have come to know Him. Whoever says, "I know Him," but does not keep His commandments is a liar and truth has no place in him. But to anyone who does keep His word, God's love truly reaches its perfection in him. So if we eat His body and drink His blood, we believe that we are in God and God is in us.

But whoever claims to remain in Him must also act as He acted. God's commandment is this, that we should believe in the name of His Son Jesus Christ and that we should love one another as He commanded us.

Whoever believes that Jesus is the Christ is a child of God, and whoever loves the Father loves the Son. In this way we know that we love God's children when we love God and keep His commandments. The love of God is keeping His commandments. But His commandments are not burdensome, because every child of God overcomes the world. And our faith is the victory that has overcome the world. Whoever keeps His commandments remains in God and God in him.

Then Jesus continued to encourage us. He said, "I've told you these things while I'm still with you. But the Counselor, the Holy

Spirit, whom the Father will send in my name, He will teach you everything and He will remind you of all that I have said to you."

"Peace I leave with you. My peace I give to you. I don't give peace to you as the world does." He seemed to be saying that the world only gives a false peace—a peace where there is just the absence of conflict. But His peace is beyond all understanding. It is the tranquility of order and includes everything which makes for our highest good.

"Let not your hearts be troubled or afraid," He continued. "You heard me tell you, 'I am going away for a while and I will come back to you.' If you truly loved me, you would rejoice that I am going to the Father; for the Father is greater than I."

"I have told you this before it takes place, so that when it does take place, you may believe. I won't go on talking much longer, for the Prince of this world is coming. He has no power over me, but the world must know that I love the Father and that I do just as the Father has commanded me. Get up! Let us go to another room."

So we left for another room in the house in order to allow the table and the Upper Room to be cleaned up. Then Jesus began teaching us again. He promised that those who believe in Him would have a new life of union with Him as intimate as a vine with its branches, a union that is attained by keeping His new commandment of love.

He said, "I am the true vine and my Father is the vinedresser. He prunes and casts away every branch of mine that bears no fruit, but every branch that does bear fruit He prunes so that it may bear more fruit. You are already pruned by the word which I spoke to you. Live in me, as I do in you. Just as a branch cannot bear fruit by itself unless it lives in the vine, neither can you, unless you live in me."

I wondered why He said that He was the true vine. The image of the vine was a familiar one for us since the land of Israel was covered with numerous vineyards. It had religious connotations as well and symbolized Israel as a nation. Isaiah spoke of the house of Israel as "the vineyard of the Lord." (Isaiah 5:7).

162

Jeremiah said that God had planted Israel "as His choice vine." (Jeremiah 2:21).

On the other hand, the Prophets also spoke of Israel's degeneration. Isaiah's prophecy spoke of Israel as a vineyard which "yielded wild grapes." (Isaiah 5:1-7). Jeremiah said that Israel had become a "degenerate and wild vine." (Jeremiah 2:21). When Jesus called Himself the true vine, He made clear that no one can claim their spiritual inheritance through their living in a particular nation, such as Judea, but rather only through Him, the King of All Nations.

Jesus continued, "I am the vine, you are the branches. Whoever lives in me and I in him, will bear much fruit, because without me you can do nothing. Anyone who does not live in me will be thrown out like a withered branch that is picked up by others, thrown into a fire and burned."

Yes, I reflected, the true vine is Jesus who feeds us, the branches, with His love, like a vine feeds its branches with its sap, by which we bear fruits of love and without which we can't bear these fruits. Jesus has pruned us, His apostles, by His words and teachings. The Father continues to prune us just like a vinedresser prunes his branches to bear more fruit, because if they are not pruned they become wild and barren. Like barren branches, we will be cast into the fire if we don't produce good fruit.

We are either fruit-bearing or non-fruit-bearing. There is no in-between. But the bearing of healthy fruit requires drastic pruning. The Lord promises that we will bear much fruit if we live in Him and allow Him to purify us. By pruning us, our heavenly Father has the same purpose as any vine grower. He prunes us in order to produce spiritual fruitfulness. Pruning does away with the old, diseased and dead branches from a plant. God works the same way in our souls. He seeks to remove the dead wood of sin and the diseased branches of vice so that our souls can enjoy greater health.

A vine grower also prunes to revitalize the plant, to encourage more growth and a greater yield of fruits. Our heavenly Father treats us in the same way. If a branch does bear fruit he prunes it so that it may bear more fruit. Only by this pruning do we produce more fruit.

We must allow the vine grower to accomplish this pruning of our souls by accepting the crosses and sacrifices that our heavenly Father gives us, such as the pains and difficulties of daily life. If we accept them with patience and love, we will bear more fruit.

The good branches live in the vine and the vine in them and they are united in life with the vine and one another as the followers of Jesus will live united with Him and one another in the Kingdom of God.

It reminds me of the time that Jesus told us, "He who eats my flesh and drinks my blood lives in me and I in him." All of our life comes from Him who pours out His life through His body and blood, just as the branches derive all their life from the vine. Without that life from Him, the branches will die. And He is the Word of life made visible, the eternal life that was present to the Father, which He has revealed to us and which we may share with Him and the Father. We can live in Him as He lives in us. It is His divine indwelling.

Jesus seemingly picked up on my thoughts and continued, "If you live in me, and my words live in you, ask for whatever you want and it will be done for you. My Father is glorified by your bearing fruit and becoming my disciples. As the Father loves me, so also I love you. Live on in my love. If you keep my commandments, you will live in my love, just as I have kept my Father's commandments and live in His love. I tell you this so that my joy may be in you and that your joy may be full."

My joy was completely full as I contemplated His words and realized that we can live in the Kingdom of God, bear fruit and glorify His Father simply by obeying His commandments.

When He said, "I am the true vine," it struck me how He had previously identified Himself as being one with His Father by using an "I AM" statement. It reminded me of the time that He said, "Before Abraham came to be, I am." In His self-revelation and identification, He used the same words that God had used with Moses at the burning bush. He told Moses, "tell them I AM sent you." Then I remembered all of His other "I am" statements in the past:

"I am the bread of life," made during His Bread of Life Discourse when He was teaching in the synagogue in Capernaum.

"I am the living bread come down from heaven," also made during His Bread of Life Discourse when He was also teaching in the synagogue in Capernaum.

"I am the light of the world," made just before He healed the man born blind.

"I am the gate," made during His discourse on the good shepherd.

"I am the good shepherd," also made during His discourse on the good shepherd.

"I am the resurrection and the life," made to Martha when He met her after the death of Lazarus.

"I am the way, and the truth, and the life," just made in answer to Thomas' question at the supper.

"I AM," made at the Feast of Tabernacles and just now to us at the supper when He implored us to "believe that I AM."

These repeated "I am" affirmations revealed the true unity between Jesus and the Father. He said, "To have seen me is to have seen the Father! . . . The Father and I are one."

Then Jesus repeated His new commandment and said, "This is my commandment, love one another as I love you. For there is no greater love than this, to lay down your life for your friends. You are my friends if you do what I command you. I no longer call you servants, for the servant doesn't know what his master is doing. But I call you friends because I revealed to you everything that I heard from my Father. You didn't choose me, but I chose you to go and bear fruit that will live, so that whatever you ask the Father in my name, He will give to you. I command you to love one another."

I thought, *Is He referring to Himself when He says "There is no greater love than this, to lay down your life for your friend"? Is He going to lay down His life for us? Is this what He meant when He said that He was going up to Jerusalem to be put to death? True love is sacrificial. It gives all to the beloved and we are His beloved. He wants us to follow His example and love one another. There is no greater proof of love than the sacrifice of one's life for the sake of another.*

He calls us His friends, just like God called Abraham His friend (see Isaiah 41:8) and God spoke to Moses as a man speaks with his friend. (See Exodus 33:11). Jesus, the Lord and Master, in turn calls us His friends rather than His servants. Friendship with God certainly entails a loving relationship which goes beyond mere duty and obedience. Jesus' discourse on friendship and brotherly love echoes the words of Proverbs, "A friend loves at all times." (Proverbs 17:17). The distinctive feature of Jesus' relationship with us disciples is His personal love for us. What a friend we have in Jesus who loves us unconditionally at all times, regardless of our sins, faults and failings. He yearns for our love for Him and one another. So our love for Him and one another should be unconditional as is His.

Jesus confirmed my belief that we can only enter and remain in the Kingdom of God by loving God and one another unconditionally, even our enemies, and, by doing so, we will bear the fruit of love to the glory of the God of love. But the Kingdom of God has always had its enemies in the Kingdom of the World who fight against it because the love of the true Kingdom is a sign of contradiction to the world's allurements of pleasure, wealth, power, glory and fame.

Jesus pointed this out to us and said, "If you find out that the world hates you, you must realize that it has hated me first. If you were of the world, the world would love you as its own. However, because you are not of the world and I chose you out of the world, the world hates you. Remember what I told you, 'A servant is not greater than his master.' If they persecuted me, they will also persecute you. If they rejected my word, they will also reject yours. They will do all these things to you on account of my name, because they do not know the Father who sent me."

"If I hadn't come and spoken to them, they would not be guilty of sin. But now they have no excuse for their sin. If they hate me, they hate my Father also. If I hadn't done such marvelous works among them, works which no one else ever did, they wouldn't be guilty. But now they have seen and they still hate both my Father and me. This fulfills the text in the Scripture, 'They hated me without cause.' But when the Counselor comes, the Spirit of Truth whom I shall send to you from the Father, who proceeds from the Father, He will bear witness on my behalf. You also must bear witness because you've been with me from the beginning."

Then Jesus explained why He was telling us all of this. "I've told you all this to you to keep you from falling away. Not only will they put you out of the synagogues, but a time will come when whoever kills you will think he is offering a service to God. They will do this to you because they haven't known the Father or me. But I've said these things to you, so that when their time comes, you will remember that I told you."

My heart shuddered to hear that those who might kill us will think that they were offering a service to God. What kind of a person could think that murder of the innocent was a service to God who commanded us not to kill?

Jesus continued, "I didn't say these things to you from the beginning, because I was with you. But now that I am going back to Him who sent me, not one of you asks me, 'Where are you going?' "

"Because I have said these things to you, your hearts are overcome with sorrow. But I tell you the truth. It's better for you that I go away. If I don't go away, the Counselor will not come to you. But if I do go, I will send Him to you. And when He comes, He will prove the world wrong about sin, about righteousness and about judgment. About sin, because they refuse to believe in me; about righteousness, because I will go to the Father and you will see me no more; and about judgment, because the ruler of this world is condemned."

In my heart, I thanked Jesus for this great gift of the Counselor, the Advocate and Spirit of Truth, whom He would send from the Father. The Spirit would prove the world wrong about sin, about righteousness and about judgment. *But how?* I wondered.

About sin, because they do not believe in Jesus! They believe in God's commandments, but they don't believe in the Commander's Son, the Son of Him who gave them. The Spirit will prove that the greatest sin is not in breaking a commandment, but in rejecting Jesus who is the Incarnation of the commandments.

About righteousness, because the Jews believed that righteousness is simply obeying the commandments. But the Spirit will prove that true righteousness is belief in Jesus, the Just One. He whom they called a devil and blasphemer is in fact the Son of God the Father.

About judgment, because in their judgment of Jesus as a devil and a blasphemer, they completely misjudged Him. He overthrew the real Devil and He will judge all people.

"I have much more to tell you," Jesus continued, "but you can't bear it now. When the Spirit of Truth comes, He will guide you to all the truth. He won't speak on His own authority, but only what He hears and He will announce to you all the things that are to come. He will glorify me, because He will receive it from me and announce it to you. All that the Father has belongs to me. That's why I said that He will announce to you what He received from me. In a little while, you won't see me anymore and then again, in a little while, you will see me because I go to the Father."

Jesus sought to uplift us because we were dragged down by sadness and were afraid that we would be left alone in the world. We were afraid to ask where He was going because we dreaded the thought of Him leaving us. He came into our lives and our hearts and everything changed. Then He told us that we won't see Him, but later we will. It sounded like a riddle to me.

Some of us said to one another, "What does He mean when He says, 'In a little while, you won't see me anymore and then again, in a little while, you will see me because I go to the Father'? We don't know what He's talking about."

Jesus knew what we wanted to ask Him, so He said to us, "You're asking yourselves what I meant. I solemnly tell you, that you will weep and mourn while the world rejoices. You will be sorrowful, but your sorrow will turn into joy. When a woman is in labor she is in pain because her time for the delivery of her child has come. But after she gives birth to her child, she no longer remembers her pain because she is joyful that her child is born into the world. In the same way, you have sorrowful pain now, but I will see you again and your hearts will rejoice with a joy that no one can take from you. On that day you won't have any questions to ask of me. I solemnly assure you, whatever you ask of the Father in my name, He will give you. Up until now, you haven't asked for anything in my name. Ask and you shall receive, so that your joy may be full."

I wanted to ask Him to explain this in plain language because I was still confused by what He meant by saying that in a little while we would not see Him and then we would see Him. However, once again, Jesus took the words right out of my mouth as if He had read my heart.

He said, "I've said these things in veiled language but a time will come when I will no longer speak to you in this way but I'll tell you plainly about the Father. On that day, you will ask in my name and I don't say that I'll pray to the Father for you. For the Father Himself loves you, because you love me and believe that I came from Him. I came from the Father and came into the world. Now I'm leaving the world and going back to the Father."

We said, "At last you're speaking plainly and not in veiled language! We are now convinced that you know everything. We don't need to ask you any more questions. We really believe that you came from God."

But how and when He was leaving the world and going back to the Father was still a mystery to me. Jesus moderated our enthusiastic confession of faith and answered us, "Do you really believe? The time is coming, indeed it's already here, when you will be scattered, each going on your own way and you'll leave me all alone. But I can never be alone, for the Father is with me. I tell you these things that you may have peace in me. You will suffer in the world, but take courage! I have conquered the world."

What world? I wondered. *The world of pleasure, wealth, power, glory and fame; the world of the flesh of lust, gluttony, drunkenness; in sum, the world of disordered bodily desires, desires of the eyes and pride in possession. We should not love this world. If anyone does love this world, the love of the Father finds no place in him. Because all of these things of the world are not from the Father, they are from the world.*

And the world with all its disordered desires is passing away. Jesus who came to the world from the Father and who goes back from the world to the Father is true God and true man. He has conquered this world and whoever does the will of God remains forever. We are in God and have conquered the world because God who is in us is greater than the Devil, the ruler of the world. His followers are from the world, but we are from God. Our faith will be the victory that conquers the world.

The Priestly Prayer of Jesus

Then we went upstairs to the flat roof of the house, into the cool and dark night air, under the full Passover moon. Jesus addressed His Father in a very moving prayer in which, as our Victim-High Priest, He offered Himself in sacrifice.

His prayer consisted of three parts. In the first, Jesus asked for the glorification of His holy human nature. In the second, He prayed for us, whom He would send out into the world to proclaim the truth of His Word. Lastly, He prayed for unity among all those who would believe in Him over the course of the centuries, until they achieved full union with Him in the Kingdom of God in heaven.

Jesus lifted up His eyes to heaven and said, "Father, the hour has come! Glorify your Son so that your Son may glorify you, since you have given Him authority over all mankind, that He might give eternal life to those whom you gave Him. This is eternal life, to know you, the only true God and Jesus Christ whom you sent. I glorified you on Earth, by accomplishing the work which you gave me to do. Now, Father, you glorify me in your own presence with the glory which I had with you before the world was created."

He continued in prayer:

> I have revealed your name to those whom you
> gave me out of the world. They belonged to you,

and you gave them to me, and they have kept your word. Now they know that everything that you gave me is from you. I gave them the words which you gave me and they have received them and know in truth that I came from you. They have believed that you sent me.

I'm praying for them. I'm not praying for the world but for those whom you gave me, for they are yours. In the same way that everything of mine is yours, and everything of yours is mine. I am glorified in them. Now I am in the world no more, but they are in the world, and I am coming to you.

Holy Father, protect them with your name which you gave me, so that they may be one, even as we are one. While I was with them, I protected them in your name which you gave me. I guarded them and none of them is lost but Judas, the son of perdition, in order to fulfill the Scripture.

When He said "the Scripture", Jesus referred to Psalm 41 as being fulfilled by the betrayal of Judas - "He who ate my bread has lifted his heel against me." Then He continued in prayer to His Father:

Now however, I am coming to you and these things I speak while I'm still in the world so that they may share my joy completely. I gave them your word and the world hated them because they are not of the world, just as I am not of the world. I do not pray that you should take them out of the world, but that you should protect them from the Evil One.

They are not of the world, even as I am not of the world. Consecrate them in the truth. Your word is truth. As you sent me into the world, so I sent them into the world. Now I consecrate myself for their sakes, so that they also may be consecrated in truth.

Then He lifted up His eyes to heaven and concluded His prayer:

> I don't pray for these only, but also for those who will believe in me through their word, that they all may be one as you, Father, are in me and I am in you, that they also may be in us, so that the world may believe that you sent me. I gave them the love which you gave to me, so that they may be one, as we are one, I in them and you in me, that they may become perfectly one, so that the world may know that you sent me and that you loved them even as you loved me.
>
> Father, I desire that all those whom you gave me may be with me where I am, to behold my glory which you gave me in your love for me before the foundation of the world. O righteous Father, the world does not know you, but I know you and these men know that you sent me. I revealed your name to them and I will continue to reveal it so that your love for me may live in them and I may live in them.

Jesus had prayed for our protection, our consecration in the truth, our union with one another and our communion with Him.

He asked the Father to protect us with His name, meaning that we would persevere in His teaching and in communion with Him. He also prayed that none of us should be lost and that His Father should guard and protect us from the Evil One, just as He Himself had protected us. And none of us was lost, except for Judas.

He prayed for our consecration in truth so that the witness of our unity in faith and morals would be a witness to the world and all nations, so that they would believe and know that the Father had sent Jesus as the true King of All Nations and that His love would live in us all with the indwelling of Jesus and we would all be perfectly one.

He prayed that, because of His protection, our union in truth and our communion with Him, we, and all who would believe through us, would share His eternal glory.

10. The Passion of Jesus

The Agony in the Garden

When the prayer of Jesus ended, we sang a hymn. Then we left the house, walked east and crossed the Kidron Valley towards the Garden of Gethsemane, about a mile away from the Upper Room. It was late in the evening. There was a wadi in the valley and a brook filled it here during the winter rains. It was the same brook that King David had crossed when he fled from his traitorous son, Absalom. We crossed the brook ahead of the traitorous Judas, who later led a crowd across it against Jesus.

The Garden of Gethsemane was an olive grove yard, at the foot of the western slope of the Mount of Olives, facing the Temple. We used to meet there with Jesus and Judas was familiar with the place.

On our way there, Jesus said, "You will all fall away because of me this night; for it is written, 'I will strike the shepherd, and the sheep of the flock will be scattered.' But after I am raised up, I will go before you to Galilee." Once again, He mentioned being "raised up" and I still didn't know what He was talking about.

As we entered the garden, we felt the gentle breeze beneath the shining full moon. Jesus said, "Pray that you may not enter into temptation. Stay here while I go over there and pray."

Then He took Peter, my brother James and me with Him a little farther away. He began to look sorrowful and troubled and said, "My soul is very sorrowful, even to the point of death. Stay here and keep watch with me."

He went about a stone's throw away from us, knelt down and prayed, "Father, you have the power to do all things. If you are willing, take this cup away from me. But not my will, but yours be done."

He was talking about the cup of His destiny, His cup for the salvation for all people. We saw an angel appear to Him from heaven to strengthen Him. In His anguish, He prayed with all the greater intensity and His sweat became like drops of blood falling on the ground. It must have been an agony of wills for Him, a mental anguish and contest between the will of His flesh, that naturally shrunk from suffering and death, and the will of His spirit that voluntarily accepted God's will. Then I remembered that Jesus had said, "I came down from heaven not to do my own will, but the will of Him who sent me."

His soul was sorrowful to the point of death because He was taking upon Himself the sins and the iniquities of the world. He was suffering for all of us. I remembered Isaiah's prophecy of the Suffering Servant, "He was despised and rejected by men; a man of sorrows. Surely he has borne our grief and carried our sorrows. He was wounded for our transgressions, he was bruised for our iniquities, upon him was the chastisement that made us whole and the Lord has laid on him the iniquity of us all." (Isaiah 53:3-5).

His sorrows included the bearing of our sins out of His love for us; the knowledge that His love would be unrequited, since many people would reject Him and His sufferings for them would be in vain, and the foreseen suffering and death that He would bear from their hands.

We, too, were filled with sorrow, fear and apprehension and fell asleep from exhaustion. Jesus needed the solace of our

176

wakefulness, but He asked for our prayers not for Himself but for ourselves, so that we might not enter into temptation. We slept.

He rose from prayer, returned to us, found us sleeping and said, "Why do you sleep? Rise and pray that you may not enter into temptation."

He said to Peter, "So, you couldn't stay awake and watch with me even for an hour? Watch and pray that you may not enter into temptation. The spirit indeed is willing, but the flesh is weak." He spoke from the experience of His own agony.

Again, for the second time, He went away and prayed, "My Father, if this cup cannot pass me by without my drinking it, your will be done." And again He came and found us sleeping, because we couldn't keep our eyes open. So, leaving us for the third time, He went away and prayed, saying the same words as before.

Finally, He returned to us and said, "Are you still sleeping and taking your rest? Behold, the hour is at hand, and the Son of Man is betrayed into the hands of sinners. Get up! Let's get going. Look, my betrayer is here."

The Arrest of Jesus

While He was still speaking, a crowd arrived, led by Judas, the betrayer. There were Roman troops as well as Temple guards supplied by the Chief Priests and the Pharisees. They carried lanterns, torches and weapons. I didn't understand why Jesus didn't just leave the garden, walk through them, and avoid their murderous intentions, as He had done several times before. However, apparently His time had finally come and He was abandoning Himself to His Father's will.

Later, I came to understand that Jesus had exercised great courage by standing His ground and not leaving the garden. It is much more noble to stand up for the truth and to face the consequences, even unto death, trusting in God's will, than to try to avoid a dangerous situation by running away like a coward.

Judas went directly to Jesus, kissed Him and said, "Peace, Rabbi!"

But Jesus said, "Judas, would you betray the Son of Man with a kiss? Friend, do what you are here for!"

How evil it was for Judas to point Jesus out and betray Him with a kiss! Yet Jesus did not condemn him, but tried to save him by addressing him as His friend and asking that question, which should have pricked Judas' conscience. However, his heart was so hardened that he wanted the new kingdom to be his way — the way of the world with its power, glory, riches and fame.

Jesus, knowing all that was to befall Him, didn't run but calmly and with great dignity came forward to the crowd and said to them, "Whom do you seek?"

They answered, "Jesus of Nazareth."

Jesus said, "I AM."

He did not say, "I am He," but again He used the same words as God had used when addressing Moses, "Tell them I AM sent you."

When He said, "I AM", they drew back and fell to the ground. It looked as if a supernatural force had struck them down.

Again He asked them, "Whom do you seek?"

They said, "Jesus of Nazareth."

Jesus answered, "I told you that I AM. So, if you seek me, let these men go."

He was always thinking of our well-being. This was to fulfill the word which He had spoken, "I have not lost one of those whom you gave me."

Then Peter suddenly drew his sword, struck the High Priest's slave and cut off his right ear. The slave's name was Malchus.

Jesus said to Peter, "Put your sword into its sheath! Shall I not drink the cup that the Father has given me? No more of this!"

Then Jesus touched Malchus' ear and healed him. This was His last public miracle—another miracle of healing—to one who seemingly neither deserved it nor appreciated it.

Then Jesus said to Peter, "All those who take up the sword will perish by the sword. Do you think that I can't appeal to my Father and He will at once send me more than twelve legions of angels? But how then should the Scriptures be fulfilled, that it must be so?"

Then Jesus said to the crowds, "Have you come out against me like a robber, with swords and clubs to capture me? Day after day I sat in the Temple teaching and you didn't seize me. But all this has taken place so that the Scriptures of the Prophets might be fulfilled. This is your hour, and the power of darkness."

Then the band of soldiers and their captain and the officers of the Jews seized Jesus and bound Him. He majestically surrendered Himself freely and voluntarily. But all of us disciples in our fear deserted Jesus, just as He had prophesied. I was saddened that we had failed to pray with Him or to protect Him, due to our sleepiness, our dullness and our cowardice.

After they arrested Jesus, I urged Peter to come with me to follow Him to see what might happen. With our Galilean clothing and accents, we were very noticeable, so we kept a safe distance away. But love spurned us on. All of the other apostles had run away to hide. They were driven by fear. I was driven by love and compassion for my Master.

First they led Jesus to Annas, the father-in-law of Caiaphas, the High Priest that year. His house was not far from the Upper Room. It was Caiaphas who had given counsel to the Jews that it was expedient that one man should die for all the people. The Jews brought Jesus first to Annas because he was the honorary High Priest and they respected his age, his political astuteness and his shrewdness.

Since I knew Annas, I was able to enter the courtyard behind Jesus, while Peter was left standing outside at the gate. I went back out and spoke to the maid who attended the gate and brought Peter in.

She said to Peter, "Aren't you also one of this man's disciples?"

"No, I'm not," he replied.

Because it was a cold April night, the servants and officers had made a charcoal fire and stood around it in the middle of the courtyard. Peter joined them, standing and warming himself.

In the light of the fire, a servant girl saw him, gazed at him intently and said, "This man was with Him."

Again, Peter denied it saying, "Woman, I don't know Him."

As Peter continued standing and warming himself, one of the servants of the High Priest, a kinsman of the man whose ear Peter had cut off, asked, "Didn't I see you in the garden with Him? This man is a Galilean, he was certainly with Him!"

Peter denied the accusation for the third time and said, "My friend, I don't even know what you are talking about."

At that moment, a cock crowed. Jesus turned around, looked straight at Peter and gave him a very sad look. Peter must have remembered Jesus' prophecy, "The cock will not crow before you deny me three times." Peter went outside and wept bitterly.

Then Annas arose from his table and began to question Jesus about His disciples and His teaching. Jesus answered him, "I have spoken openly to the world. I have always taught in synagogues or in the Temple, in public where Jews come together. I have said nothing in secret. Why do you question me? Question those who heard what I said to them. They know what I said." Jesus was the serene master of this situation.

At this reply, one of the Temple guards standing by struck Jesus with his hand, a hard blow on His face. He said, "Is that any way to answer the High Priest?"

Jesus meekly answered him, "If I said anything wrong, show me, but if I spoke the truth, why do you strike me?"

He said this to prick the man's conscience, but it was to no avail. The guard apparently wanted to impress Annas. Then Annas bound Jesus and sent Him to Caiaphas, the real High Priest. Caiaphas was one of 71 members of the Sanhedrin, the Jewish

Council and supreme religious court. They should have followed the Law and held their trial in their court, located near the north wall of the Temple. But they, the supreme men of the Law, disobeyed it and took Jesus to the house of Caiaphas. I followed Jesus.

The Chief Priests, with the whole Sanhedrin, were busy soliciting testimony against Jesus that would lead to His death, but they couldn't find any. Many spoke against Him falsely under oath, but their testimony did not agree. Some, for instance, on taking the stand, testified falsely by alleging, "We heard Him declare, 'I will destroy this Temple made by human hands and in three days I will construct another not made by human hands.' "

But still, their testimony did not agree. Of course, what Jesus actually had said was not, "I will destroy this Temple" but, "Destroy this Temple (meaning His body) and I will re-build it in three days."

Then Caiaphas saw that the false accusations were getting nowhere, so he asked Jesus directly, "Have you no answer to make to these charges? What do you have to say about what these men testify against you?" But Jesus remained silent.

So Caiaphas tried to get Jesus to convict Himself of blasphemy out of His own mouth, without the need of any witnesses. He asked Him, "I adjure you by the living God, tell us if you are the Messiah, the Son of God." Since Caiaphas had invoked the living God, Jesus felt compelled to answer.

Jesus looked straight into the eyes of Caiaphas and said, "I AM. And you will see the Son of Man seated at the right hand of the Power and coming on the clouds of heaven." This was His final "I AM" statement, His final self-identification with God, the statement that was still rejected, but now would be used as the basis of a charge of blasphemy.

At that, Caiaphas tore his tunic straight down from his chest and said, "Why do we still need witnesses? You have heard His blasphemy. What is your verdict?"

The Sanhedrin condemned Him as guilty with the sentence of death. Some began to spit in His face. They blindfolded Him, struck Him and said, "Prophesy!" And the guards laid blows upon Him.

This entire process was illegal under Jewish Law. No trial could be held at night, blasphemy could not be charged unless the name of God was used by the accused and after a verdict of guilty, a sentence of death could not be imposed until at least the next day. Jesus was imprisoned in Caiaphas' dungeon.

At dawn, the Sanhedrin met again. They were determined to have their revenge on Jesus, who was the sign of contradiction to them as Simeon had prophesied at the Presentation of Jesus. They met in the daytime to finalize the criminal charge and to impose the death sentence that they had decreed the night before. However, that sentence was not legal because the initial meeting was at night and not in the daytime, as required by the Law.

The Sanhedrin had condemned Jesus to death for blasphemy. They could have executed a death sentence upon Jesus for blasphemy, but they wanted the sentence to be executed by the Romans to make the Sanhedrin look better before the eyes of the people. However, blasphemy was not a Roman crime, so the Romans could not execute Him for that.

Then the Sanhedrin framed Jesus with the false charge of sedition, after His illegal trial for blasphemy and, without any new trial whatsoever, they imposed the death sentence on the grounds of sedition. However, they couldn't execute it under the Jewish Law on that ground, but only on the grounds of blasphemy. Only the Romans could execute the death sentence on the grounds of sedition.

So, early on Friday morning, after Jesus' sleepless night, they led Him, bruised, dehydrated, and exhausted, to the praetorium, the residence of Pontius Pilate, the Procurator or Roman governor. It was located at the fortress Antonia near the northwest corner of the Temple. Pilate usually lived at Caesarea by the Sea, but stayed in Jerusalem during the Passover Feast because of the possibility of public disturbances or insurrection from the large crowds.

Pilate was the fifth Roman governor of Judea. His administration was characterized by corruption and violence that included terroristic public murders in the streets by his agents, who blended in with the crowds. In one horrific and blasphemous case, he ordered some Galileans slaughtered and mingled their blood with the blood of the Temple sacrifices. He had ordered many executions without even the pretense of a trial.

The Trial of Jesus before Pontius Pilate

The Jews did not enter Pilate's praetorium because they thought that they would defile themselves by entering it and they wanted to avoid ritual impurity before they celebrated the Passover. I was amazed to see their hypocrisy in attempting to remain ritually pure while in reality being impure because they wanted to kill an innocent man who had only done good for them.

Pilate then came down from his house and met the Jews at the praetorium gate. He said, "What accusation do you bring against this man?" As a judge, he wanted a formal charge.

The Jewish leaders offered no criminal evidence and vaguely, without any formal specific accusation, replied, "If this man weren't a criminal, we would not have handed Him over to you."

Pilate said contemptuously, "Take Him yourselves and judge Him by your own law."

The Jewish leaders answered, "It isn't lawful for us to put any man to death." This was not true, because they could execute the death sentence for blasphemy. But they didn't accuse Jesus of blasphemy, because Pilate would have dismissed the case as simply a Jewish religious issue.

The Jews wanted a Roman public crucifixion that would give the appearance of legitimacy to their accusation and the execution of the Roman sentence of death. This was to fulfill the word which Jesus had spoken to show by what death He was to die.

Pilate was taken aback by the Jews' demand for the death of Jesus and wondered what this man could possibly have done to deserve the death penalty.

So the Jews began to accuse Jesus of sedition, a Roman crime. They said, "We found this man subverting our nation, opposing the payment of taxes to Caesar and calling himself the Messiah, a king."

Of course, it was a lie that Jesus opposed the payment of taxes since He had said, "Render unto Caesar what is Caesar's and to God what is God's." He never opposed the payment of taxes to Caesar and He even had Peter pay taxes from a coin that Peter miraculously gathered from a fish, after Jesus had told him to catch a fish and take the coin from its mouth.

After the accusation by the Jews, Pilate went back into the praetorium in confusion. He called Jesus to come to him and asked Him, "Are you the King of the Jews?"

Jesus appealed to Pilate's conscience, gave him an opportunity to show his sincerity and answered, "Do you say this of your own accord, or did others say it to you about me?"

But Pilate's heart was closed to this appeal and he said, "I'm not a Jew! Your own nation and the Chief Priests have handed you over to me. What have you done?"

Jesus answered, "My kingdom is not of this world. If my kingdom were of this world, my subjects would be fighting for me to save me from being handed over to the Jews. But my kingdom is not of this world."

The Kingdom of Jesus was over the hearts, minds and wills of all people, of all nations, a Kingdom of God, a kingdom of truth, beauty, goodness, justice, love, peace and joy, not a kingdom of worldly riches, power and glory.

Pilate, surprised that He claimed to be a king, asked Him, "So then, you are a king?"

Jesus replied, "It's you who say that I am a king. The reason that I was born and came into the world is to testify to the truth. Anyone who is committed to the truth hears my voice."

Pilate then showed his skepticism and cynicism and rhetorically asked, "What is truth?"

Before Pilate stood the man who had said, "I am the way, the truth and the life." But, for Pilate, there was no objective, absolute truth. All of his decisions were relative and dependent upon his own self-interest, especially as to how they might appear to Caesar, upon whose favor his position as governor depended.

Pilate could find no evidence of sedition, so he went out to the Jews and told them, "I find no case against Him."

That should have been the end of the so-called trial and Jesus should have been released immediately for lack of proof. But, to assure that the Jews would agree to Jesus' release, Pilate offered them a choice between the release of Jesus and that of a real criminal, Barabbas. Ironically, he had been convicted of sedition, the same charge that the Jewish leaders were now bringing against Jesus!

Pilate said, "Recall your custom that I should release one man for you at the Passover. Do you want me to release for you the King of the Jews?"

They cried out again, "Not this man, but Barabbas!" Now Barabbas was a seditionist, a robber and a murderer. Pilate must have thought surely that Barabbas was a much worse criminal than the innocent Jesus and therefore that the crowd would want to release Jesus. But they had hardened their hearts against Him.

While Pilate was sitting on the judgment seat, his wife sent word to him, "Don't have anything to do with that righteous man, for I have suffered a great deal today in a dream because of Him."

Then the Chief Priests and the elders persuaded the people to ask for Barabbas and to crucify Jesus. Pilate again said to them, "Which of the two do you want me to release for you?"

They said, "Barabbas."

Pilate said to them, "Then what shall I do with Jesus who is called Christ?"

They all said, "Let Him be crucified."

But Pilate still asked, "Why, what evil has He done?"

They just shouted all the louder, "Let Him be crucified."

Pilate seemed to be totally baffled by Jesus and concerned about what should be done with Him and why, exactly, the crowd was so filled with hatred of Him. He wanted to release Jesus since he knew that He was innocent of any crime. So he said to the Chief Priests and the multitudes, "I find no crime in this man."

But they insisted and cried out, "He stirs up the people, teaching throughout all Judea, from Galilee even to this place."

Pilate used this as an excuse to remove himself from jurisdiction over the case. When he heard that Jesus was from Galilee, he thought he had an out. Since Jesus was a Galilean, He belonged to the jurisdiction of King Herod Antipas. So Pilate sent Jesus over to King Herod Antipas, who was in Jerusalem at that time just a few blocks away. He was the son of King Herod the Great who had had John the Baptist beheaded. Peter and I followed along in sorrow.

When Herod saw Jesus, he was very glad, for he had long desired to see Him because he had heard about Him and he was hoping to see some sign done by Him. He was like many of the people who were only curious about Jesus. They didn't want to change. They just wanted to see a show of signs and wonders.

Herod taunted Jesus to perform a miracle, but Jesus refused because Herod was not well disposed. He questioned Jesus at some length, but He made no answer.

The Chief Priests and the Scribes stood by, vehemently accusing Him. Herod and his soldiers treated Jesus with contempt and mocked Him.

Because Jesus did not perform any signs, Herod contemptuously dismissed Him. He had Him marched back to Pilate. We followed along in deeper sorrow. On that day, Herod and Pilate became friends, whereas before that they were enemies. Pilate was happy that Herod was in solidarity with him.

Pilate still wanted to release Jesus, so he called together the Chief Priests and the rulers and the people and said to them, "You brought me this man as one who was perverting the people. However, after examining Him before you, I didn't find Him guilty of any of your charges. Neither did Herod, since he has sent Him back to us. Look, he said, He hasn't done anything deserving death." Pilate knew that Jesus was totally innocent of any crime and probably thought that He was just some idealist who had religious disputes with the Jews.

But they still shouted out, "Crucify Him, crucify Him!"

So, for a third time, Pilate said to them, "Why, what evil has He done? I have found in Him no crime deserving death; I will therefore chastise Him and release Him."

I wondered why Pilate would chastise Him, if he believed that He was innocent. He was acting totally out of his own self-interest and seeking only human respect. He should have immediately released Jesus, but he decided to chastise Him, an innocent man, just to please the crowd.

When Pilate saw not only that he was gaining nothing, but rather that a riot was beginning, he took water and washed his hands before the crowd, saying, "I am innocent of this innocent man's blood. You see to it yourselves."

Pilate hypocritically acted as if his symbolic act of washing his hands could in reality demonstrate his innocence and absolve him of his personal guilt.

The Jews all answered, "Let His blood be upon us and on our children!"

So, Pilate released Barabbas to them, but he sent Jesus to be scourged. I watched through the gate into the courtyard. I saw Jesus tied to a metal ring at the top of a small post. The soldiers whipped Him with leather tongs that were tipped with lead balls and small pieces of bone. These caused His skin to swell which was then ripped. Much blood flowed. I was shocked and saddened to see that the scourging gradually exposed Jesus' innermost veins and arteries and eventually His bones.

Then they plaited a crown of long spiked thorns, put it on His head, clothed Him as a mock king in a purple robe and put a reed in His right hand as the mock scepter of a king. They knelt before Him, took the reed and struck Him on the head with it, spat upon Him, mocked Him and said, "Hail, King of the Jews!"

Pilate went out again, and said to them, "See, I am bringing Him out to you, that you may know that I find no crime in Him."

Jesus came out and stood before us in total humiliation. He was bleeding profusely and horribly disfigured by the wounds caused by the scourging. He wore the purple robe and the crown of long thorns that the soldiers had plaited and pressed into His scalp which caused much bleeding. His appearance was a mockery of His true Kingship.

He looked pathetic and Pilate thought that the Jews would finally be compassionate and accept His release. So he said to them, "Behold the man!" in the hope of eliciting some mercy from them.

But when the Chief Priests and the officers saw Him, they cried out, "Crucify Him, crucify Him!"

Pilate said to them, "Take Him yourselves and crucify Him, for I find no crime in Him."

The Jewish leaders answered him, "We have a law, and by that law He ought to die, because He has made Himself the Son of God."

The charge now shifted from sedition back to blasphemy, the original charge of the Jewish leaders, but which was not a Roman crime.

When Pilate heard these words, he became more afraid than ever. He couldn't understand the crowd's demand for the execution of Jesus. So he went back into the praetorium and asked Jesus out of superstitious fear, "Where are you from?"

But Jesus didn't answer him. He remained curiously passive, virtually silent. The Prophets had predicted that the Redeemer would be silent, just like a lamb that puts up no resistance before it is slaughtered. Jesus accepted His victimhood like the lambs sacrificed for the Feast of Passover.

Then I remembered that John the Baptist had called Jesus "the Lamb of God who takes away the sin of the world." This reminded me of the Prophet Isaiah who had prophesied, "He was offered because it was his own will, and he opened not his mouth;

188

he shall be led as a sheep to the slaughter, and shall be dumb as a lamb before his shearer, and he shall not open his mouth." (Isaiah 53:7).

Then Pilate said to Jesus, "Do you refuse to speak to me? Don't you know that I have power to release you and power to crucify you?"

Jesus answered him, "You would have no power over me whatsoever unless it were given you from above. That is why he who delivered me to you has the greater sin."

After this, Pilate was still eager to release Jesus, but the Jewish leaders cried out, "If you release this man, you are not a friend of Caesar's. Anyone who makes himself a king sets himself up against Caesar."

Now the charge was back to sedition, again amplified by the intimidation of the Jews. Pilate began to fear for his future as governor if Rome learned that he let a supposed king and enemy of Caesar go free.

When Pilate heard the threats of the Jewish leaders, he made up his mind to protect himself and his position. He brought Jesus out and sat down on the judgment seat at a place called the Stone Pavement, Gabbatha in Hebrew. Now it was Preparation Day for the Passover. It was about mid-day, the time during which the Temple priests were preparing the Passover lambs for sacrifice and the time when Jesus prepared Himself as the new sacrificial Passover Lamb.

Pilate said to the Jews, "Behold, your king!"

At this, they shouted, "Away with Him! Away with Him! Crucify Him!"

Pilate said to them, "Shall I crucify your king?"

The Chief Priests answered, "We have no king but Caesar."

The hypocritical Jewish leaders, who really hated Caesar, now proclaimed their loyalty to him and blasphemously denied that God was their true king. They continued to insist and demand with loud cries that Jesus should be crucified. Finally, their voices prevailed.

189

Pilate granted their demand and signed the death sentence for Jesus. He had released the guilty Barabbas, the man who had been thrown into prison for sedition and murder, and passed the death sentence upon the innocent Jesus.

Pilate also wrote a title on a sign which they hung on the neck of Jesus and later on the Cross. It read, "JESUS OF NAZARETH, THE KING OF THE JEWS." Ironically, the sign told the truth, but the leaders did not recognize it.

Many of the Jews would read this title, for the place where Jesus was to be crucified was near the city and the sign was written in Hebrew, Latin and Greek. So the Chief Priests of the Jews said to Pilate, "Do not write, 'The King of the Jews,' but, 'This man said, I am King of the Jews.' "

Pilate answered, "What I have written I have written." Then he handed Him over to them to be crucified.

The Way of the Cross

So they took Jesus and He went out and carried His own Cross. It was about eight feet long and weighed about seventy pounds. He was led southwest outside the walls of Jerusalem to the Place of the Skull (Golgotha in Hebrew, Calvary in Latin), so-named because it was a hill fifteen feet high whose contour resembled a human skull. It was about a half mile from Jerusalem.

Jesus tried to walk upright, but the weight of the heavy Cross, together with the shock produced by His copious loss of blood, caused Him to stumble and fall. The rough wood of the beam gouged into the lacerated skin and muscles of His shoulder.

As they led Him away, the soldiers seized one Simon of Cyrene, who was coming in from the fields and ordered him to help Jesus carry the Cross. As Jesus carried the heavy Cross on His right shoulder, dragging the base behind Him along the road, the soldiers stopped Him. They dragged Simon to the base of the Cross. Simon knelt down at the base of the Cross and lifted it up onto his right shoulder.

As they walked on, I thought, *Jesus once told us, "Whoever wishes to come after me must deny himself, take up his cross daily and follow me." But we must do it without shame and voluntarily, not just because we may be forced to do so like Simon. Because Jesus had gone on to say, "For whoever wishes to save his life will lose it, but whoever loses his life for my sake will save it. What profit is there for one to gain the whole world yet lose or forfeit himself? Whoever is ashamed of me and of my words, the Son of Man will be ashamed of him when He comes in His glory and in the glory of the Father and of the holy angels."*

When I looked at Jesus' tortured body, it was hard for me to believe that He could ever come in glory. The weakness of Jesus from lack of food, water and sleep caused Him to fall several more times. The soldiers beat Him to make Him get up. They plucked His beard and spit at Him. It was terrible.

It reminded me of the Prophet Isaiah who had prophesied about this when he said, "I gave my back to those who beat me and my cheeks to those who plucked my beard. I did not shield my face from their spitting." (Isaiah 50:61).

A great crowd of people followed Him, including some women who bewailed and lamented over Him. Jesus turned to them and prophesied, "Daughters of Jerusalem, do not weep for me, but weep for yourselves and for your children. The days are coming when they will say, 'Blessed are the barren, the wombs that never bore and the breasts that never nursed!' Then they will begin to say to the mountains, 'Fall on us,' and to the hills, 'Cover us.' For if they do this when the wood is green, what will happen when it is dry?"

I wondered if this was another prophecy of the destruction of Jerusalem.

The Crucifixion

When they got to Calvary, they gave Him a drink of wine flavored with gall which He tasted but refused to drink. The soldiers stripped Jesus of His garments which re-opened His clotted wounds. Then they threw Jesus down on His back with His shoulders against the Cross. They felt for the depression at

191

the front of His wrist and drove a heavy, square, six-inch long wrought-iron nail through it and deep into the wood. Quickly, they moved to His other wrist and did the same. Then they nailed the sign at the top of the Cross, "JESUS OF NAZARETH, THE KING OF THE JEWS." Next, they pressed Jesus' left foot over His right and drove another nail through them into a piece of wood fastened to the Cross to bear up His body. I felt weak at the sound of the hammer on the nails and the sight of the flowing blood.

Then they raised the Cross and dropped it into its pre-dug hole. I shuddered at the sound of the Cross hitting the bottom of the hole that shook the crucified body of Jesus from His head to His toes. They placed the Cross between those of two crucified criminals.

His body slowly sagged down which then placed more weight on the nails in His wrists. Jesus grimaced from the excruciating pain that must have shot along His fingers and up His arms into His brain.

Jesus pushed His body upward to avoid this stretching torment, but this movement placed His full weight on the nail in His feet. Again He grimaced from the searing agony of the nail tearing through the nerves of His feet. Then, as His arms tired, cramps swept over His body that caused relentless, throbbing pain.

Blood continually trickled from His wounds. His hair and beard were covered by dried blood. The terrible crown of thorns prevented Him from raising His head without intense pain. His lips were caked in white from thirst that caused His mouth to hang open. In spite of His horrible appearance, He maintained an aura of dignity, goodness and love. He kept praying the psalms and was fulfilling their prophecies before our eyes.

The soldiers took His garments and divided them into four parts, one for each soldier. But the tunic was without a seam, woven from top to bottom, so they said to one another, "Let us not tear it, but cast lots for it to see whose it shall be."

They divided His garments among them, casting lots for them, to decide what each should take. This was to fulfill the psalm, "They divided my garments among them and for my clothing they cast lots." (Psalm 22).

192

Jesus began to struggle to breathe. The weight of His body on His lungs made it extremely difficult for Him. He had to arch His back and try to stand up in order to be able to take a breath. He fought with great effort to raise Himself up, take a small gulp of air, but then collapse, over and over again. This tore His already lacerated back even more as He moved up and down against the rough timber of the Cross. This was called the "The Dance of the Crucified."

I remembered the psalm, "I am poured out like water, and all my bones are out of joint; my heart is like wax; it is melted in the midst of my bowels." (Psalm 22:14).

Jesus groaned, "Father, forgive them for they don't know what they are doing."

The people stood by, watching; but the rulers scoffed at Him, saying, "He saved others; let Him save Himself, if He is the Christ of God, His Chosen One!"

The soldiers also mocked Jesus. They came up to Him and offered Him sour wine or vinegar and said, "If you are the King of the Jews, save yourself."

One of the criminals hanging next to Jesus railed at Him and said, "Are you not the Christ? Save yourself and us!"

But the other criminal rebuked him, saying, "Do you not fear God, since you are under the same sentence of condemnation? And we indeed justly; for we are receiving the due reward of our deeds; but this man has done nothing wrong."

He then turned to Jesus and said, "Jesus, remember me when you come into your kingdom."

Jesus answered him in love, "Truly, I say to you, today you will be with me in Paradise."

The people going by kept insulting Him, saying, "So you are the one who was going to destroy the Temple and rebuild it in three days! Save yourself, why don't you? If you are the Son of God, come down from the Cross!"

The leaders also joined in the jeering, "He saved others but He can't save Himself! So He is the King of Israel! Let's see Him come down from that Cross and then we will believe in Him. He trusts in God; let God rescue Him now if He wants to. After all, He claimed, 'I am the Son of God.' "

The bystanders could not believe that a man who had done such miraculous works and who was called the Son of God could become a helpless victim on His Cross. They thought that if He was truly the Messiah and Son of God, surely He could save Himself! They didn't realize that the greatest love is to lay down your life for your friends as He was now doing. However, the good criminal realized this.

The good criminal saw the sign that proclaimed Jesus as the King of the Jews. He heard Jesus forgive everyone for His crucifixion. His heart was moved to faith and he believed that Jesus' Kingdom was certainly not of this world that they both were leaving through death. The good criminal now believed that through Jesus' death, he was coming into a new Kingdom of God and he humbly prayed that Jesus would remember him. Jesus mercifully granted his prayer of faith that very day!

Standing by the Cross of Jesus were His mother Mary, His mother's cousin, Mary the wife of Clopas, Mary Magdalene and me. Jesus' mother stood at the foot of the Cross in silent sorrow. She looked as if a sword had pierced her heart. She clutched her right hand near her heart while tears streamed down her face with her plaintive moans.

It reminded me of Simeon's prophecy to Mary in the Temple when she made the Presentation of the infant Jesus. Simeon told her that Jesus would be a sign that would be contradicted and that a sword would pierce her so that the thoughts of many would be revealed. Here at Calvary the prophecy was fulfilled. Jesus, the great sign of God's love for man, received His final rejection and Mary received the piercing of her final sword of sorrow.

My heart was overwhelmed with grief for Jesus and anger for His executioners. I was horrified by their cruelty to both Him and His mother.

When Jesus saw His mother and me standing near, He said to His mother, "Woman, behold, your son!"

194

As at the wedding at Cana, Jesus didn't use the term "woman" in disrespect of His mother. He spoke it with reverence as if she were the woman that God referred to in Genesis when He told Satan that He would put enmity between him and the woman. (See Genesis 3:15).

Then He said to me, "Behold, your mother!"

I did so, and, like the Son of Thunder that Jesus had previously called me, I wanted to scream, "Stop! You are killing this mother's innocent son!" I wanted to pull the soldiers away from her son. I wanted to cover her eyes and protect them from looking on His tortured body.

My anger was rising and it felt like my blood was boiling, but it seemed useless to cry out and resist. Jesus was silent. He wasn't resisting. He hung there like a lamb, waiting for the knife of death.

Then I noticed that His mother was reacting in the same way that He was — in silence, calmly accepting what seemed to be the will of God. I tried to imitate them. I restrained my emotions and my reactions.

I looked at Mary who became my mother of example. She gave me strength. She, a woman, gave strength to me, a man. A supposed Son of Thunder! She was a pillar of strength, while I was a broken reed of fear and anxiety. But then I remembered that Isaiah wrote, "A bruised reed, He shall not break!" (Isaiah 42:3). I was emotionally bruised, but not broken. I took a deep breath and calmed myself down.

I was humbled that Jesus would entrust His mother to me as her son. Then I began to think. At first, I thought that Jesus had only meant that I should take care of His mother. So from that moment, I resolved to take her into my home. But later, as I reflected on His words, I understood that He meant that *all* people of all nations forever should take her as their spiritual mother. All should live in a spiritual relationship with her by consecrating themselves to Jesus through her and totally dedicating themselves to His service. All should accept her help and rely on her intercession with Him as she interceded at Cana, and Jesus performed His first miracle by changing the water into wine.

The Death of Jesus

Beginning at noon and for the next three hours, there was darkness over the whole land from an eclipse of the sun. Then Jesus cried out in distress, not despair, with a loud voice, *"Eloi, Eloi, lama sabachthani?"* which means, "My God, my God, why have you forsaken me?"

Some of the bystanders hearing it said, "Listen! He's calling Elijah. Wait, let's see whether Elijah will come to take Him down."

After this, Jesus, knowing that all was now finished, said, "I thirst." This was to fulfill the prophecy of the psalm, "As dry as a potsherd is my throat; my tongue sticks to my palate." (Psalm 22).

When He said, "I thirst," it was not just for water but for the love of souls. He appealed from the Cross to the personal freedom of men and women of all nations for all time and called each one to follow Him on the path of complete abandonment into the hands of God.

A bowl full of common wine stood there. So they put a sponge full of the wine on hyssop and held it to His mouth. When Jesus had received it, He said, "It is finished."

This hyssop branch was the very same kind of branch used to sprinkle a lamb's blood during the Passover Feast done in remembrance of the sprinkling with hyssop of the lamb's blood on the doorposts of the Israelites in Egypt. Because of that, the angel of death had passed over them while the firstborn of the Egyptians died.

Now, Jesus' blood was sprinkled on the new doorpost of the Cross so that the punishment of eternal death might pass over us. This was the completion of Jesus' fourth and final cup of wine, and the consummation of His Last Supper and new Passover meal. That is why He said, "It is finished." It was the finality of the sacrifice of Jesus, the true Passover lamb. He had finished His work of doing His Father's will. He had accomplished His mission of salvation for all peoples and nations through the forgiveness of sins.

Jesus also initiated the Kingdom of God and fulfilled His Last Supper prophecy that He would never again drink wine until "I drink it new in the Kingdom of God." Now He had done so.

Then, with one last surge of strength, Jesus pressed His torn feet against the nail for the last time, straightened His legs, took a deep breath and uttered His last cry, "Father! Into your hands I commit my spirit."

Then He bowed His head and gave up His spirit. His entire body collapsed forward from the Cross. It was 3 p.m. on Friday, April 3, in the year 33. I was 27 years old.

It was mid-afternoon, when the Passover lambs were being slain in the Temple, that Jesus was also slain. In the Temple, rows of priests assembled with their silver bowls. They caught the blood of the slaughtered Passover lambs as it gushed out of them. Then the priests carried their bowls to the altar and poured out the blood on it in sacrifice. Similarly, Jesus, the true Passover Lamb, had shed His sacrificial blood that gushed out from Him, slaughtered on the altar of His Cross. He was truly the Lamb of God who takes away the sin of the world, as John the Baptist had called Him.

Suddenly, the curtain of the Temple was torn in two, from top to bottom. The earth shook and the rocks were split. Tombs were also opened and many bodies of dead saints were raised. They came out of the tombs and went into Jerusalem and appeared to many people.

When the centurion, and those who were with him, keeping watch over Jesus, saw the earthquake and what took place, they were filled with awe, and said, "Truly this man was the Son of God!"

It was the day of Preparation of the Passover. The Feast of Passover fell this year the next day on Saturday the Sabbath. So, in order to prevent the bodies from remaining on the Cross on the

Sabbath, the Jewish leaders went to ask Pilate if the soldiers could break Jesus' legs while He hung on the Cross, so that He could no longer use them to lift Himself up to breathe. In that way, He would die sooner and they could take Him off the Cross before the Sabbath.

Pilate granted their request and the soldiers came back and broke the legs of the two criminals who had been crucified with Jesus. But, when they came to Jesus, they saw that He was already dead. So they didn't break His legs. Jesus, the true Passover Lamb, fulfilled the Scripture that no bones of the Passover lamb should be broken. (See Exodus 12:46).

I thought, He is the true Lamb of God, the true Passover Lamb who is pure and innocent and who is sacrificed to protect us from the justice of God, just like the Passover lambs' blood protected the Israelites in Egypt on the first Passover. His Cross is like their doorposts, covered in blood by which we are saved from sin and eternal death. His Cross is our door to eternal life.

None of His bones were broken, just like the Passover lamb whose bones should not be broken. He is the new Passover victim whose blood protects us from God's justice of eternal damnation. But He's not only the victim, He is also the priest who offers Himself – priest and victim are one in this holy sacrifice. This is what He meant during His new Passover meal at our Last Supper when He said that He was offering His body and blood for the forgiveness of our sins.

His sacrifice accomplishes what the sacrifice of thousands of lambs could not. The forgiveness of sins could be accomplished only by the perfect sacrifice of Jesus, the Lamb of God who takes away the sin of the world, as John the Baptist had first identified Him.

From now on, we must eat the sacrificed Lamb and drink His blood because He told us to take and eat what looked like bread and wine, but was really His body and blood. This is what He meant when He said, "Unless you eat the flesh of the Son of Man and drink His blood, you do not have life within you. He who eats my flesh and drinks my blood has eternal life and I will raise him up at the last day. For my flesh is real food, and my blood is real drink. Whoever eats my flesh and drinks my blood lives in me, and I in him."

In order to guarantee the death of Jesus, one of the soldiers pierced His side with a spear, and at once there came out blood and water. As I winced in pain, I wondered how His mother could stand such a sight. When the soldier saw what had taken place, he praised God and said, "Certainly this man was innocent!"

Later, Flavius Josephus, the Jewish historian, wrote, "There lived Jesus, a wise man for He was a performer of marvelous feats and a teacher of such men who received the truth with pleasure. He attracted many Jews and many Greeks. He was called the Christ. Pilate sentenced Him to die on the Cross, having been urged to do so by the noblest of our citizens; but those who loved Him at the first did not give up their affection for Him."

I really and truly saw all of what I have just set forth. I bear witness, my testimony is true and I know that I tell the truth so that you also may believe. I never gave up my affection for Him. All of this happened so that the Scripture passage might be fulfilled. I remembered it, "They will look upon him whom they have pierced." (Zechariah 12:10).

This passage was from the prophecy of Zechariah and was now fulfilled, "I will pour out on the house of David and the inhabitants of Jerusalem a spirit of compassion and supplication, so that, when they look on him whom they have pierced, they shall mourn for him, as one mourns for an only child, and weep bitterly over him, as one weeps over a firstborn. And on that day there shall be a fountain opened for the house of David in the inhabitants of Jerusalem to cleanse them from sin and uncleanness." (Zechariah 12:10). This was the prophecy of His fountain of blood and water that had gushed forth from His pierced heart and side as a fount of mercy for us.

I stood there at the foot of that Cross and I looked on Him whom they had pierced. I couldn't take my eyes off of His holy face. His battered face disturbed me. It was swollen by blows, black and blue, covered with spittle, torn by thorns, running with blood and splotched with dried blood. I could hardly recognize Him.

Then I looked up above His head to the top of the Cross at the sign that said, "JESUS OF NAZARETH, THE KING OF THE

JEWS." I thought, *What kind of a king is this? I expected a victorious warrior king, but we have a king who was apparently defeated and is dead. Can His death bring His victory and usher in His Kingship? Could His victory be over sin and death, our true enemies, rather than over His human enemies, the Jewish leaders and the Romans who have just killed Him?*

As I continued to ponder this, I beheld His beautiful face that was now so disfigured. This reminded me of what Isaiah prophesied for the Suffering Servant, "He had no form or comeliness that we should look at him, and no beauty that we should desire him. He was despised and rejected by men; a man of sorrows, and acquainted with grief; and as one from whom men hide their faces he was despised." (Isaiah 53:2).

If only the people would have let themselves be moved by the unmistakable features of Christ's holy face. From the contemplation of the disfigured, loving face of the Son of God made man, I drew the strength to overcome this hour of darkness and tears.

My hope increased as I remembered the beauty of His transfigured holy face that I had witnessed on Mount Tabor when Moses and Elijah had appeared with Him. Then His face had shone with radiance like the sun and His garments had become white as light. It was as if the light came out from inside of Him. Perhaps I would see that countenance again.

But now, as I continued to look at Jesus, lifted on the Cross, I was also reminded of the story of Moses and the serpents in the desert. (See Numbers 21:4-9). The patience of the wandering Israelites had been worn out by their journey in the desert after their Exodus from Egypt. They complained against God and Moses, "Why have you brought us up from Egypt to die in this desert, where there is no food or water? We are disgusted with this wretched food!"

In punishment, the Lord sent serpents among them, which bit the people so that many of them died. Then the people came to Moses and said, "We have sinned in complaining against the Lord and you. Pray the Lord to take the serpents from us."

So Moses prayed for the people, and the Lord said to Moses,

"Make a serpent and mount it on a pole, and if any who have been bitten look at it, they will live."

Accordingly, Moses made a bronze serpent and mounted it on a pole, and whenever anyone who had been bitten by a serpent looked at the bronze serpent, he lived.

Now I looked upon Jesus and thought, *so too shall we live by looking upon and contemplating you mounted on this pole.*

I also remembered that He had told Nicodemus, "No one has gone up to heaven except the one who has come down from heaven, the Son of Man. And just as Moses lifted up the serpent in the desert, so must the Son of Man be lifted up, so that everyone who believes in Him may have eternal life."

So Jesus was lifted up for us on this Cross for our eternal life. Just as God saved the Israelites who were bitten by the serpents, so will Jesus save those bitten by the serpent of sin. If we only look upon Him with faith, we will have eternal life in the Kingdom of God. For God so loved the world that he gave His only Son, so that everyone who believes in Him might not perish but might have eternal life. God did not send his Son into the world to condemn the world, but that the world might be saved through Him.

I remembered that Jesus had also said, "When I am exalted I will draw all to myself." Now God had exalted Him upon this humble Cross and His drawing of all peoples and nations to Himself had begun.

We apostles had all shared the primordial human longing to seek the face of God. That's why we followed Jesus. We originally thought that He was the Messiah sent to us by God to become a warrior king over Israel and to liberate us from the oppression of the Romans. We had forgotten that the Messiah had to suffer. We had forgotten Isaiah's prophecy of the Suffering Servant and we came to realize that His Kingship would not merely be over Israel but over all nations.

Then, remembering that Jesus had asked us to pray for our enemies, I prayed for the salvation of Judas, His betrayer; for the Jewish leaders, His accusers; for Pontius Pilate, His judge; and for the Roman soldiers, His executioners; that Jesus would also draw them to Himself.

When the crowd saw all that had happened, they returned home beating their breasts. The women who had followed Him from Galilee stood at a distance watching everything. Among these women were Mary, His mother; Mary Magdalene; Mary, His mother's cousin, wife of Clopas and the mother of James the younger and Joses; and my own mother, Salome. All of them had ministered to Him when He was in Galilee and came up with Him to Jerusalem. These women were women of great courage. They defied the danger of openly showing themselves and came to console Jesus. All of His male apostles, except me, had scattered and abandoned Him. These women were not scandalized by Jesus nor by the ignominy of His Cross.

The Burial of Jesus

When evening came, Joseph of Arimathea was bold enough to go to Pilate. He asked for the body of Jesus, since it was the day before the Sabbath, a day on which they could not bury His body because it was a work that was forbidden on the Sabbath.

Joseph was a secret disciple of Jesus and a respected member of the Sanhedrin. He had not consented to their evil deed of condemning Jesus. He was searching for the Kingdom of God.

Pilate wondered whether Jesus could already be dead. So he summoned the centurion and asked him whether Jesus was already dead. When he learned from the centurion that He was indeed dead, he granted the body to Joseph.

Joseph brought a linen shroud and, with me and others, took Jesus down from the Cross and wrapped Him in it. Nicodemus also came. He had at first come to Jesus by night and now he came bringing a 100-pound mixture of myrrh and aloes for use against the expected stench of His decaying flesh. They took the body of Jesus and bound it in linen cloths with the spices, as was the burial custom of the Jews.

In the place where He was crucified, there was a garden with a newly hewed tomb where no one had ever been buried. So, because of the Jewish Preparation Day and the upcoming Sabbath and as the tomb was close at hand, they buried Jesus there.

Joseph rolled a stone across the entrance to the tomb and departed. On the next day, the Sabbath, they all rested according to the commandment.

I reflected on the meaning of Jesus' crucifixion to me. I remembered the dialogue between Jesus and Pilate, during which the scourged Jesus had claimed for Himself the title of King and witness of truth. But what is the truth that Christ came to testify to in the world?

His whole life was a revelation that God is love and that He was truly the Son of God and the Son of Man who came to bring us eternal life through the forgiveness of our sins. This is the truth to which He bore full witness with the sacrifice of His very own life on Calvary.

The Cross was His throne from which this King, wearing His crown of thorns, revealed the sublime royalty of God's love. He offered Himself in expiation for the sins of the world. He defeated the dominion of Satan, the prince of this world, and He definitively installed the Kingdom of God, a kingdom of all nations.

The way to enter into the Kingdom of God does not permit shortcuts. Rather, every person must freely welcome the truth of the love of God. He is Love and Truth and both love and truth never impose themselves, rather they knock at the door of the heart and mind and, wherever they may enter, they bring peace and joy and rest.

Jesus had always done that for us. He told the truth when He said, "Come to me, all you who labor and find life burdensome, and I will give you rest. Take my yoke upon you and learn from me, for I am meek and humble of heart; you will find rest for yourselves. For my yoke is easy, and my burden light." He never asked anything of us that we could not handle with His help.

We open the door to the Kingdom of God by faith, repentance and conversion to the love of the one true God. This is God's way of reigning. This is His project of salvation, a plan that will be revealed little by little throughout history.

Then I came to understand what love is. He laid down His life for us. So we too ought to lay down our lives for others. How can God's love survive in one who has enough of this world's goods, yet closes his heart to another when he sees him in need?

We should love in deed and in truth and not merely talk about it. This is how we know that we are committed to the truth and we are at peace before God, no matter what our consciences may charge us with. For God is greater than our hearts and all is known to Him. The man who does not love is among the living dead. Anyone who hates his brother is a murderer and eternal life doesn't live in the heart of a murderer.

I remembered that Jesus said that He was the Good Shepherd who lays down His life for the sheep. He said that the Father loved Him "because I lay down my life, that I may take it again. No one takes it from me, but I lay it down of my own accord. I have power to lay it down, and I have power to take it again; this charge I have received from my Father."

The men of power did not take His life from Him. He freely laid it down, just as His friends had laid Him in the tomb. I wondered now, would He take it up again and would He rise from the dead on the third day as He said He would?

We disciples returned to the house with the Upper Room.

Jesus in the Tomb

On the next day, Saturday, the Sabbath, the Chief Priests and the Pharisees called on Pilate at his residence. "Sir," they said, "we remember how that impostor said, while He was still alive, 'After three days I will rise again.' Please order the tomb to be made secure until the third day. Otherwise, His disciples will steal Him away, and tell the people, 'He has risen from the dead.' This fraud will be worse than the first."

204

Pilate told them, "You have a guard of soldiers. Go and secure the tomb as best as you can."

So they went and made the tomb secure by sealing the stone and setting a guard. Of course, they were hypocritically performing manual work on the Sabbath which was against the Jewish Law.

They had often accused Jesus of breaking the Sabbath by working, but He did not perform any manual labor, only good deeds by performing miracles. These were not violations of the Sabbath law for which they had accused Him.

I went out for a walk to ponder on these great mysteries. I walked to a valley where my attention was stirred by the raucous cries of birds. I looked in the distance and came upon the dead body of Judas Iscariot hanging from an olive tree. Vultures and crows circled in flight above it.

In his great pride, Judas probably thought that he had committed an unforgiveable sin and so he had committed suicide in despair. But God's mercy is greater than our sins. Peter learned this.

Peter was devastated for having denied the Master three times, just as Jesus had prophesied that he would. He wept and was beside himself with grief. So I went back to the Upper Room to talk to him.

I told Peter about Judas' suicide and that I hoped that Peter would not fall into despair like he did. I told Peter that God is merciful and forgives our human weaknesses. He is Love itself and he who lives in love, lives in God and God in him. He loved sinners so much that He sent His only begotten Son so that we might have eternal life in Him. He came not to condemn us but to save us. This was a great consolation to Peter.

11. The Resurrection of Jesus

Appearances to the Women

Early in the morning on Sunday, while it was still dark, Mary Magdalene went to the tomb with ointments to anoint the body of Jesus. Although the tomb was blocked by a stone, she later told us that she went off, moved by love, trusting that God would provide His help.

We disciples remained in the nearby house with the Upper Room. We sat around the supper table in the Upper Room that was locked for fear of our being arrested by the authorities.

We discussed what we should do. Some thought that we should run and hide before they found us. Others just wanted to go to their homes. Peter said, "My wife has waited this long to see me, a few more days won't make any difference. Remember that Jesus said that He would rise on the third day, whatever that means. He forgave me three times for my three denials of Him. The least I can do for Him is to wait until the end of today, which is the third day."

Then we discussed whether Jesus would really rise from the dead on the third day and what that could mean. Our minds told us that He was really dead. I was a witness to it. So how could He rise? But He had said that He would and He had raised Lazarus from the dead, right before our very eyes. And Lazarus had been dead for four days! So, since this was the third day, we all decided to wait it out.

After a while, we heard loud, rapid knocking at the door and we all trembled. I carefully and slowly opened it. Mary Magdalene stood there puffing, catching her breath and excitedly announced, "The Lord has been taken from the tomb! I don't know where they've put Him!" She also said that the stone at the entrance to the tomb was rolled back and that the soldiers were gone.

We doubted her, but Peter and I decided to check it out anyway. So we went back to the tomb with Mary. Peter and I ran, but I outran him and reached the tomb first. Then Peter came up and I let him go into the tomb first, out of deference to the primacy that Jesus had granted him.

Then I entered the tomb. We saw the linen burial cloths lying there. The cloth that had covered Jesus' head, was rolled up in a separate place. They were neat, tidy and undisturbed. I believed that Jesus had really risen from the dead, but I didn't say anything to Peter. He looked confused and uncertain. I didn't want to embarrass him by saying that I believed. Then we left Mary there and went back to the Upper Room.

It was the third day after His crucifixion. I saw and I believed. I saw His undisturbed burial cloths and I believed that Jesus had really risen from the dead, as He had said that He would. If others had taken out the body, they would have left the burial cloths in a disturbed manner and not as I saw them, undisturbed.

Jesus had prophesied that He would be condemned to death, crucified and that He would be raised from the dead on the third day. I had heard Him say it, but the words passed over my head. I couldn't grasp them. I didn't understand them. No one had ever prophesied and fulfilled his own suffering, death and resurrection.

However, I now believed that He was the Messiah King, true God and true man, risen from the dead. From the beginning, I had heard that Jesus was the Son of God and the Son of Man. I heard His heavenly Father say at His baptism, "This is my beloved Son." John the Baptist had said, "He is the Son of God." Jesus often called himself the Son of Man. Nathaniel recognized Him as the "King of Israel." Others recognized Him as the Messiah. I struggled to believe these titles. But I could not understand them. I could not comprehend them. I now realized that they were mysteries, that I would never fully understand or comprehend them with my intellect. And it was not necessary to do so. I came to believe by submitting my intellect and my will to His revelation. Although my reason could not comprehend everything, my belief was not contrary to reason. My belief was not unreasonable.

I believed these mysteries because God revealed them through the words of His Prophets and through the words and actions of Jesus. I believed them because God revealed that Jesus Christ was true man and true God and God cannot deceive us.

I now believed that He is really the Son of Man and the literal Son of God, just as John the Baptist had said He was and just as I heard His Father identify Him in His loud voice from heaven when I first saw Jesus at His baptism.

It was His mother Mary's intercessory prayers that brought me to this belief. I had asked her for her prayers for this belief because I was struggling to believe that He was truly man and truly God when she first told me of her own belief. That was when we walked along the road to Capernaum after His rejection in Nazareth. Her prayers were now realized in my own faith.

Later, Mary Magdalene came knocking again at the Upper Room. She seemed to be beside herself and gasped, "I have seen the Lord!" She proceeded to tell us that after we had left her at the tomb, she stood there weeping, wondering where Jesus was. As she wept, she stooped to look into the tomb and saw what appeared to be two young men. She believed that they were angels. They sat where the body of Jesus had lain, one at the head and one at the feet. They said to her, "Woman, why are you weeping?"

She said to them, "Because they have taken away my Lord and I do not know where they have laid Him." As she said this, she turned around and saw Jesus standing there but she didn't recognize Him.

He said to her, "Woman, why are you weeping? Whom do you seek?"

She thought that He was the gardener and said, "Sir, if you have carried Him away, tell me where you have laid Him, and I will take Him away." She didn't understand that Jesus' dead body was really alive again, right in front of her. She thought that someone must've taken it away.

He said to her, "Mary."

Then she turned to Him again, said, "Teacher!" and rushed up to hug Him.

But Jesus said to her, "Don't cling to me, for I have not yet ascended to the Father; rather go to my brothers and tell them, 'I am ascending to my Father and your Father, to my God and your God.' "

As she reported this message to us about His ascending, the others didn't know what she was talking about and didn't believe any of this, since it all sounded like nonsense. They had not received the grace to believe as I had. I said nothing. I kept my belief to myself.

We stayed on in the Upper Room and Mary went back to the tomb with Joanna and Mary, the mother of James, and others to inspect the tomb.

Later, for a third time, Mary Magdalene returned from the tomb with the other women and said, "The Lord is risen! I saw an angel and later Jesus and they said to tell you that He has risen from the dead and that He goes ahead of you to Galilee where you will see Him."

I believed, but the others didn't. Peter asked her to calm down and tell us what she was talking about. Then she began her story.

"We came to the tomb at daybreak and felt a great earthquake as an angel of the Lord descended from heaven, came and sat upon the stone. His appearance was like lightning, and his raiment white as snow. It was awesome! We were frightened and bowed our faces to the ground."

"Then the angel said to us, 'Do not be afraid. I know that you are looking for Jesus who was crucified, but He is not here. He has risen, just as He said that He would. Remember how He told you, while He was still in Galilee, that the Son of Man must be delivered into the hands of sinful men, and be crucified, and on the third day rise. Come and see the place where He was laid. Why do you seek the living among the dead? Now go quickly and tell His disciples that He has risen from the dead and that He goes ahead of you to Galilee where you will see Him. That is my message for you.' "

"So," Mary continued, "We fled from the tomb with mixed emotions of fear, trembling and joy. On the way here, Jesus himself met us. We embraced His feet and did Him homage."

"Then He said the same as the angel, 'Do not be afraid. Go tell my brothers to go to Galilee and there they will see me.' So here we are to deliver their message — Jesus is risen from the dead! Go to Galilee where you will see Him."

Appearance to the Emmaus Disciples

Later that day, we were still hiding in the Upper Room for fear of being arrested. We sat around in a stupor, confused in a jumble of emotions of fear, sorrow and grief. We were haggard and tired from three sleepless nights. We carried the emotional burdens of not responding to Jesus' request for our prayers, but sleeping instead, during His hour of need in the Garden of Gethsemane and of running and abandoning Him there when He was arrested on Thursday.

Others intermittently held their heads in their hands in shame for abandoning the way of His Cross, His crucifixion on it and His burial on Friday. And, except for the excursion by Peter and me to the tomb with Mary, we all continued to sit in the Upper Room in a dazed state that had begun on Friday and had continued on until this day, Sunday, the third day.

211

Suddenly, without any warning, Peter impulsively got up and said, "I'm going for a walk." He left the room and went outside without any explanation. A short time later, he came running into the room excitedly screaming, "I have seen the Lord! I have seen the Lord! I have really seen Him! Please believe me!"

We all shouted, "We do!" We believed Peter based on his authority as our leader.

Just then, two disciples from Emmaus came into the room. Emmaus was a small village about seven miles northwest of Jerusalem. We all shouted to them, "The Lord has really risen and has appeared to Simon!"

Then one of them, who was also greatly excited, told us that he believed us and that he had an amazing story of his own. He said, "Today we were walking on the way back from here to Emmaus and talking with each other about Mary's tale that Jesus' body was not in the tomb and that an angel had said that He was alive. It made no sense to us and we were trying to figure out its meaning."

"Then a stranger approached us and said, 'What are you talking about as you are walking?' "

"Cleopas, looking sad, answered Him, 'Are you the only visitor to Jerusalem who doesn't know what's happened there in these days?' "

"'What things?' the stranger asked."

"Cleopas said, 'About Jesus of Nazareth, who was a Prophet mighty in deed and word before God and all the people, and how our Chief Priests and rulers delivered Him up to be condemned to death and crucified Him. We had hoped that He would be the one who would set Israel free. Today is the third day since these things happened.' "

"Then Cleopas told the stranger that Mary had told us some astounding news. He said that she had gone to the tomb early in the morning, didn't find Jesus' body and came back and reported that she had seen a vision of an angel who had announced that He was alive. So, some of us went to the tomb and found things just as she had described, but they did not see Jesus."

"Then the stranger said to us, 'O foolish men! Why are you so slow of heart to believe all that the Prophets have spoken! Wasn't it necessary that the Messiah had to suffer these things in order to enter into His glory?' "

"Then He began with Moses and all the Prophets and He interpreted for us every passage of Scripture that referred to the Messiah. We began to understand that we had mistakenly expected an earthly king who would rule over the new Kingdom of Israel. We expected a kingdom that would overcome Rome, eliminate evil, dispense justice and restore Israel to its former glory."

"As the stranger continued to interpret the Scriptures, we began to understand that the Messiah was a heavenly king. That He came not to rule but to serve. That to reign is to serve. His reign of service was to save our souls for eternity by the forgiveness of our sins. His kingdom was eternal. It was a Kingdom of God, a kingdom of faith, peace, love and joy for all people, for all nations, for all time."

"As we drew near to the village, the stranger acted as if He were going farther, but we stopped Him and said, 'Stay with us, for it's almost evening and the day is now far spent.' "

"So He came and stayed with us and we sat down to eat. He took bread, blessed it and broke it and gave it to us. And suddenly our eyes were opened and we recognized Him. It was Jesus! As soon as we recognized Him in the breaking of the bread, He vanished out of our sight."

"We said to each other, 'Weren't our hearts burning within us as He explained the Scriptures to us?' "

"Then we got up and came right here to tell you all about it."

I believed their story while some of the other apostles still remained in their unbelief.

Later that evening, as we were in the Upper Room, Jesus Himself suddenly came right through the locked doors.

He said, "Peace be with you." We were startled and frightened, and thought that we had seen a ghost.

But He said to us, "Why are you afraid and troubled? Why do questions cross your mind? Look at my hands and my feet. It is really I. Touch me and see for yourselves. A ghost doesn't have flesh and bones as I do."

He stood among us in His glorified body dressed in a dazzlingly white robe that emanated light. The light shone through Him like sunlight through a crystal. The light came out from Him in all of the colors of the rainbow. The red crucifixion wounds in His wrists and feet were still showing and contrasted with His white robe. Rays of light shone from His wounds. I was ecstatic to see Him but I winced at His wounds.

Once again He said, "Peace be with you. As the Father has sent me, so I send you." When He had said this, He breathed on us and said, "Receive the Holy Spirit. If you forgive people's sins, they are forgiven. If you don't and hold them bound, they are held bound." I was in awe that He gave us His own power to forgive sins. As He had forgiven sins, so now we were called to do so, acting in His name.

I remembered His last discourse with us after our Last Supper when He also granted us peace and said, "Do not let your hearts be troubled or afraid. You heard me tell you, 'I am going away and I will come back to you.' " And now He had come back, just as He had promised.

Then He asked us, "Do you have anything to eat?" So we gave Him a piece of cooked fish which He took and ate.

He said, "Remember all the words that I spoke to you when I was still with you. Everything written about me in the Scriptures had to be fulfilled." Then He opened our minds to the understanding of the Scriptures, just as He had done for the disciples from Emmaus.

He said, "The Messiah had to suffer and rise from the dead on the third day. In His name, penance for the remission of sins is to be preached to all the nations, beginning at Jerusalem. You are witnesses of this. I will send down upon you the promise of my Father. Stay here in the city until you are clothed with power from on high."

Now I understood how wrong we had been to expect a warrior Messiah King who would be victorious over our Roman oppressors. He is so much more! He is victorious for all nations over sin and death, our true and greatest enemies. He absorbed all of the sin and injustice of his persecutors and crucifiers and died, but He has been resurrected as the eternal King of All Nations.

Then He disappeared as we all wondered what He meant about the promise of His Father. Nevertheless, we obeyed and continued to stay in the Upper Room.

We found out later that the tomb guards went into the city and told the Chief Priests all that had taken place. The Chief Priests assembled with the elders and decided to give a bribe of money to the guards. They told the guards to tell the people that His disciples came during the night and stole Jesus' body away while they were asleep. They assured the guards that when Pilate learned about this, they would keep them out of trouble. So the guards took the money and did as they were told.

This false story that His disciples had stolen His body spread among the Jews. However, if someone had taken the body away, they would have taken the burial cloths or left them in disarray. But they were left behind without any disturbance, and I was an eyewitness to this.

Thomas, one of the disciples, wasn't with us when Jesus came through the doors. So when he arrived later at the Upper Room, we told him, "We have seen the Lord."

But he said, "Unless I see in His hands the print of the nails, and place my finger in the mark of the nails, and place my hand in His side, I will not believe." He would have his chance to do that one week later.

Appearance to Thomas

We were still in the Upper Room on Sunday of the next week and Thomas was with us. Again, the doors were shut for fear of the authorities, but again Jesus came right through them, stood among us and said again, "Peace be with you."

Then, in His great love and kindness, He said to Thomas, "Put your finger here, and see my hands. Put out your hand and place it in my side. Do not be unbelieving, but believe."

Thomas fell to his knees and shouted, "My Lord and my God!"

Jesus said to him, "Have you believed only because you have seen me? Blessed are those who have not seen and yet believe."

Appearance by the Sea of Galilee

Then we returned to Galilee, as Jesus had asked us to do. I went with Peter, Thomas, Nathaniel, my brother James and two other disciples. We hadn't seen the Lord or received any instructions and we didn't know what to do. After a few days, Peter said to us, "I'm going fishing."

We said, "Okay, we'll go with you."

So we got into the boat and went fishing in the Sea of Galilee. We fished all night but caught nothing. We were discouraged.

Just as day was breaking, a man stood on the shore but we didn't recognize Him. He called out to us, "Children, have you any fish?"

I wondered why He called us "children". We were grown men! It was a fatherly call, but He didn't look old enough to be calling us children. I thought that He was just looking for a free meal. However, we couldn't help Him since we hadn't caught any fish. I yelled back, "No, we've caught nothing!"

Then He said, "Cast the net on the right side of the boat and you'll find some."

Sure, I thought, *here we've been fishing all night, caught nothing and now some stranger comes, calls us children and tells us the fish are on the right side of the boat.*

He didn't look like a fisherman. How could He know where the fish were? But we had caught none and had nothing to lose, so we followed His advice and cast the net to the right side of the boat. We started to haul it in, but it was very heavy from the many fish in it.

This reminded me of my first net haul as a teenager with my father Zebedee and my brother James. That was a heavy haul also and I had come a long way since then. Still I wondered why He had called us children.

Then I remembered that Jesus had told Mary near the tomb, "I'm ascending to my Father and your Father." He called us children because we are all children of the same Father. Suddenly I knew in a flash who He was and I yelled out, "It is the Lord!"

Then I remembered that Mary had told us, "The Lord is risen! I saw an angel and later Jesus and they said to tell you that He has risen from the dead and that He goes ahead of you to Galilee where you will see Him." Now we were in Galilee and we had seen Him, just as they had said we would.

When Peter heard me say, "It is the Lord," he tucked in his garment, for he was lightly clad, and excitedly jumped into the water while we rowed the boat in, dragging the net full of fish. We were only about a hundred yards off shore. When we got out on the shore, we saw a charcoal fire with fish and bread lying on it. It reminded me of the charcoal fire at which Peter had warmed himself when he denied that he knew Jesus to the servant girl in the courtyard of Annas.

Jesus said, "Bring some of the fish that you've just caught."

So, under Peter's leadership, we heaved and hauled the net ashore. Even though it was so full of large fish, the net wasn't torn. We counted 153 fish of all varieties.

Later as I reflected on this scene, it seemed very symbolic to me. The sea represented the world, over which we would sail under the leadership of Peter in the boat of the Church to fish for the various souls of all nations that would be caught in its untorn net of the unity of all nations under Jesus, King of All Nations.

Then Jesus said, "Come and have breakfast."

Not one of us dared to ask Him, "Who are you?" We knew it was the Lord Jesus. He took the bread and gave it to us with the fish, just as He had given us the bread at His Last Supper. He was always giving. This was now the third time that Jesus was revealed to us after He was raised from the dead.

After we finished the breakfast, Jesus asked Peter, "Simon, son of John, do you love me more than these?" He referred to the others of us.

Peter answered, "Yes, Lord. You know that I love you."

Jesus said, "Feed my lambs."

A second time Jesus asked him, "Simon, son of John, do you love me?"

Peter said, "Yes, Lord. You know that I love you."

Jesus said, "Tend my sheep."

Jesus then asked him for a third time, "Simon, son of John, do you love me?"

Peter was grieved because He had asked him three times, "Do you love me?" With pain on his face, Peter said, "Lord, you know everything. You know that I love you."

Jesus said to him, "Feed my sheep. Truly, truly, I say to you, when you were young, you used to dress yourself and go where you wanted. But when you grow old, you will stretch out your hands and someone else will dress you and lead you where you don't want to go."

And then He said, "Follow me."

In this way, Jesus conferred the prime authority of His Church on Peter as the chief shepherd of His flock, the Church, for him to tend and to feed it spiritually.

But, I wondered, what does He mean ". . . someone else will dress you and lead you where you don't want to go?" Maybe someone will kill

Peter for his faith in Jesus. Once he had boasted about his willingness to die for Jesus, but now he may learn that martyrdom is a grace given by God, not something to be boastfully sought. Why did Jesus ask him three times, "Do you love me?" Maybe He was giving Peter a chance to make up for his three denials that he knew Jesus. Peter had made those denials after Jesus was arrested while Peter warmed himself at the charcoal fire. Yes, that's probably it – three affirmations of faith, and ultimately martyrdom, to make up in some way for his three denials.

My thoughts were interrupted by Peter who, having heard Jesus' prophecy of his own future, turned, pointed to me, his friend, with concern and asked Jesus, "Lord, what about him?"

Jesus answered, "What if I want him to remain until I come? What concern is it of yours? You follow me."

This saying spread abroad and people interpreted it to mean that I wouldn't die. But Jesus didn't say that. He merely said, "What if I want him to remain until I come? What concern is it of yours? You follow me."

Later, I came to understand that when Jesus said, "Until I come," He didn't mean until His judgment at the end of the world. He meant His judgment and coming through the Romans who fulfilled His prophecy and destroyed Jerusalem in the year 70. I lived in Ephesus then and survived that time and that is how I fulfilled Jesus' prophecy that I would remain until He came.

Then Jesus ordered us to leave the Sea of Galilee and to go up to a mountain in Galilee. We went there and He appeared to all eleven of us. We saw and worshiped Him, but some still doubted that He was the true King of All Nations.

He approached us and said, "All authority in heaven and on Earth has been given to me. Go, therefore, and make disciples of all nations, baptizing them in the name of the Father, and of the Son, and of the Holy Spirit, teaching them to observe all that I have commanded you. And behold, I am with you always, until the end of the age."

I was in awe of Jesus' claim of universal power over heaven, Earth and all nations. He was truly the King of All Nations and He gave us His Great Commission. He commanded us to go and make disciples of all nations by baptizing them into His community, the Church, and by teaching them His commandments. I was consoled by His promise to be with us always as we all returned to Jerusalem.

12. The Ascension of Jesus

Jesus continued to appear to us during the forty days after His resurrection, speaking of the Kingdom of God. One day, while we were on the Mount of Olives, He told us not to leave Jerusalem. He said, "Wait, rather, for the fulfillment of my Father's promise, which you heard me speak about. John baptized with water, but within a few days you will be baptized with the Holy Spirit."

I had seen and understood John's baptism with water since I was one of his disciples, but I didn't know what Jesus was talking about now or how the Holy Spirit would baptize us.

Some of us were still thinking about the restoration of Israel to a kingdom like King David's Kingdom. So, while we were with Him, they asked Him, "Lord, now are you going to restore the Kingdom to Israel?"

He answered, "It is not for you to know the exact time. My Father has fixed the time by His own authority. But you shall receive power when the Holy Spirit comes down upon you. Then you will be my witnesses in Jerusalem and throughout Judea and Samaria and even to the ends of the earth." He was speaking about a much greater kingdom than that of King David, a kingdom of all nations.

When He had said this, He was lifted up right before our eyes in a cloud that took Him out of our sight. While we were gazing up in awe into the skies as He went, two men dressed in white robes suddenly appeared and stood beside us. They looked like angels and said, "Men of Galilee, why do you stand here looking into the sky? This Jesus, who was taken up from you into heaven, will come back in the same way as you saw Him go into heaven."

I remembered that Jesus had said, "I am going to prepare a place for you, so that where I am you may be also." However, the words of the angels seemed to be a gentle reproach because we fixed our minds on that place. They seemed to say that we must not stay looking up to heaven to discover where Jesus is, but rather to go on living, continuing His mission, taking His Gospel of Love to the ends of the earth and being ready to greet Him when He returns from heaven.

While this was the end of Jesus' physical presence with us, it marked the beginning of His presence with us in a new way. He had promised to send us the Holy Spirit who would anoint us with power. We greatly anticipated this anointing so that we would be empowered to fulfill His Great Commission to be the witnesses of Jesus, King of All Nations, not just to Judea, but to all nations.

Then, as Jesus had requested, we returned in awe to Jerusalem and entered the Upper Room. With me were Peter and his brother, Andrew; my brother James; Philip; Thomas; Bartholomew; Matthew; James, the son of Alphaeus; Simon the Zealot and Judas, the son of James. We all devoted ourselves to constant prayer in one accord together with the women, Mary, the mother of Jesus, and His cousins.

Peter said that Judas Iscariot, whom I had seen hanging dead from a tree, had bought a field with the money that he received for betraying Jesus. He had died in that field. His body burst open in the middle and all his bowels gushed out. The field became known as the Field of Blood.

Then Peter quoted the psalm, "Let his habitation become desolate and let there be no one to live in it. Let another take his office." (Psalm 69:25). So, to replace Judas, we proposed Joseph, called Barsabbas, who was surnamed Justus, and Matthias, two men who had accompanied us from the beginning with the baptism of John.

We prayed, "Lord, who knows the hearts of all men, show which one of these two you have chosen to take the place in this apostolic ministry from which Judas turned aside to go to his own place."

Then we cast lots and the lot fell on Matthias. He then joined the other eleven of us.

13. The Descent of the Holy Spirit at Pentecost

When the day of Pentecost came, we were all gathered in the Upper Room together with some women and Mary, the mother of Jesus. Suddenly, we heard a sound coming from the sky like the rush of a mighty wind and it filled the whole house. Then we saw what looked like tongues of fire coming through the air. They came, parted and rested on each of us. We were all filled with the Holy Spirit and began to speak in other tongues, as the Spirit enabled us.

This reminded me of the Scripture about the first Pentecost that took place at Mount Sinai, fifty days after the Passover in Egypt. The lambs' blood had been shed in Egypt and God had freed the Israelites from their bondage. Fifty days later, God came down in fire upon the mountain and gave Moses the Ten Commandments.

It was the same with us on this Pentecost. It was fifty days after the resurrection of the Lamb of God, Jesus, whose blood was shed when God freed us from the bondage of sin. Jesus had made good on His promise that the Father would send the Holy Spirit to us in His name as our Counselor to teach us everything and to remind us of everything that He had told us.

This also fulfilled the prophecy of John the Baptist that someone was coming who was mightier than he who would baptize us with the Holy Spirit and fire.

Since we were celebrating the Feast of Pentecost, there were Jewish pilgrims from every nation staying in Jerusalem who spoke different languages. When they heard the sound of the mighty wind, they tried to find its source. They were bewildered, because all of them heard and understood us speaking in their own language.

They were amazed and wondered, saying, "Are not all these who are speaking Galileans? And how is it that we hear, each of us in his own native language? Parthians and Medes and Elamites and residents of Mesopotamia, Judea and Cappadocia, Pontus and Asia, Phrygia and Pamphylia, Egypt and the parts of Libya belonging to Cyrene, and visitors from Rome, both Jews and proselytes, Cretans and Arabians, we hear them telling in our own tongues of the mighty works of God."

The confusion of languages, understanding and dispersal that came because of man's pride in building the Tower of Babel (see Genesis 11:7) was now reversed to a union of understanding as a sign that the Holy Spirit had now come not just for Israel, but for all nations to be one in faith, hope and love in the Kingdom of God. This reminded me of Christ's prophecy to us at His ascension, "But you shall receive power when the Holy Spirit comes down upon you. Then you will be my witnesses in Jerusalem and throughout Judea and Samaria and even to the ends of the earth."

The Jewish pilgrims were all amazed and perplexed and said to one another, "What does this mean?"

But others mocked and implied that we were drunk. They said, "They are filled with new wine."

Peter was standing with us. The pilgrims' slander did not deter him. He boldly lifted up his voice and addressed them, "Men of Judea and all who dwell in Jerusalem, let this be known to you, and give ear to my words. For these men are not drunk, as you suppose, since it is only nine in the morning. They are acting like this in fulfillment of the prophecy of Joel. His prophecy of the outpouring of the Spirit in messianic times is now fulfilled. This is what the Prophet Joel said:

And in the last days it shall be, God declares, that I will pour out my Spirit upon all flesh, and your sons and your daughters shall prophesy and your young men shall see visions, and your old men shall dream dreams; yea, and on my menservants and my maidservants in those days I will pour out my Spirit; and they shall prophesy.

And I will show wonders in the heaven above and signs on Earth beneath, blood and fire and vapor of smoke; the sun shall be turned into darkness and the moon into blood, before the day of the Lord comes, the great and manifest day. And it shall be that whoever calls on the name of the Lord shall be saved. (Joel 3:1-5).

"Men of Israel," Peter continued, "hear these words. Jesus of Nazareth, a man attested to you by God with mighty works, signs and wonders that God did through Him in your midst, as you yourselves know — this Jesus, delivered up according to the definite plan and foreknowledge of God, you crucified and killed by the hands of lawless men. But God raised Him up, having loosed the pangs of death, because it was not possible for Him to be held by it." He had put them to shame.

Then Peter quoted the psalm and said, "For David says concerning Him, 'I saw the Lord always before me, for He is at my right hand that I may not be shaken; therefore my heart was glad, and my tongue rejoiced; moreover my flesh will dwell in hope. For you will not abandon my soul to Hades, nor let your Holy One see corruption. You have made known to me the ways of life; you will make me full of gladness with your presence.' " (Psalm 16).

"Brothers," continued Peter, "this psalm referred not to David but to the Christ. I may say to you confidently of the Patriarch David that he both died and was buried, and his tomb is with us to this day. Being therefore a Prophet and knowing that God had sworn with an oath to him that he would set one of his descendants upon his throne, he foresaw and spoke of the

227

resurrection of the Christ, that He was not abandoned to Hades, nor did His flesh see corruption. This Jesus, God raised up and of that we all are witnesses. Being therefore exalted at the right hand of God and having received from the Father the promise of the Holy Spirit, He has poured out this which you see and hear."

"For David did not ascend into the heavens; but he himself says, 'The Lord said to my Lord, Sit at my right hand, till I make your enemies a stool for your feet.' Let all the house of Israel therefore know assuredly that God has made Him both Lord and Christ, this Jesus whom you crucified. He is the Messiah!"

Now when they heard all of this from Peter, they were cut to the heart and said to him and the rest of the apostles, "Brothers, what shall we do?"

Peter said to them, "Repent, and be baptized every one of you in the name of Jesus Christ for the forgiveness of your sins; and you shall receive the gift of the Holy Spirit. For the promise is to you and to your children and to all that are far off, everyone whom the Lord our God calls to Him."

Peter continued to testify with many other words and exhorted them, saying, "Save yourselves from this crooked generation."

Then those who received his word were baptized, amazingly about 3000 souls that day. They devoted themselves to our teaching and fellowship, to the breaking of bread and to the prayers.

14. The Acts of the Apostles

Signs and Wonders

Soon awe came upon every soul. God performed many signs and wonders through us apostles. All who believed were together and had all things in common. We sold our possessions and goods and distributed them to all, according to need. Day by day, attending the Temple together and breaking bread in our homes, we partook of food with glad and generous hearts, praising God and were in favor with all the people. The Lord Jesus continued to add to our number day by day those who were being saved.

One day, Peter and I were going up to the Temple at mid-afternoon. A man who was lame from birth was being carried. Daily they laid him at the Temple's Beautiful Gate to ask alms of those who entered the Temple. Seeing Peter and me about to go into the Temple, he asked for alms.

Peter and I looked directly at him and said, "Look at us." He fixed his attention upon us, expecting to receive something from us. But Peter said, "I have no silver and gold, but I give you what I have; in the name of Jesus Christ of Nazareth, walk."

Then Peter took him by the right hand and raised him up. Immediately, the man's feet and ankles were made strong. He leapt up, walked and entered the Temple with us, leaping and praising God. All the people saw him walking and praising God and recognized him as the one who sat for alms at the Beautiful Gate of the Temple. They were filled with wonder and amazement at what had happened to him.

While he clung to Peter and me in Solomon's Portico, all the people ran together to us, astounded. Peter saw this and addressed them. "Men of Israel, why do you wonder at this, or why do you stare at us, as though by our own power or piety we had made him walk? The God of Abraham and of Isaac and of Jacob, the God of our fathers, glorified His servant Jesus, whom you delivered up and denied in the presence of Pilate, when he had decided to release Him. But you denied the Holy and Righteous One, and asked for a murderer to be granted to you and you killed the Author of life, whom God raised from the dead. We are witnesses to this. By faith in His name, He has made this man strong whom you see and know. The faith which is through Jesus has given this man this perfect health in the presence of all of you."

"Now brothers," Peter continued, "I know that you acted in ignorance, as did your rulers. But what God foretold by the mouth of all the Prophets, that His Christ should suffer, He had fulfilled. Therefore, repent and turn again to God so that your sins may be blotted out and that times of refreshment may come to you from the presence of the Lord, and that He may send the Christ appointed for you, Jesus, whom heaven must receive until the time for restoring all that God spoke by the mouth of His holy Prophets from of old."

Peter continued, "Moses said, 'The Lord God will raise up for you a Prophet from your brothers as He raised me up. You shall listen to him in whatever he tells you. Every soul that does not listen to that Prophet shall be destroyed from the people.' And all the Prophets who have spoken, from Samuel and those who came afterwards, also proclaimed these days. You are the sons of the Prophets and of the covenant which God gave to your fathers, saying to Abraham, 'And in your posterity shall all the families of Earth be blessed.' God, having raised up His servant, sent Him to you first, to bless you in turning every one of you from your wickedness."

The First Arrest of Peter

As Peter was speaking to the people, the priests, the Sadducees and the captain of the Temple came upon us. They were annoyed because we were teaching the people and proclaiming Jesus and His resurrection from the dead. So they arrested us and took us into their custody since it was already evening. But many of those who had heard the word believed. There were about 5000 of them.

The next day, the rulers and elders and Scribes were gathered in Jerusalem, together with Annas, Caiaphas, John and Alexander, and all who were of the high-priestly family. When they had set us in their midst, they inquired, "By what power or by what name did you do this to a crippled man?"

Then Peter, filled with the Holy Spirit, said to them, "Rulers of the people and elders, if we are being examined today concerning a good deed done to a cripple, by what means this man has been healed, be it known to you all, and to all the people of Israel, that by the name of Jesus Christ of Nazareth, whom you crucified, whom God raised from the dead, by Him this man is standing before you well. This is the stone which was rejected by you builders, but which has become the cornerstone. There is salvation in no one else, for there is no other name under heaven given among men by which we must be saved."

When they saw Peter's boldness and perceived that we were uneducated, common men, they wondered how he could teach and heal. They recognized that we had been with Jesus. But seeing the man that had been healed standing beside them, they had nothing to say in opposition. Then they commanded us to leave the Sanhedrin while they conferred with one another. They probably wondered what they should do with us. They could not deny that a great sign had been performed through us since it had been witnessed by many. But in order that our teaching and healing might not spread any further among the people, they warned us not to teach or speak any more to anyone in the name of Jesus.

However, Peter and I answered them, "Whether it is right in the sight of God to listen to you rather than to God, you must judge for yourselves. However, we must speak of what we have seen and heard."

Then they threatened us further, but let us go. They found no way to punish us because of all of the witnesses who were praising God for what had happened.

When we were released, we went to our friends and reported what the Chief Priests and the elders had said to us. When our friends heard it, they lifted their voices together to God, referred to the psalm (Psalm 2) and prayed, "Sovereign Lord, maker of heaven and Earth and the sea and all that is in them, you said by the Holy Spirit through the mouth of your servant David, 'Why did the nations rage, and the peoples utter folly? The kings of Earth took their stand and the rulers gathered together, against the Lord and against his Anointed.' For truly in this city there were gathered together against your holy servant Jesus, whom you anointed, both Herod and Pontius Pilate, with the Gentiles and the peoples of Israel, to do what your hand and your will had long ago planned to take place. Now, Lord, look upon their threats, and enable your servants to speak your word with all boldness, while you stretch out your hand to heal, and signs and wonders are performed through the name of your holy servant Jesus."

When we prayed, the place where we were gathered shook. We were all filled with the Holy Spirit and spoke the word of God with boldness.

The Unity of the Church

The community of believers had one mind and heart. No one claimed that any of his possessions were his own but we held everything in common. With great power we gave our testimony to the resurrection of the Lord Jesus and great grace was upon us

232

all. There was not a needy person among us. Those who owned land or houses sold them, brought the proceeds of the sale and laid them at our feet. We distributed them to each according to need. For example, Joseph, whom we surnamed Barnabas, (which means, "son of encouragement"), a Levite and a native of Cyprus, sold a field that he owned and brought the money to us for our distribution.

But then a man named Ananias, with his wife Sapphira, sold a piece of property and, with his wife's knowledge, he kept back some of the proceeds and brought only a part and laid it at our feet.

Peter said, "Ananias, why has Satan filled your heart to lie to the Holy Spirit and to keep back part of the proceeds of the land? While it remained unsold, didn't it remain your own? And after it was sold, wasn't it at your disposal? How is it that you have contrived this deed in your heart? You haven't lied to men but to God."

When Ananias heard these words, he fell down dead. Great fear came upon all who heard of it. The young men rose and wrapped him up and carried him out and buried him.

About three hours later, his wife came in, not knowing what had happened to Ananias. Peter said to her, "Tell me whether you sold the land and gave us all of the proceeds."

She said, "Yes." Then Peter said to her, "How is it that you have agreed together and lied to tempt the Spirit of the Lord? Look, the feet of those that have buried your husband are at the door and they will carry you out too!"

Immediately she fell down dead at his feet. When the young men came in they found her dead and they carried her out and buried her beside her husband. God's severe punishment for the pride, greed, lies and hypocrisy of Ananias and Sapphira was a great lesson to all. Great fear came upon the whole Church and upon all who heard of these things.

Many signs and wonders were done by God among the people through our hands. We were all together in Solomon's Portico. The people held us in high honor. More and more believers were added to the Lord, multitudes both of men and women. They even carried out the sick into the streets and laid them on beds and pallets, in the hope that when Peter came by at least his shadow might fall on some of them and heal them. The people also gathered from the towns around Jerusalem, bringing the sick and those afflicted with unclean spirits, and they were all healed.

The Second Arrest of Peter

The High Priest and the party of the Sadducees rose up. They were filled with jealousy. They arrested us apostles and put us in prison. But that night an angel of the Lord opened the prison doors and brought us out. The angel told us, "Go and stand in the Temple and tell the people everything about this Life."

So, we entered the Temple at daybreak and began to teach. Meanwhile, the High Priest and those who were with him had called together the Sanhedrin, the Council of Israel, and sent for us to be brought to them from the prison. Of course, when the officers came, they did not find us there. So they returned and reported to the Chief Priests, "We found the prison securely locked and the guards stationed at the doors, but when we opened them we found no one inside."

When the Chief Priests and the captain of the Temple heard this report, they were really perplexed and wondered what this would come to. Then someone came and reported to them, "The men whom you put in prison are standing in the Temple area and are teaching the people." Then the captain and the court officers came and got us, but without force because they were afraid of being stoned by the people.

They brought us and set us before the Sanhedrin. The High Priest questioned us and said, "Didn't we give you strict orders not to teach in this name? Yet you have filled Jerusalem with your teaching and you want to bring this man's blood upon us."

Peter answered, "We must obey God rather than men. The God of our fathers raised Jesus whom you killed by hanging Him on a tree. But God exalted Him at His right hand as Leader and Savior to give repentance to Israel and forgiveness of sins. We are

234

witnesses to these things, and so is the Holy Spirit whom God has given to those who obey Him."

When they heard this, they were enraged and wanted to kill us. However, a Pharisee in the Sanhedrin named Gamaliel, a teacher of the Law, who was held in honor by all the people, stood up and ordered us to be put outside for a while.

He said to the Sanhedrin, "Men of Israel take care what you do with these men. Some time ago, Theudas appeared, claiming to be someone important, and about four hundred men joined him, but he was killed, and all those who were loyal to him were disbanded and came to nothing."

"After him came Judas the Galilean at the time of the census. He also drew people after him, but he too perished and all who were loyal to him were scattered. So now I tell you, stay away from these men, and let them go. For if this endeavor or this activity is of human origin, it will destroy itself. But if it comes from God, you will not be able to destroy them. You may even find yourselves fighting against God."

So the Sanhedrin took his advice, and when they had called us back inside, they flogged us and told us once again not to speak in the name of Jesus. Then they let us go. We left their presence rejoicing that we were counted worthy to suffer dishonor for the sake of the name of Jesus. Every day in the Temple and at home we never stopped teaching and preaching Jesus as the Christ.

As the number of disciples continued to grow, the Greeks complained against the Israelites because their widows were being neglected in the daily distribution. So the Twelve called together the community of the disciples and said, "It is not right for us to neglect the word of God to serve at table in the daily distribution. Brothers, select from among you seven reputable men, filled with the Spirit and wisdom, whom we shall appoint to this task, whereas we shall devote ourselves to prayer and to the ministry of the word."

The proposal was acceptable to the whole community. So they chose Stephen, a man filled with faith and the Holy Spirit, also Philip, Prochorus, Nicanor, Timon, Parmenas, and Nicholas of Antioch, a convert to Judaism. They presented these men to us

235

and we prayed and laid our hands on them. The word of God continued to spread and the number of the disciples in Jerusalem increased greatly. Even a large group of priests were becoming obedient to the faith. And soon the Gentiles would be baptized.

The Baptism of the Gentiles

One day, Peter was on a roof terrace praying. He saw heaven opened and something resembling a large sheet coming down, lowered to the ground by its four corners. In it were animals that were unclean to the Jews, but a voice said to him, "What God has made clean, you are not to call profane."

As Peter was pondering the vision, the Spirit said to him, "There are three men here looking for you. So get up, go downstairs, and accompany them without hesitation, because I have sent them." So Peter went with the men to Caesarea to the home of a man named Cornelius, whose house was filled with his Gentile relatives and close friends.

Peter said, "You know that it is unlawful for a Jewish man to associate with or visit a Gentile, but God has shown me that I should not call any person profane or unclean. In truth, I see that God shows no partiality. Rather, in every nation whoever fears Him and acts uprightly is acceptable to Him. You know the word that He sent to the Israelites as He proclaimed peace through Jesus Christ, who is Lord of all. You have heard what has happened all over Judea, beginning in Galilee after the baptism that John preached, how God anointed Jesus of Nazareth with the Holy Spirit and power. He went about doing good and healing all those oppressed by the devil, for God was with Him. We are witnesses of all that He did both in the country of the Jews and in Jerusalem. They put Him to death by hanging Him on a tree. This man God raised on the third day and granted that He be visible, not to all the people, but to us, the witnesses chosen by God in advance, who ate and drank with Him after He rose from the dead. He commissioned us to preach to the people and testify that He is the one appointed by God as judge of the living and the dead. To Him all the Prophets bear witness, that everyone who believes in Him will receive forgiveness of sins through His

236

name."

While Peter was still speaking these things, the Holy Spirit fell upon all who were listening. The circumcised believers who had accompanied Peter were astounded that the gift of the Holy Spirit should have been poured out on the Gentiles also, for they could hear them speaking in tongues and glorifying God.

Then Peter responded, "Can anyone withhold the water for baptizing these people who have received the Holy Spirit even as we have?"

So he ordered them to be baptized in the name of Jesus Christ. Now we realized that God had granted life-giving repentance not just to the Jews, but to the Gentiles and to all nations.

The Persecution of King Herod

In the year 42, a great persecution broke out against the Church in Jerusalem under King Herod Agrippa I, grandson of Herod the Great, who had slaughtered the innocent babies of Bethlehem. Peter was imprisoned and my brother James was beheaded. Except for us apostles, the Church was scattered throughout the region of Judea and Samaria.

I remembered Jesus' prophecy, "The hour is coming when everyone who kills you will think he is offering worship to God. They will do this because they have not known either the Father or me. I have told you this so that when their hour comes you may remember that I told you." That hour had now come, I remembered what Jesus had said and the killings had begun.

Deacon Stephen was stoned to death at the feet of Saul of Tarsus. Devout men buried him and we were all in great sorrow. But Saul, a fanatic Pharisee, was ravaging the Church, entering house after house. He dragged off men and women and committed them to prison.

However, those who were scattered still went about preaching the word. Philip went down to a city of Samaria and proclaimed to them that Jesus was the Messiah. The people heeded to what he said when they heard him and saw the signs which he did.

Unclean spirits, crying with a loud voice, came out of many who were possessed. Many who were paralyzed or lame were healed and there was much joy in that city.

However, there was a man named Simon who had previously practiced magic in this city and had amazed the nation of Samaria, saying that he himself was somebody great. They all heeded him, from the least to the greatest, saying, "This man is that power of God which is called Great." And they followed him, because for a long time he had amazed them with his magic. But when they believed Philip as he preached good news about the Kingdom of God and the name of Jesus Christ, they were baptized, both men and women. Even Simon himself believed and, after being baptized, he followed Philip. He saw signs and great miracles performed that amazed him.

When we apostles at Jerusalem heard that Samaria had received the word of God, Peter and I were sent to the people. We went down and prayed for them that they might receive the Holy Spirit, since it had not yet fallen on any of them. They had only been baptized in the name of the Lord Jesus. So we laid our hands on them and they received the Holy Spirit. I remembered how I once had wanted fire to rain down from heaven on the unbelieving Samaritans. Now I was the first to happily receive them as brothers.

When Simon saw that the Spirit was given through the laying on of our hands, he offered us money, saying, "Give me also this power, that anyone on whom I lay my hands may receive the Holy Spirit."

But Peter said to him, "May your silver perish with you because you thought you could obtain the gift of God with money! You have neither part nor lot in this matter, for your heart is not right before God. Repent therefore of this wickedness of yours, and pray to the Lord that, if possible, the intent of your heart may be forgiven you. For I see that you are in the gall of bitterness and in the bond of iniquity."

Simon answered, "Pray for me to the Lord that nothing of what you have said may come upon me."

When we had testified and spoken the word of the Lord, we

returned to Jerusalem, preaching the gospel to many villages of the Samaritans.

The Third Arrest of Peter

When King Herod saw that it pleased the Jews that he had killed my brother James with the sword, he then proceeded to arrest Peter. This was during the days of Unleavened Bread. He put him in prison and delivered him to four squads of soldiers to guard him, intending after the Passover to bring him out to the people. We earnestly prayed for Peter.

On the night before Herod was about to bring him to trial, Peter was asleep between two soldiers, bound with two chains while sentries were outside the door guarding the prison. Suddenly, an angel of the Lord appeared and a light shone in the cell. The angel struck Peter on the side and woke him, saying, "Get up quickly." Immediately, the chains fell off his hands. Then the angel said to him, "Dress yourself and put on your sandals."

Peter did so and the angel said to him, "Wrap your mantle around yourself and follow me." Then the angel went out and Peter followed him. Peter didn't know that what had been done by the angel was real, but thought that he was seeing a vision.

When they had passed the first and the second guard, they came to the iron gate leading into the city. It opened to them of its own accord, and they went out and passed on through one street. Then the angel left him.

Peter came to himself and said, "Now I am sure that the Lord has sent His angel and rescued me from the hand of Herod and from all that the Jewish people were expecting." He went to the house of Mary, the mother of John, who was called Mark, where many were gathered together and were praying.

He knocked at the door of the gateway and a maid named Rhoda came to answer. She recognized Peter's voice. In joy she didn't open the gate, but ran in and told everyone that Peter was standing at the gate.

They said to her, "You are mad," but she insisted that it was so.

239

They said, "It is his angel!"

Peter kept knocking. When they finally opened the door, they saw him and were amazed. He motioned to them with his hand to be silent and described to them how the Lord had brought him out of the prison. Then he said, "Tell this to James and to the brothers." Then he departed and went to another place.

When day came, the soldiers were all stirred up over Peter's escape. When Herod had sought for him and could not find him, he examined the sentries and ordered that they should be put to death. Then he went down from Judea to Caesarea and remained there.

I later learned that in the year 44, King Herod held a festival at Caesarea in honor of Claudius, the Roman Emperor. Herod put on his royal robes, took his seat upon the throne in the theater and addressed the people.

The rays of the sun reflected from his garments and made him look like shining silver. The people shouted, "This is not the voice of a man but of a god!" The king accepted this blasphemous flattery.

Immediately, an angel of the Lord struck Herod down because he did not give God the glory, but took it for himself. Worms literally ate him and he died.

King Herod's persecution ended with his horrible death. I had fled Jerusalem for Ephesus two years before his death to protect Mary, the mother of Jesus from him. It was a difficult flight.

15. My Ministry in Ephesus

With Mary

From the day of the crucifixion, when Jesus had entrusted His mother to my care, I took her and cared for her in my home and in my heart. After the persecution under King Herod Agrippa I, we left Jerusalem in the year 42 and I brought Mary to safety in Ephesus, about 600 miles away. We sailed on a coastal schooner from Jerusalem up the Mediterranean and Aegean coasts to the city of Ephesus. There were no cabins on these schooners. They were merchant ships and we had to sleep and eat on deck with the rough sailors.

Ephesus was in the province of Asia. It was the rich center of the Roman Empire in the East with a population of 250,000. Among them was a community of both Jews and Jewish Christians who enjoyed freedom of religion.

When the boat docked at the harbor at Ephesus, we looked up at the magnificent marble-paved and colonnaded Harbor Road that led to the southern end of the city and to the great amphitheater built into the hillside with a seating capacity for 25,000 spectators. Mary temporarily lived in the city while I built her a little stone house on nearby Nightingale Mountain. A tiny

Christian community lived there in peace and Mary soon joined them.

Mary lived in her house, tended by a maidservant. She ate vegetables grown on the plateau and drank water from a spring. Here she prayed and fasted for our salvation. Up the mountainside behind her house, Mary built the first Stations of the Cross, symbolizing the significant places along the original route over which Jesus had carried His Cross to Calvary. She laid them out the same distances between them as she had measured out the original ones in Jerusalem. There she had retraced the route and measured the places along the Way of the Cross of Jesus from the place of Pilate's judgment to the place of Jesus' crucifixion on Calvary. When she was about 70 years old, Mary died and I buried her in the year 51, nine years after our arrival in Ephesus.

I buried Mary in a little grotto that I had previously built at the end of her Way of the Cross, to represent her son's tomb. On the next day, I returned to the grotto to pray. I looked into the grotto, as I had done into the tomb of Jesus after He rose from the dead. I was astonished to see the burial cloths there, but not her body, just as I had seen in the tomb of Jesus. As I had done at Jesus' tomb, I saw and I believed. I believed that her son had assumed her body and soul into heaven to join Him.

I preached and taught at Ephesus. In penance, I prayed and fasted. I ate no flesh. In the year 51, after Mary's death, I returned to Jerusalem for the Council of the Apostles. Peter said that God had granted the Holy Spirit to the Gentiles just as He had done to us without any distinction between us and them. He believed that we are saved through the grace of the Lord Jesus, in the same way as they are. So people of all nations can be saved by Jesus King of All Nations, not only the Chosen Jewish People.

We decided not to burden the Gentiles with all of the Mosaic Law, including circumcision, but asked only that they abstain from meat sacrificed to idols, from blood, from meats of strangled animals and from sexual immorality.

I returned again to Jerusalem in the year 62 to meet the rest of the apostles who were then living. We met and chose Simeon as the second Bishop of Jerusalem. Then I came back once again to Ephesus.

Some Jews had first introduced Christianity or The Way in Ephesus. The original community was under the leadership of Apollo and they were disciples of St. John the Baptist. They were converted by Aquila and Priscilla. Then came Paul.

Paul in Ephesus

Saul of Tarsus had a tremendous conversion on the road to Damascus while he was on his way to arrest the followers of Jesus. He then became known as Paul. Through him the word of God grew and conversions multiplied. Paul eventually came to Ephesus about the year 54. He found some disciples and asked them, "Did you receive the Holy Spirit when you first believed?"

They said, "No, we have never even heard that there is a Holy Spirit."

Then Paul asked, "Into what then were you baptized?"

They said, "Into John's baptism."

Paul responded, "John baptized with the baptism of repentance, telling the people to believe in the one who was to come after him, that is, Jesus." On hearing this, they were baptized in the name of the Lord Jesus. When Paul had laid his hands upon them, the Holy Spirit came upon them and they spoke with tongues and prophesied. There were about twelve of them in all.

Then Paul entered the synagogue and for three months spoke boldly, arguing and pleading about the Kingdom of God. However, when some were stubborn and disbelieved, speaking evil of the Way before the congregation, he withdrew from them, taking the disciples with him, and argued daily in the hall of Tyrannus. This continued for two years, so that from the center of Ephesus all the residents of the surrounding cities heard the word of the Lord, both Jews and Greeks.

God did extraordinary miracles by the hands of Paul. When

handkerchiefs or aprons were carried away from his body to the sick, diseases left them and evil spirits came out of them. Then some of the itinerant Jewish exorcists undertook to pronounce the name of the Lord Jesus over those who had evil spirits, saying, "I adjure you by the Jesus whom Paul preaches."

Seven sons of a Jewish High Priest named Sceva were doing this, but the evil spirit answered them, "Jesus I know, and Paul I know; but who are you?" Then the man who was possessed leaped on them, mastered all of them, and overpowered them, so that they fled out of that house naked and wounded.

When this became known to all of the residents of Ephesus, both Jews and Greeks, fear fell upon them all and the name of the Lord Jesus was extolled. Many of the new believers also came, confessing and divulging the Way. A number of those who practiced magic arts brought their books and burned them in the sight of all. Then they counted the value of them and found it came to fifty thousand pieces of silver. The word of the Lord grew and prevailed mightily.

Soon after, a controversy arose concerning the Christian Way in Ephesus. A silversmith, who sold silver statues of the false goddess Artemis, brought a lot of business to the craftsmen. He gathered them together with other similar workers, and said, "Men, you know that from this business we have our wealth. And you see and hear that not only at Ephesus but almost throughout all Asia this Paul has persuaded and turned away a considerable company of people, saying that gods made with hands are not gods. There is danger not only that this trade of ours may come into disrepute but also that the Temple of the great goddess Artemis may count for nothing and that she may even be deposed from her magnificence, she whom all Asia and the world worship."

When they heard this, they were enraged and cried out, "Great is Artemis of the Ephesians!" The city was filled with confusion and they rushed together into the amphitheater, dragging with them Gaius and Aristarchus, Macedonians who were Paul's companions in travel.

Paul wished to go in among the crowd, but his disciples would not let him. Some of the magistrates, who were friends of his, sent to him and begged him not to venture into the theater. Now some cried one thing and some another because the assembly was in confusion and most of them did not know why they had come together.

Some of the crowd prompted Alexander, whom the Jews had put forward, and he motioned with his hand, wishing to make a defense to the people. But when they recognized that he was a Jew, they cried out for about two hours with one voice, "Great is Artemis of the Ephesians!"

When the town clerk had finally quieted the crowd, he said, "Men of Ephesus, what man is there who does not know that the city of the Ephesians is Temple keeper of the great Artemis, and of the sacred stone that fell from the sky? Seeing then that these things cannot be contradicted, you ought to be quiet and do nothing rash. You have brought these men here who are neither sacrilegious nor blasphemers of our goddess. If therefore Demetrius and the craftsmen with him have a complaint against anyone, the courts are open, and there are proconsuls; let them bring charges against one another. But if you seek anything further, it shall be settled in the regular assembly. For we are in danger of being charged with rioting today, there being no cause that we can give to justify this commotion." When he had said this, he dismissed the assembly.

Paul later left Timothy as Bishop of the city while I continued to preach the word in other parts of Asia, and cared for and consecrated bishops for them. I tried to teach the truth against the various heresies that arose, particularly against those of Cerinthus.

One day, I went to a public bath, but then I learned that Cerinthus was in there so I started back and said to some of my friends who were with me, "Let us, my brothers, make haste and be gone, lest the bath, wherein is Cerinthus, the enemy of the truth, should fall upon our heads."

I always taught my flock to beware of the conversation of those who willfully corrupted the truth of religion and who by their ensnaring speeches endeavored to seduce others. I preached and

245

taught until the persecution of the Roman Emperor Domitian broke out in the year 95. At that time, I was apprehended by the proconsul of Asia and sent to Rome. I was thrown into a cauldron of boiling oil in front of the Latin Gate, but the Lord delivered me without suffering any injury. Then I was exiled to the island of Patmos, because I had proclaimed God's word and gave testimony to Jesus. Patmos is a beautiful island that lies off the west coast of Ephesus in the Aegean Sea. Here I had time and solitude to reflect and to write.

16. My Revelation at Patmos

On a Lord's Day in the year 96, while I was lying prostrate praying in a cave on Patmos, facing its opening towards the sea, a huge bolt of lightning hit the cave and shattered the ceiling. It was as if the hand of God had smote a cleft in it.

I was caught up in spirit and heard behind me a voice as loud as a trumpet which said, "Write on a scroll what you see and send it to the seven churches: to Ephesus, Smyrna, Pergamum, Thyatira, Sardis, Philadelphia, and Laodicea."

I got up and turned around to see whose voice it was that had spoken to me. I saw seven gold lampstands and, in the midst of the lampstands, one like a Son of Man wearing an ankle-length robe with a gold sash around His chest. It was Jesus! His hair was as white as white wool or snow and His eyes were like a fiery flame. His feet were like polished brass refined in a furnace and His voice was like the sound of rushing water.

In His right hand He held seven stars. A sharp two-edged sword came out of His mouth and His face shone like the sun at its brightest. When I caught sight of Him, I fell down at His feet as though dead.

He touched me with His right hand and said, "Do not be afraid. I am the first and the last, the one who lives. Once I was dead, but now I am alive forever and ever. I hold the keys to death and the netherworld. So write down what you have seen, and what is happening, and what will happen afterwards."

The Letters to the Seven Churches

So, as I was instructed, I wrote letters to the seven churches of Asia. These letters were dictated by Jesus Christ, the faithful witness, the firstborn of the dead, the ruler of the world and the King of All Nations. He loves us, has freed us from our sins by His blood and has made us into a Kingdom of God, priests for His God and Father. They were letters of warning to these churches to repent or to suffer from God's chastisements. I shuddered when I remembered God's chastisement upon Jerusalem and the destruction of the Temple 26 years before.

During his ministry, Jesus had prayed and wept over Jerusalem. He had prophesied that not a stone upon a stone would be left standing there. This was God's chastisement for their failure to recognize the day of His visitation and to accept His way to peace. Jesus' prophecy was fulfilled to the letter by the Roman General Titus in the year 70 when he annihilated the city of Jerusalem and the Temple.

In the letters that I wrote, Jesus recognized the good deeds of the seven churches, but warned them that their love had grown cold. He urged them to repent and to return to their first love or to suffer chastisements.

In particular, Jesus told the church of Ephesus, "Realize how far you have fallen. Repent, and do the works you did at first. Otherwise, I will come to you and remove your lampstand from its place, unless you repent."

These were not mean-spirited, vindictive threats, but words of love for God's children to return to Him. Yes, God is a God of love, but what Father does not reprove His children? Jesus said, "I reprove and train those whom I love, so be earnest and repent."

God loves us, but He does not force His love upon us. He stands at the door of our hearts and knocks. If we open the door He will enter. Jesus said, "Look, I am standing at the door knocking. If one of you hears me calling and opens the door, I will come in to share a meal at that person's side. Anyone who proves victorious I will allow to share my throne, just as I myself have overcome and have taken my seat with my Father on His throne. Let anyone who can hear, listen to what the Spirit is saying to the churches."

Visions of Heavenly Worship

Next, I had some amazing visions of creatures and the worship of God in heaven. I had a vision of an open door to heaven, and I heard the trumpet-like voice that had spoken to me before saying, "Come up here and I will show you what must happen afterwards."

At once I was caught up in spirit. A throne was there in heaven and on the throne sat one whose appearance sparkled like jasper and carnelian. Around the throne was a halo as brilliant as an emerald. Surrounding the throne, I saw twenty-four other thrones on which twenty-four elders sat, dressed in white garments and with gold crowns on their heads. From the throne came flashes of lightning, rumblings, and peals of thunder. Seven flaming torches burned in front of the throne, which are the seven spirits of God.

In front of the throne was something that resembled a sea of glass like crystal. In the center and around the throne, there were four living creatures covered with eyes in front and in back. Day and night they do not stop exclaiming, "Holy, holy, holy is the Lord God almighty, who was, and who is, and who is to come."

Whenever the living creatures give glory and honor and thanks to the one who sits on the throne, who lives forever and ever, the twenty-four elders fall down before the one who sits on the throne and worship Him. They throw down their crowns before the throne, exclaiming, "Worthy are you, Lord our God, to receive glory and honor and power, for you created all things; because of your will they came to be and were created."

Then I saw a scroll in the right hand of the one who sat on the throne. It had writing on both sides and was sealed with seven seals. I understood that the scroll contained God's plan for all peoples and nations. I cried because no one was found worthy to open the scroll. One of the elders said to me, "Do not weep. The lion of the tribe of Judah, the root of David, who is Jesus the Messiah and the King of All Nations, has triumphed and will be worthy to open the scroll with the seven seals."

Then I saw standing in the midst of the throne and the four living creatures and the elders, a Lamb that seemed to have been slain. He had seven horns and seven eyes. I understood that this image symbolized Jesus Christ, the Lamb who has universal power and knowledge. The number seven is the symbol of the universal, the horns are the symbol for power and the eyes are the symbol for knowledge.

The Lamb came and received the scroll from the right hand of the one who sat on the throne. When He took it, the four living creatures and the twenty-four elders fell down before the Lamb. Each of the elders held a harp and gold bowls filled with incense, which are the prayers of the holy ones.

They sang a new hymn:

> Worthy are you to receive the scroll and to break open its seals, for you were slain and with your blood you purchased for God those from every tribe and tongue, people and nation.
>
> You made them a Kingdom of God and priests for our God, and they will reign on Earth.

I looked again and heard the voices of many angels who surrounded the throne and the living creatures and the elders. They were countless in number, and they cried out in a loud voice, "Worthy is the Lamb that was slain to receive power and riches, wisdom and strength, honor and glory and blessing."

Then I heard every creature in heaven and on Earth and under Earth and in the sea, everything in the universe, cry out, "To the one who sits on the throne and to the Lamb be blessing and honor, glory and might, forever and ever."

The four living creatures answered, "Amen," and the elders fell down and worshiped. Then the Lamb broke open the seals of the scroll. I had a vision as He opened each one of them. Most of these visions were of the evils of men and disasters such as conquest, war, famine, death, martyrdom and a great earthquake. The sun turned black and the moon became like blood. The stars in the sky fell to Earth, the sky was torn like a scroll curling up and every mountain and island was moved from its place. The people hid themselves in the mountains and cried out in terror because the great day of the wrath of God and His Lamb had come.

I understood that, faced with these calamites, we should never lose hope, but should firmly believe that the power of evil is always conquered by the omnipotence of God. We must not be overcome by evil, but overcome evil with good. God calls us to live through history courageously amid suffering, with the faith that ultimately evil will not conquer good. That is why we pray that the Kingdom of Jesus King of All Nations will be recognized on Earth.

After this I had a vision of a great multitude, which no one could count, from every nation, race, people, and tongue. They stood before the throne and before the Lamb, wearing white robes and holding palm branches in their hands.

They cried out in a loud voice, "Salvation comes from our God, who is seated on the throne, and from the Lamb."

All the angels stood around the throne and around the elders and the four living creatures. They prostrated themselves before the throne, worshiped God, and exclaimed, "Amen. Blessing and glory, wisdom and thanksgiving, honor, power and might be to our God forever and ever. Amen."

Then one of the elders spoke up and said to me, "Who are these wearing white robes, and where did they come from?"

I said to him, "My Lord, you are the one who knows."

He said to me, "These are the ones who have survived the time of great distress; they have washed their robes and made them white in the blood of the Lamb. For this reason, they stand before God's throne and worship Him day and night in His Temple."

"The one who sits on the throne will shelter them. They will not hunger or thirst anymore, nor will the sun or any heat strike them. For the Lamb who is in the center of the throne will shepherd them and lead them to springs of life-giving water, and God will wipe away every tear from their eyes."

I understood that this vision represented the definitive establishment of the Kingdom of God amongst peoples of all nations. They were saved by the blood of Jesus, the Lamb of God, offered in sacrifice for all peoples and extending His grace and mercy to all nations. They were saved from the Kingdom of the World for eternal happiness with Jesus King of All Nations in the Kingdom of God and offered God their praise and blessing.

The Lamb was first identified as Jesus by John the Baptist who said, "Behold the Lamb of God, who takes away the sin of the world!"

Now I saw the total self-giving of Jesus to the Father, represented by the innocent lamb who was slain. It symbolized Jesus who went like a lamb to the slaughter and was slain for us on Calvary. All of the people in heaven are priests who assist in the offering of the firstborn Son of God to the Father and join themselves in the sacrifice.

Jesus is the Lamb who died, resurrected from the dead and ascended into heaven where He continues His Passover sacrifice. He does not die, bleed or suffer again, but continues to offer up Himself as the firstborn and as the unblemished Lamb, as the perpetual, timeless, everlasting sacrifice of praise to the Father.

The vision seemed to be a mirror of the Eucharistic celebration instituted by Jesus on Earth at His Last Supper when He, the innocent Lamb offered Himself to the Father as both man and God, and pre-presented His sacrifice on Calvary. Now He re-presents that sacrifice, but in an unbloody manner, for all time. Our Lamb, who looks as though He is slain, is truly the firstborn Son, our Victim High Priest, True Prophet and Sovereign King of All Nations. He lives and reigns forever in His resurrected and glorified body.

There were loud voices in heaven, saying, "The Kingdom of the World now belongs to our Lord and to His Anointed, and He will reign forever and ever."

I understood that our earthly worship also participates in the heavenly worship. In our earthly worship we share in a foretaste of the celebration of that heavenly worship where Christ is sitting at the right hand of God, Minister of the sanctuary and of the true tabernacle. We worship God with all the angels and all the warriors of the heavenly army.

Then I saw that an angel stood at the altar, holding a gold censer. He was given a great quantity of incense to offer, along with the prayers of all the holy ones. The smoke, along with the prayers, went up before God. The angel then took the censer, and filled it with fire from the altar and threw it on Earth. There were peals of thunder, loud noises, flashes of lightning and an earthquake.

I understood that these images symbolized that our imperfect prayers are purified and are a sweet aroma that reaches the heart of God. No prayers are useless prayers. God responds to all of them in the mystery of His providential love and mercy. He intervenes, makes His voice heard on Earth and disrupts the structures of evil.

Then the twenty-four elders who sat on their thrones before God prostrated themselves and worshiped God and said:

We give thanks to you, Lord God almighty, who
are and who were.

For you have assumed your great power and have established your reign.

The nations raged, but your wrath has come, and the time for the dead to be judged, and to recompense your servants, the Prophets, and the holy ones and those who fear your name, the small and the great alike, and to destroy those who destroy the earth.

The Woman and the Dragon

Then I saw God's Temple in heaven opened and the Ark of His Covenant could be seen in the Temple. This was the Ark that had been missing since the time of the Prophet Jeremiah. There were flashes of lightning, rumblings, and peals of thunder, an earthquake, and a violent hailstorm.

Next a great sign appeared in the sky. It was a woman clothed with the sun, with the moon under her feet, and on her head a crown of twelve stars. She was with child and wailed aloud in pain as she labored to give birth. I understood that she represented Mary, Queen of heaven.

Then another sign appeared in the sky. It was a huge red dragon, with seven heads and ten horns, and on its heads were seven diadems. I understood that this represented Satan and the kingdoms of this world. Its tail swept away a third of the stars in the sky and hurled them down to Earth.

The dragon stood before the woman about to give birth, to devour her child when she gave birth. She gave birth to a son, a male child, who represented Jesus, destined to rule all the nations with an iron rod. Her child was caught up to God and His throne. The woman herself fled into the desert where she had a place prepared by God, that she might be taken care of there for a period of time.

War broke out in heaven. Michael and his angels battled against the dragon. The dragon and its angels fought back, but they did not prevail and there was no longer any place for them in heaven.

254

The huge dragon, the ancient serpent, who is called the Devil and Satan, who deceived the whole world, was thrown down to Earth, and its angels were thrown down with him.

Then I heard a loud voice in heaven say:

> Now have salvation and power come, and the kingdom of our God and the authority of His Anointed.

> For the accuser of our brothers is cast out, who accuses them before our God day and night.

> They conquered him by the blood of the Lamb and by the word of their testimony. Love for life did not deter them from death.

> Therefore, rejoice, you heavens, and you who dwell in them.

> But woe to you, Earth and sea, for the Devil has come down to you in great fury, for he knows he has but a short time.

When the dragon saw that it had been thrown down to Earth, it pursued the woman who had given birth to the male child. But the woman was given the two wings of the great eagle, so that she could fly to her place in the desert where, far from the serpent, she was taken care of for a period of time.

The serpent, however, spewed a torrent of water out of his mouth after the woman to sweep her away with the current, but Earth helped the woman and opened its mouth and swallowed the flood that the dragon spewed out of its mouth.

Then the dragon became angry with the woman and went off to wage war against the rest of her offspring, those who keep God's commandments and bear witness to Jesus.

When I saw the heavens opened and the Ark of the Covenant, I remembered that the Ark had once contained the Ten Commandments as the Word of God, the priestly staff of Aaron

255

and a golden jar containing some manna that had miraculously come to the Israelites during their time in the desert. Later in the Temple of Jerusalem, the Ark was kept in the Holy of Holies, the inner core of the Temple where God dwelt.

The Prophet Jeremiah hid the Ark to prevent its capture and desecration by the Babylonians. He had said, "The place is to remain unknown until God gathers His people together again and shows them His mercy." (2 Maccabees 2:7).

In my vision, I saw the Ark and then I saw the woman who represented Mary. Mary carried Jesus in her womb. He is the Word of God and the Bread of Life and our Victim High Priest, True Prophet and Sovereign King. I understood that Mary is a symbol of the Ark of the New Covenant. Jesus as priest had made this New Covenant with us by giving us His life and by pouring out His blood in the sacrifice of the Cross, whereby He reconciled us to Himself by the forgiveness of sins so that we would have eternal life with Him.

As I contemplated the vision of the Woman Clothed with the Sun, I saw it as symbolic of God's plan for the salvation of humanity. There is no time with God. One day is the same as a 1000 years. All time is present to Him. This vision spoke to me in the past, the present and the future.

In the past, I saw the vision as the Woman prophesied in the book of Genesis whose son would strike at Satan's head. (See Genesis 3:15). In the present, I saw the vision as Mary to whom Jesus gave me from His Cross as my mother and whom I believed was now assumed into heaven since I had buried her body but could not find it upon my return to venerate it.

I also saw the vision in the past as the presentation by God to Satan of His plan for our salvation. The plan was that God would create humanity, who would fall by the original sin of Adam and Eve, but who were promised a Redeemer. The Redeemer was to be a man born of a woman. Jesus Christ, true God and true man, was born of the Virgin Mary, who was pregnant with Him in the vision. The red dragon symbolized Satan. He rebelled against God's plan for the redemption of humanity. In his pride, envy and jealousy, Satan wished to be the Redeemer or, if not the

Redeemer, the mediator of the redemption. This was not God's plan and so Satan rebelled against it and he and his angels fell from heaven.

I saw the vision in the present as Mary, Queen Mother of heaven by virtue of her crown of twelve stars, Queen of the twelve tribes of Israel and Queen of the twelve apostles and of all those in union with them in the New Covenant. I also saw the vision in the present and future as Satan's rebellion continued throughout history against the children of God. I saw it as a futile battle for him because the true King of All Nations had defeated Satan with His iron rod.

I also understood that this great sign was the prefigurement of God's plan that He made before His creation, of Mary's virgin birth of Jesus, King of All Nations, Son of God and Son of David, whose throne He would inherit and whose kingdom would be without end, as prophesied by the angel Gabriel at his Annunciation to Mary.

The Woman was with child, the child king as prophesied by the angel Gabriel. I understood that her son is Jesus, now raised, ascended and glorified, who is the new Adam, the new David who fulfills Gabriel's prophecy and rules His Kingdom without end as Jesus King of All Nations.

After I had later meditated on the vision of the Woman Clothed with the Sun, I concluded that she represented both the Church and the Virgin Mary as Mother of God and Mother of the Church, immaculately conceived, perpetual virgin and assumed into heaven. I reasoned this out with my mind and in faith from God's revelation.

The Church is our Mother. It is Christ's Church, the Kingdom of God that He personally founded upon Peter when He told him, "You are Peter, and upon this rock I will build my Church, and the gates of hell shall not prevail against it." The Church is our Mother because it is one, holy, catholic and apostolic. It is the mystical body of Christ who is its head with all of us believers in Him as its members. Christ is one and all-holy.

The Church is catholic because it is universal and the means of salvation for all humanity. The Church is apostolic because it

257

originated with the twelve apostles, represented by the twelve stars of the crown in the vision. Mary is the Mother of the Church and the Mother of God because the Church is Christ and she is the mother of Christ who is both God and man. Mary's cousin Elizabeth was the first to recognize this when the Holy Spirit inspired her to cry out to Mary, "Who am I that the Mother of my Lord should come and visit me?"

Mary was immaculately conceived because she is full of grace, as the angel Gabriel told her. Grace is the life of God and no one could have the fullness of the life of God unless they were always without sin. I believed that Mary had to be without sin from her conception because of the revelation of the angel Gabriel and the fact that I believed that only a sinless person could conceive and bear the Son of God. I never saw the slightest fault in her. She had to be free from the original sin of Adam and Eve and from any actual sin during her entire life. She is the New Eve, Mother of All the Living, as Jesus is the New Adam, both of whom were sinless, humble and obedient, unlike the sinfulness, pride and disobedience of the first Adam and Eve.

Mary was also a perpetual virgin, as she had told me. She was assumed into heaven, just as I had seen Jesus ascend into the sky and to heaven with my very own eyes after His resurrection from the dead. My vision showed Mary surrounded by the clouds in the sky and I had found her tomb emptied of her body with her burial clothing lying there, just as I had found the tomb of Jesus emptied of His body with His burial clothing lying there.

The Woman Clothed with the Sun is in a great struggle against the red dragon, the enemy of the mission of Christ and His Church. I saw Mary both as a prefigurement of God's plan and as its realization with her in eternal happiness, yet laboring in mysterious childbirth for the birth of those who are yet to be with her and Jesus in eternal happiness.

The dragon appeared to be winning the battle, but in reality he had already been defeated since, as I saw, he was cast down to Earth, and his angels were cast down with him. He was defeated by Christ through His obedience and humility, death and resurrection. So, even though the dragon may continue in battle, we should not be afraid since he has already been defeated. When his allotted time is up, he will be thrown into the pool of fire and sulfur, where he and his fallen angels and all the evildoers will be tormented day and night forever and ever.

The New Heaven, the New Earth and the New Jerusalem

Then I saw a vision of a new heaven and a new Earth. The former heaven and the former Earth had passed away, and the sea was no more. I also saw the holy city, the New Jerusalem, coming down out of heaven from God, prepared as a bride adorned for her husband.

I heard a loud voice from the throne saying, "Behold, God's dwelling is with the human race. He will dwell with them and they will be His people and God Himself will always be with them. He will wipe every tear from their eyes, and there shall be no more death or mourning, wailing or pain, for the old order has passed away."

The one who sat on the throne said, "Behold, I make all things new." Then He said, "Write these words down, for they are trustworthy and true. They are accomplished:

> I am the Alpha and the Omega, the beginning and the end. To the thirsty I will give a gift from the spring of life-giving water. The victor will inherit these gifts, and I shall be his God, and he will be my son.

> But as for cowards, the unfaithful, the depraved, murderers, the unchaste, sorcerers, idol-worshipers, and deceivers of every sort, their lot is in the burning pool of fire and sulfur, which is the second death."

Then an angel came and said to me, "Come here. I will show you the bride, the wife of the Lamb."

He took me in spirit to a great, high mountain and showed me the holy city, the New Jerusalem coming down out of heaven from God.

It gleamed with the splendor of God. Its radiance was like that of a precious stone, like jasper, clear as crystal. It had a massive, high wall, with twelve gates where twelve angels were stationed and on which the names of the twelve tribes of the Israelites were inscribed.

There were three gates facing east, three north, three south, and three west. The wall of the city had twelve courses of stones as its foundation, on which were inscribed the twelve names of the apostles of the Lamb.

I saw no Temple in the city, for its Temple is the Lord God almighty and the Lamb. The city had no need of sun or moon to shine on it, for the glory of God gave it light, and its lamp was the Lamb.

All nations will walk by its light, and to it the kings of Earth will bring their treasure. During the day its gates will never be shut, and there will be no night there.

The treasure and wealth of all nations will be brought there, but nothing unclean will enter it, nor anyone who does abominable things or tells lies. Only those whose names are written in the Lamb's book of life will enter.

Then the angel showed me the river of life-giving water, sparkling like crystal, flowing from the throne of God and of the Lamb down the middle of its street. On either side of the river grew the tree of life that produces fruit twelve times a year, once each month; the leaves of the trees serve as medicine for all nations.

Nothing accursed will be found there anymore. The throne of God and of the Lamb will be in it, and His servants will worship Him. They will look upon His face, and His name will be on their foreheads. Night will be no more, nor will they need light from lamp or sun, for the Lord God shall give them light, and they shall reign forever and ever.

Isaiah had prophesied that Israel would be a light to the nations, whose wealth would be brought to it and that its gates would be open to people of all nations. (See Isaiah 49:6; 60:3,5; 60:11).

I understood that my vision of the New Jerusalem fulfilled these prophecies. It was the Church, the Kingdom of God, the Kingdom of All Nations with its foundation of the twelve apostles and its gates of the twelve tribes of Israel through which all nations would now come.

These Prophetic Words

Then the angel said to me, "These words are trustworthy and true, and the Lord, the God of prophetic spirits, sent His angel to show His servants what must happen soon."

Jesus said, "Behold, I am coming soon."

It is I, John, who heard and saw these things, and when I heard and saw them I fell down to worship at the feet of the angel who showed them to me.

However, he said to me, "Don't do that! I am a fellow servant of yours and of your brothers the Prophets and of those who keep the message of this book. Worship God."

Then he said to me, "Do not seal up the prophetic words of this book, for the appointed time is near. Let the wicked still act wickedly, and the filthy still be filthy. The righteous must still do right, and the holy still be holy."

Jesus said:

Behold, I am coming soon. I bring my reward with me, to repay each as their deeds deserve. I am the Alpha and the Omega, the first and the last, the beginning and the end.

Blessed are they who wash their robes so as to have the right to the tree of life and enter the city through its gates. Outside are the dogs, the sorcerers, the unchaste, the murderers, the idol-worshipers, and all who love and practice deceit.

Then Jesus said, "I, Jesus, sent my angel to give you this testimony for the churches. I am the root and offspring of David, the bright morning star."

I, John, say that the Spirit and the Bride say, "Come." Let the hearer say, "Come." Let him who is thirsty come, let him who wants the water of life take it without price.

I warn everyone who hears the prophetic words in this book. If anyone adds to them, God will add to him the plagues described in this book, and if anyone takes away from the words in this prophetic book, God will take away his share in the tree of life and in the holy city described in this book.

Jesus, the one who gives this testimony, says, "Yes, I am coming soon." Amen! Come, Lord Jesus!

The History of God's Kingdom

After my visions on Patmos, I reflected on the history of God's Kingdom, His plan for our salvation, our Jewish kings and on the Lord Jesus, King of All Nations.

God's Kingdom began in the Garden of Eden when God gave Adam kingship and dominion over all Earth and all the creatures and fish and birds. God shared His own kingship with man, whom He had made in His image and likeness.

However, Adam and Eve forfeited their kingdom when they listened to Satan and, in their pride, disobeyed God, wanting to be like gods. Their original sin caused suffering, death and the loss of eternal life to humanity. However, God promised humanity a Redeemer who would conquer Satan.

Then Adam's son Cain murdered his brother Abel and humans continued to sin. So God in His justice brought the chastisement of the Great Flood upon Earth, but He saved a remnant in the family of the just man, Noah.

Sin returned with the arrogance of the building of the Tower of Babel and God in His justice brought the chastisement of confused speech upon the world and dispersed the human family into exile.

Down to about 2000 BC, the time of Abraham's father, our fathers had worshiped false gods. God led Abraham out from Ur to the land of Canaan. He made a covenant with Abraham for all the nations and re-established the bonds of kinship between God and the human family. He promised Abraham that he would be the father of many nations and that his descendants would be as countless as the number of the sands on the seashore. He promised him that in his descendants, all the nations of Earth would find blessing. He promised him that He would be their God and they would be His people and that He would give them the land of Canaan.

However, the Israelites broke this covenant through their sins. So in 1700 BC, God in His justice brought upon them the chastisement of their enslavement in Egypt for over 200 years, as God had prophesied to Abraham.

In His mercy, God liberated the Israelites in about 1500 BC under the leadership of Moses who led them out of Egypt, through the waters that God miraculously parted in the Red Sea and into the desert. There they worshipped a golden calf, complained against God and did not trust Him. In justice, God brought upon them the chastisement of their wandering in the desert for 40 years. But, He still cared for them and fed them manna from heaven as He led them to the Promised Land.

Just as the waters of the Red Sea had miraculously parted, so did the waters of the River Jordan as Joshua led the Israelites into the Promised Land. God destroyed seven nations in the land of Canaan and gave the Israelites the Promised Land as their inheritance, as He had promised Abraham.

Zechariah had prophesied that the Lord would become King over the whole Earth and on that day the Lord would be the only one, and His name the only one.

The Lord was the King of the Israelites for over 325 years. He worked through mediators called judges. God wanted to remain as King of Israel, but Israel wanted a human king like the other nations. They wanted worldly power and prestige. They demanded that the Prophet Samuel appoint a king for them and they rebelled against God's rule.

Samuel warned them that their demands would harm the people. He said that a king would tax them for his own purposes, wage war and bring them unhappiness. But they were insistent. God told Samuel that they had rejected God as their King and to grant them what they wanted.

Around 1000 BC, God chose Saul, son of Kish, as King of Israel and Samuel anointed him. However, Saul disobeyed God by not annihilating his enemies and by looting their goods. Samuel told Saul that God had rejected him. He chose David as King. Saul became envious of David and tried to kill him. Saul later committed suicide.

Samuel anointed David as King and he was re-anointed publicly as King of Judah for seven years and later anointed again as King of all Israel. He marched north and conquered Jerusalem and made it his capital. David moved the nation's capital to Jerusalem in order to unite the tribes. He brought the Ark of the Covenant there which made Jerusalem the religious and political center of Israel. God wanted to build a kingdom for David so that he would rule over all the nations. God wanted to establish the throne of His kingdom forever. God made a covenant with King David and Israel was united under him as one kingdom, free from foreign oppression.

God told the Prophet Nathan to tell David, "I will raise up your heir after you, sprung from your loins, and I will make his kingdom firm. It is he who shall build a house for my name. And I will make his royal throne firm forever. I will be a father to him, and he shall be a son to me. Your house and your kingdom shall endure forever before me; your throne shall stand firm forever." (2 Samuel 7:12-13).

In his psalms, David wrote that God had made a covenant with him and that He swore to him, "Forever will I confirm your posterity and establish your throne for all generations." (Psalm 89:29).

God would come to rule Earth and would rule the world with justice and the peoples with equity. David wrote that God was King of Earth and reigns over the nations. He wrote, "All the ends of Earth will remember and turn to the Lord, and all the families of the nations will bow down before Him, for dominion belongs to the Lord and He rules over the nations." (Psalm 22:27-28).

Isaiah prophesied, "God's dominion is vast and forever peaceful, from David's throne, and over His kingdom, which He confirms and sustains by judgment and justice, both now and forever." (Isaiah 9:6).

But, like Adam and the Israelites before David, David's son Solomon sinned grievously. He built the first Temple but turned to foreign gods and sacrificed his own children to them. In His justice, God brought the chastisement of rebellion. The northern ten tribes rebelled against Solomon's son Rehoboam. After his death, the kingdom was divided in two around 926 BC. Judah was left as one nation with only the two tribes of Benjamin and Judah.

Sins continued and so did the chastisements. The northern kingdom of Israel was destroyed in 722 BC by the Assyrians and the other ten tribes ultimately disappeared. In 587 BC, Babylon destroyed Jerusalem, the Temple and the southern kingdom of Judah, sending its people into exile. Later, around 538 BC, after Babylon had fallen to Persia, some Israelites returned to Jerusalem and they began to rebuild the Temple.

From David's descendants, God eventually brought to Israel a savior, Jesus, according to His promise, as the King of All Nations. The angel Gabriel told Mary that her son, conceived by the Holy Spirit, was to be called Jesus. He would be great and would be called Son of the Most High, who would inherit the throne of David His father, and He would rule over the house of Jacob forever, and of His kingdom there would be no end.

John the Baptist heralded His coming by proclaiming a baptism of repentance to all the people of Israel. Jesus proclaimed that the kingdom was at hand.

Jesus went about doing good, healing the sick, casting out demons, raising the dead and forgiving sins. Finally, at His Last

265

Supper with us, He established His new covenant of eternal life through the forgiveness of sins for many. He sealed it with His own blood when He changed the wine into His blood and gave it to us to drink with the eating of His body after He had changed the bread into His body.

At the end of His earthly ministry, He told us disciples, "I assigned to you, as my Father assigned to me, a Kingdom." The High Priest Caiaphas prophesied that Jesus was going to die for the nation and not only for the nation, but also to gather into one the dispersed children of God — all nations.

Jesus was the King of All Nations and His Father assigned to Him the Church as His Kingdom. He wanted His Kingdom to be recognized on Earth. However, the inhabitants of Jerusalem and their leaders failed to recognize His Kingdom or to recognize Jesus as their King. They condemned Him and put Him to death as the Prophets and Jesus Himself had foretold.

But God raised Him from the dead and for many days He appeared to those who had come up with Him from Galilee to Jerusalem. They were His witnesses before the people.

After His death and resurrection, Jesus spoke as the King of All Nations. He told us that all authority in heaven and on Earth had been given to Him. In His Great Commission, He commanded us to make disciples of all nations, baptizing them in the name of the Father, and of the Son, and of the Holy Spirit, teaching them to observe all that He had commanded us.

Jesus is the fulfillment of God's covenant with David, whose throne He inherited, and of whose Kingdom there will be no end. He reigns now as King of All Nations over His Church, both in His Kingdom in heaven and in His Kingdom on Earth.

Jesus King of All Nations is the priest who offered Himself on the Cross as the victim in sacrifice for the forgiveness of our sins. He is also the Prophet foretold by Moses. He is truly our Victim High Priest, True Prophet and Sovereign King.

In order to reunite all of His children scattered by sin, the Father willed to call the whole of humanity together into His Son's Kingdom for their unity and salvation.

We enter His Kingdom and are incorporated in it through baptism when we become adopted children of God. He shares His divine life with us and dwells within us through sanctifying grace, which comes to fulfillment in eternal life in heaven.

The Kingdom of God actually means that God reigns. He Himself is present and crucial to human beings in the world. His Kingdom does not come in such a way that we can see it paraded along a highway. It is in us and in our midst. It develops wherever charity and love prevail and God's will is done.

The Kingdom is present wherever there are people who are open to His arrival. So let Jesus enter into the world and their hearts so that He may reign there and His reign will be recognized on Earth. He wants His reign to be recognized on Earth and that there be unity in one flock with one shepherd to save it from condemnation, so that the world might believe that His Father sent Him to the world as true God and true man for our eternal life.

In the Kingdom of God, we receive from God's mercy the forgiveness of our sins, the healing of our brokenness and the renewal of our hearts in the faith, hope, love and joy of His Kingdom so that we may be one in Him. He created us for a life with Him, full of peace, truth, beauty, goodness, and meaning. A life that begins now, lasts forever, and can't be taken away. This life is what is called the Kingdom of God.

Ultimately, the Kingdom of God is the person of Jesus Christ Himself. He is the face of this Kingdom. He reveals the love of the Father and the nature of His Kingdom, especially through His healing and His forgiveness of our sins.

The Kingdom of God has come because of the redemption of Jesus, but it is still coming towards the fulfillment of His prophecy of one flock and one shepherd, Jesus Christ. This is what we ask for when we pray as He taught us, "Thy Kingdom come."

When King David's throne was overthrown and had been vacant for centuries, God promised to raise up a new king who would rule forever. The kind of king which God promised His people was different from our understanding. We had hoped for

267

a Messiah King who would rule over the land of Israel and free us from Roman oppression, but God's plan of redemption was to free us from sin and it included not only Israel, but all the nations of Earth as well.

How did God accomplish His plan? By sending Jesus, the Messiah, the King of All Nations, who defeated sin, death, and Satan through His victory on the Cross and over the grave. Through His death and resurrection Jesus makes us friends of God and citizens of heaven. The Lord Jesus wants us to live in joyful hope and confident expectation that He will come again to fully establish His Kingdom of truth, life, holiness, grace, justice, love and peace.

My revelations revealed that Jesus is the firstborn of the dead and the ruler of the kings of Earth. The Kingdom of the World has become the Kingdom of our Lord and of His Christ, and He shall reign forever and ever.

This is why we should believe in the name of Jesus Christ and love one another as He loved us, just as He commanded us. We should love one another because love is of God. Everyone who loves is begotten by God and knows God. Whoever is without love does not know God, for God is love. The way the love of God was revealed to us was that God sent His only Son into the world so that we might not be condemned, but have eternal life through Him.

Love is not that we have loved God, but that He loved us and sent His Son as expiation for our sins. Beloved, if God so loved us, we also must love one another. No one has ever seen God. Yet, if we love one another, God remains in us, and His love is brought to perfection in us. Those who keep His commandments remain in Him, and He in them.

We have come to know and to believe in the love God has for us. God is love, and whoever lives in love, lives in God and God in him. In this is love brought to perfection among us, that we have confidence on the Day of Judgment because as He is, so are we in this world.

We believe and take Jesus at His word. We believe that God loved us so much that He sent His only begotten Son who was

268

sacrificed on the Cross as the innocent Lamb to reconcile us to Himself, to redeem us from the slavery of sin, death and eternal judgment to damnation, through the forgiveness of our sins and the gift of eternal life with Him in happiness in heaven. But there will be a final judgment.

One day, while Jesus was still with us, He told us that someday He would come in glory as the King of All Nations with all the angels with Him and sit upon His glorious throne with all of the nations assembled before Him. There would be a final judgment. He told us that He would separate all from one another, as a shepherd separates the sheep from the goats. He would place the sheep on His right and the goats on His left. Then as King He would say to those on His right, "Come, you who are blessed by my Father. Inherit the Kingdom prepared for you from the foundation of the world."

Then as King He would say to those on His left, "Depart from me, you accursed, into the eternal fire prepared for the devil and his angels." He explained that these will go off to eternal punishment, but the righteous to eternal life. He also explained that His judgment would be based upon their actions and whether they showed mercy to those in need, especially the hungry, the thirsty, the strangers and the prisoners. He identified Himself with them and said that what was done or not done for one of them, His least brothers, was done or not done for Him and that they would be judged accordingly.

My revelations were filled with mysteries of things that were and of things that are to come. They are the final warnings that the world will surely end and judgment will be eternal heaven for the good and eternal damnation for the evildoers. I saw heaven and all of the glories awaiting we who keep our robes white.

Our struggle with Christ against the Kingdom of Satan and his fallen angels will continue, but Christ has won the victory. Jesus' victory over Satan ushered in the everlasting reign of God. In the face of apparently insuperable evil, we are called to trust that Jesus is with us. We who remain steadfast in our faith and confidence in the risen Christ need have no fear, for perfect love

269

casts out all fear.

Suffering, persecution, even death by martyrdom, though remaining part of the mystery of iniquity, are not the end. No matter what sufferings we may endure, in the end we will triumph over Satan and his forces because of our fidelity to Christ the victor.

Jesus is the sovereign Lord of history. We will survive the great tribulations and the final fire that all evildoers will face for eternity with Satan and his fallen angels. We will live forever and ever with Jesus, the King of All Nations in the New Jerusalem, the everlasting Kingdom of God.

Before I received my revelations, the Prophet Daniel had also been given revelations regarding the restoration of all things when the everlasting Kingdom of God would be established. He wrote, "The God of heaven will set up a Kingdom that will never be destroyed, nor will it be left to another people. It will crush all those kingdoms and bring them to an end, but it will itself endure forever. (Daniel 2:44). The saints of the Most High will receive the Kingdom and will possess it forever — yes, forever and ever. (Daniel 7:17, 18). Then the sovereignty, power and greatness of the kingdoms under the whole heaven will be handed over to the saints, the people of the Most High. His Kingdom will be an everlasting Kingdom, and all rulers will worship and obey Him. 'This is the end of the matter...' " (Daniel 7:27, 28).

Yes, this was the end of the matter, just as I had seen in my vision of those who were standing on the sea of glass, holding harps and praising God. They sang the song of Moses, and the song of the Lamb, saying:

Alleluia! The Lord has established His reign, our God, the Almighty.

Let us rejoice and be glad and give Him glory. For the wedding day of the Lamb has come, His bride has made herself ready.

Great and marvelous are your works, O Lord God, the Almighty. Righteous and true are your

270

ways, King of All Nations!

Who will not fear, O Lord, and glorify your name? For you alone are holy.

All nations will come and worship before you, for your righteous acts have been revealed.

As the song ended, I understood that the Kingdom of the World had become the Kingdom of Jesus King of All Nations and that He shall reign forever and ever. May these revelations be a message of hope and consolation for all nations because the prophecy of the psalm will soon be fulfilled:

Proclaim to the nations: "God is King." He made the world firm in its place; He will judge the people in fairness.

Let the heavens rejoice and Earth be glad, let the sea and all within it thunder praise, let the land and all it bears rejoice, all the trees of the wood shout for joy at the presence of the Lord for He comes.

He comes to rule Earth. He will rule the world with justice, He will judge the peoples with His truth.   (Psalm 96:10-13).

17. My Return to Ephesus

My exile on Patmos lasted only 18 months. The Emperor Domitian was slain in the year 96 and all of his edicts and public acts were declared void by a decree of the Roman Senate on account of his excessive cruelty. His successor, Nerva, recalled all those whom Domitian had banished, including me. And so I left Patmos and returned to Ephesus in the year 97 at the age of 91.

Because Timothy had suffered martyrdom in Ephesus the preceding January, the faithful asked me to lead them. In imitation of the High Priest of the Jews, I wore a plate of gold upon my forehead, as a sign of my Christian priesthood.

When the faithful earnestly pressed me to write my Gospel, I agreed to do it, but only if, by ordering a common fast, they would all offer up their prayers together to God. I prepared myself for this divine undertaking through retirement, prayer, fasting and contemplation. When it ended, I was replenished with the clearest and fullest revelation coming from heaven and I immediately began to write. I completed it in the year 98, at the age of 92.

After my return to Ephesus, I was no longer able to walk very far. My disciples carried me to the public square in Ephesus. There I continually exhorted the faithful to love one another.

One day I preached:

> Children, let us love not in word or speech but in deed and truth.
>
> Now this is how we shall know that we belong to the truth and reassure our hearts before Him in whatever our hearts condemn, for God is greater than our hearts and knows everything.
>
> Beloved, if our hearts do not condemn us, we have confidence in God and receive from Him whatever we ask, because we keep His commandments and do what pleases Him.
>
> And His commandment is this: we should believe in the name of His Son, Jesus Christ, and love one another just as He commanded us.
>
> Those who keep His commandments remain in Him, and He in them, and the way we know that He remains in us is from the Spirit He gave us.

When the faithful wearied with constantly hearing my exhortation to love one another, they asked me why I always repeated the same words. I answered them, "Because it is the precept of the Lord, and if you comply with it, you do enough."

They asked me the same question that the young Greek, Odysseus, had asked me a year before when I was preaching from the Teacher's Chair in this same public square and that was also my response to him at that time.

My Lost Sheep

Odysseus had returned to listen to me day after day as I had preached the year before. He had repented of his past sins, believed the good news of eternal salvation through faith in Jesus Christ and His forgiveness of his sins, had converted and had been baptized. I then entrusted him to the care of the bishop of another city. I said, "In the presence of Christ, and before this congregation, I earnestly recommend this young man to your care."

The bishop took the trust upon him and promised to faithfully discharge it. Then I visited the other churches of Asia to correct abuses and to supply them with worthy pastors. I wrote three letters for the universal Church.

Almost one year later, I visited the bishop to whom I had entrusted Odysseus and I asked him about the young man's progress in the faith. The bishop told me that he had lodged him in his own home, instructed him in the faith, and helped him to lead a good life.

I asked the bishop, "Restore to me the trust which Jesus Christ and I committed to you in the presence of your church." The bishop was surprised, imagining that I meant some trust of money. But I explained myself that I spoke of Odysseus and his soul which I had entrusted to his care.

Then the bishop, with sighs and tears, said, "He is dead!"

"What did he die from?" I asked.

The bishop's countenance changed to sadness and he replied, "He is dead to God. He turned into a robber, and instead of remaining in the Church with us, he went into the mountains where he lives with a company of wicked men like himself."

When I heard this, I rent my garments and with a deep sigh and tears I said, "Oh what kind of a guardian did I provide to watch over my brother's soul?"

The bishop confessed that he had assumed that Odysseus was safe in the hands of God and that he, the bishop, had slackened and had become less watchful over him. This was quickly observed by a company of idle robbers who lured Odysseus into their gang.

In this evil company, he soon forgot Christian teachings and passed from one degree of wickedness to another. He finally stifled all remorse, put himself at the head of his own gang of robbers and took to the highway.

When I heard this, I called for a horse and a guide and we rode away to the mountains where Odysseus and his gang were living in hiding. I was captured by his lookouts. I didn't try to escape or to beg for my life, but cried out, "I know your leader, please take me to him."

They led me to him. He was armed, but when he saw that it was me he was seized with a mixture of shame and fear. He ran away in confusion.

I forgot my feebleness and old age and I hobbled in pursuit of him. I cried out after him, "Child, why do you run from me, your father, unarmed and an old man? My son, have compassion on me. There is room for repentance, God will forgive you. I will answer for you to Jesus Christ. I am ready and most willing to lay down my life for you, as Jesus Christ laid down His life for all men. I will pledge my soul for yours. Stay, believe me, I am sent by Christ."

At these words, Odysseus stood still, with his eyes fixed upon the ground. Then he threw away his weapons, trembled and burst into tears. When I came up to him, he was repentant. He embraced me as his father and implored my forgiveness.

I fell on my knees before him, kissed his hand, assured him of God's forgiveness and implored him to return to Christ and His Church. He responded by making his Confession to me and received my absolution as I acted in the person of Christ.

I remembered that the Master had said, "If a man has a hundred sheep and one of them goes astray, will he not leave the ninety-nine in the hills and go in search of the stray? And if he finds it, he rejoices more over it than over the ninety-nine that did not stray."

In the same way, I rejoiced in finding the lost Odysseus. I brought him to the congregation the next Sunday and told the congregation, "Rejoice, as the Master taught us, for I have found my lost sheep. And little children, let us always remember the Master's new law to love one another as He loved us. For no greater love has a man than to lay down his life for his friends."

I was happy that Odysseus had returned to the Church and

276

rejoiced with the congregation to hear the testimony of his re-conversion. He became faithful in all that he did for the brothers, especially for strangers. They testified to his new life.

My hope was that Odysseus would become a missionary of Jesus Christ. I entrusted him with a letter to another one of my spiritual children named Gaius. I congratulated Gaius for walking in the truth, for nothing gave me greater joy than to hear that my children were doing so. I encouraged Gaius to give hospitality and help to Odysseus and to all of the missionaries who taught the truth about Jesus Christ and His Church. I warned Gaius against Diotrephes who was spreading evil about me and was refusing to afford hospitality to the true missionaries. Even worse, he was expelling from the community those Christians who did help them.

There were many false missionaries who were antichrists and taught that Jesus was not really a true man but a pure divine spirit who just looked like a man. Since He wasn't really human, He couldn't have really died. They taught that He came to us in order to pass on to us secret knowledge needed for spiritual enlightenment and that the greed and lust that they saw all around them was only because we had physical bodies. True salvation for them was liberation from the prison of the body so that the soul could escape from it to heaven.

But we know that Jesus, the Word of God, was true God and true man. For in the beginning was the Word, and the Word was with God, and the Word was God. He was in the beginning with God. All things came to be through Him, and without Him nothing came to be. What was from the beginning, what we have heard, and what we have seen with our eyes, we looked upon and touched with our hands concerns the word of life—for the life was made visible; we have seen it and testify to it and proclaim to you that eternal life that was with the Father and was made visible to us—what we have seen and heard we proclaim now to you, so that you too may have fellowship with us; for our fellowship is with the Father and with His Son, Jesus Christ. I am writing this so that your joy may be complete.

What came to be through Him was life, and this life was the

light of the human race; the light shines in the darkness, and the darkness has not overcome it. He was the true light, which enlightens everyone, and He came into the world. He was in the world, and the world came to be through Him, but the world did not know Him. He came to what was His own, but His own people did not accept Him.

To those who did accept Him, He gave power to become children of God, to those who believe in His name, who were born not by natural generation nor by human choice nor by a man's decision but of God.

And the Word became flesh and made His dwelling among us, and we saw His glory, the glory as of the Father's only Son, full of grace and truth. From His fullness we have all received grace in place of grace, because while the Law was given through Moses, grace and truth came through Jesus Christ. No one has ever seen God. The only Son, God, who is at the Father's side, has revealed Him.

He really died for us and rose from the dead on the third day after His death, just as He had said that He would. I heard Him say from the Cross of His crucifixion, "Father, into your hands I commend my spirit. It is finished." I saw Him die with my own eyes. I saw the soldier pierce His side with a lance and the blood and water gush forth from His heart. I saw them wrap His dead body in burial cloths. I saw Him buried in the new tomb in the garden near where He was crucified. I saw the empty tomb on Sunday morning and the undisturbed burial cloths lying in it.

Jesus appeared to us after His death. We saw Him with our very eyes, we heard Him speak to us with our very ears and we touched Him with our very hands. He said. "Look at my hands and my feet, that it is I myself. Touch me and see, because a ghost does not have flesh and bones as you can see I have." He was not a ghost, but real flesh and blood and He even ate with us to prove it.

The false missionary antichrists also taught that we are sinless. If we believe this, we deceive ourselves and the truth is not in us. However, if we acknowledge our sins, Jesus, who is true God and true man, is faithful and just and will forgive us, cleanse us from every wrongdoing and fulfill His promise to us of eternal life with Him in the Kingdom of God. Then we will walk in the light as He is in the light. We will have fellowship with one another and the blood of Jesus will cleanse us from all sin. He laid down His life for us; so we ought to lay down our lives for our brothers. The Father sent His Son as savior of the world. So we should see what love the Father has bestowed on us that we may be called the children of God. Yet so we are.

Jesus Christ is the Messiah, the Lord and Savior, the Son of Man and the Son of God, the King of Love and the King of All Nations. I write this to you so that you may know that you who believe this have eternal life.

For whoever is begotten by God conquers the world. And the victory that conquers the world is our faith. Who indeed is the victor over the world but the one who believes that Jesus is the Son of God? And this is the testimony: God gave us eternal life, and this life is in His Son. Whoever possesses the Son has life; whoever does not possess the Son of God does not have life.

This is the Gospel of Love that I preached and wrote in Ephesus.

Author's Afterword

Mary's House

On my first visit to Ephesus in September 2001, I had tried to experience Ephesus for myself, as St. John might have done, by walking in his footsteps to Mary's House. The early morning sun beat down on me as I prayed at his tomb located in the ruins of the Basilica devoted to him on Ayasuluk Hill outside of the city of Ephesus. John wrote his gospel and his letters in Ephesus and he often walked through the ancient city and up the mountain to Mary's House where the Blessed Virgin Mary lived for the last nine years of her life.

I walked in the footsteps of John down from his Basilica and west to the ancient city of Ephesus. I stopped there for a visit at the ruins of Mary's Church. This was the first church in the world that was dedicated to Mary. The Council of Ephesus was held there in 431. It proclaimed the first Marian dogma that Mary is the Mother of God.

After a refreshing drink of water, I continued through the magnificent ruins of Ephesus and began the climb up Nightingale Mountain, from which I could see the powder blue sky, the cobalt blue Aegean Sea and the Island of Samos glistening like a

281

diamond in the sea. As I climbed the road up the mountain, I passed the huge statue of Mary that overlooks the valley below. I took it as a sign that she was encouraging me to keep climbing up to her House.

Three and a half hours after I left St. John's Basilica, I reached a plateau hidden on the back of the mountaintop. As the sweat poured off my face, I stood before Mary's House which is nestled in the mountainside. The restored House is made of stone and its foundation has been there for almost 2000 years. This House was the fountain of grace from which sprang the dogma of Mary Mother of God and the great basilicas of Ephesus dedicated to Mary and to St. John. Here she died and was buried and from here her body and soul were assumed into heaven.

I walked up to her House and entered the chapel which was once Mary's living room. I prayed there and then exited through what was once Mary's bedroom.

Then I walked behind her House and prayed while on the path of the Stations of the Cross that Mary herself made, according to the visions of Blessed Sister Catherine Emmerich, and then at the likely place of her burial and assumption. I reflected on her House that had lain here in ruins for almost 1900 years, little known by the world except for local venerators, until the Church ruled in the late 19th century that the ruins were the remains of Mary's House.

Pilgrims Visit Mary's House

Today, pilgrims of all faiths come to visit Mary's House, especially Muslims. They call the House, *Meryem Anna Evi*, Mother Mary's House.

The Muslims have a great devotion to Mary who is mentioned several times in the Koran. Chapter 3 verse 40 says, "Mary, God gives the good tidings of a word from Him whose name is Messiah, Jesus, Son of Mary, high honored shall she be in this world and the next, near stationed to God."

Pope Pius XII said, "The holy House should be a Marian center which is unique throughout the world, a place where Christians and Moslems of all rites and denominations and of all nationalities can meet each other to venerate the Mother of Jesus, and make true the prophecy, 'All Generations will call me blessed.' " (*L'Osservatore Romano*, April 24, 1954).

St. John XXIII, as a bishop, and Popes Paul VI, St. John Paul II and Benedict XVI all made pilgrimages to Mary's House. Over one million visitors journey there each year.

Pope Benedict XVI celebrated Mass there on November 29, 2006 at the open air altar before a large crowd of pilgrims, just five years after the 9/11 attack on America. In his homily he proclaimed peace among all nations:

> In this Eucharistic celebration we praise the Lord for Mary's divine motherhood, a mystery solemnly confessed and proclaimed in Ephesus at the Ecumenical Council of 431. To this place, so dear to the Christian community, my venerable predecessors the Servants of God Paul VI and John Paul II came as pilgrims; the latter visited this Shrine on 30 November 1979, just over a year after the beginning of his Pontificate....
>
> Christ "came to proclaim peace" (Ephesians 2:17), not only between Jews and non-Jews, but between all nations, since all have their origin in the same God, the one Creator and Lord of the universe. Strengthened by God's word, from here in Ephesus, a city blessed by the presence of Mary Most Holy — who we know is loved and venerated also by Muslims — let us lift up to the Lord a special prayer for peace between peoples. From this edge of the Anatolian peninsula, a natural bridge between continents, let us implore peace and reconciliation, above all for those dwelling in the Land called "Holy" and considered as such by Christians, Jews and Muslims alike: it is the land of Abraham, Isaac and Jacob, destined to be the

home of a people that would become a blessing for all the nations. (See Genesis 12:1-3). Peace for all of humanity! May Isaiah's prophecy soon be fulfilled: "They shall beat their swords into ploughshares, and their spears into pruning hooks; nation shall not lift up sword against nation, neither shall they learn war anymore." (Isaiah 2:4). We all need this universal peace; and the Church is called to be not only the prophetic herald, but even more, the "sign and instrument" of this peace.

Pilgrim's Apparition of Mary

Elizabeth Fraser of Vermont made a pilgrimage to Mary's House on April 4, 1959. She was temporarily living in Greece, across the Aegean Sea west of Ephesus. During Mass in Mary's House she prayed for her sister and her sister's disabled children and for all those who suffer. Her sister had four children. One son had severe cerebral palsy and she had just learned that her fourth child, also a son, had Downs Syndrome.

Mrs. Fraser wrote:

It was a fresh spring day and so quiet and peaceful up there on the mountain, I stood outside Mary's House and looked all over to enjoy the same scenery that she must have enjoyed, especially at that time of year, with daisies scattered over the mountainside, a little olive grove beside the house, the view of the blue sea below and the mountain top not far above. There were many clouds in the sky and they kept passing in front of the sun, creating problems for taking pictures.

Before long it was time to enter Mary's House for Mass. Right away I wanted to be sure I prayed for everyone who couldn't have the privilege of visiting there. I think I mentioned everyone by name or group, and especially those who suffer. As I stood for the Gospel, I thought, "How beautiful it is here with the sun shining in and Mass being celebrated!"

Now there were thoughts coming to me as though Mary herself was speaking to me, "We love them, dear. Why, the reward for suffering is so great that even if you were told you wouldn't know. Your minds aren't meant to know. This life is no more than a short wave of the hand with no more than a veil between." These and other ideas were like wonderful news to me, although I knew I had always believed them. I felt I could hardly wait to go to my sister and tell her. How happy she would be to know how truly blessed are children who are handicapped.

Then I thought I should say the rosary—surely a rosary in Mary's House, of all places. As I recited the Apostles' Creed, each truth was so real to me, and the following prayers so meaningful! After a few Hail Marys of the first decade, with the realization that Mass was proceeding, I tried to make myself more conscious of the precise part and moment of the Mass. Despite my attempt to do this I could not, because the rays of the sun, shining in on the Gospel side of the altar, were too distracting. The fact that they were not constant, but kept going off and on as though little clouds were quickly passing before the sun, was the main source of distraction.

I looked at the light and mentally answered as in reply to a wish of the Blessed Mother, "All right, Mary! How do you look in your little House?" Then, without knowing why and with a strong impression of "statue" in the back of my mind, I looked to the other side of the altar. At first she wasn't there—then she was.

There was no surprise in all of this except that the Blessed Mother didn't look as I had always pictured her. Her hair was black instead of light. And because of this I said to her in my mind, "Of course you look like this; you were Jewish." Then I looked at her eyes. Because of having heard that Mary's smile was the most beautiful thing about her appearance, I continued, "They're wrong. It's your eyes that are most beautiful! So this is how love and happiness look—it's all in your eyes!" Then, looking at her cheek, "No, it's your cheek that is most beautiful!" I looked at her mouth, her lips were parted as if she were about to speak. "No," I said, "It's your mouth that is most beautiful." Mary then smiled broadly. "Oh yes, they are right! It is your smile that is most beautiful." Mary looked toward the altar, and I said to her, "Oh, you are so pleased that we came to visit and that Mass is being said in your little House." I was so happy that she was pleased. I wish that more could be said about this moment, but there just aren't words.

Mary's hair was loose around her forehead. She wore a sheer veil, pale in color, which seemed to be folded back on her head and to fall longer than her shoulders. And I remember so well thinking of those beautiful amber eyes, so very round and full that all creation could be seen in them. I simply couldn't take my eyes from her face and, therefore, am unable to describe anything else Mary wore— I really don't know.

While I was admiring her beauty, there were still thoughts coming from Mary such as these, "Don't worry so, dear. You aren't meant to understand. We know! And we know that you don't know, that is why God is so merciful. Everything is as it should be according to God's plan. We are with them."

I was looking at Mary, her cheek especially because I could see all her face that way, when the *Sanctus* announced the beginning of the Consecration. I looked away from Mary and thought no more about her until I went up to Communion.

I thought I'd look at the beautiful statue now that I was at the altar, and when I did I was looking at the old statue up in back of the altar. It was black metal; the nose was broken off, and the arms were broken at the wrists. The statue looked so ugly to me after expecting to see such beauty that I couldn't look away and put it out of my mind fast enough.

It wasn't until the Last Gospel that I looked back at the same statue above the altar. The sun was shining in once more, and in place of the ugly black statue I saw Mary once again. At the time I wondered how the statue could be so ugly from up close and so beautiful from the kneeling bench.

After Mass, I picked up my belongings and walked up to the altar. I was ready to remark how pretty it was with the sun shining in, and at the same instant I looked up to see the window through which the sunshine should have been coming. There was no window — just a blank wall!

I asked the priest, who had just finished Mass, where the light had been shining from, and he answered that the only places any light could enter were the miniature skylight of the chapel itself or a window of an adjoining room, all of which were too far removed from the spot whence the light should have come. I realized that none of the sources could have possibly produced the direct rays that I saw!

The whole day continued to be just wonderful. After the visit at Mary's House I walked through the ruins of the old city of Ephesus. At one point beyond the edge of the ruins there was a shepherd with his flock standing under a flowering tree on a hillside. He was singing and it carried over to Ephesus. I couldn't help but say aloud, "I am so happy!"

Mary's Image

Mrs. Fraser said that Mary looked like Our Lady of Guadalupe. Like the image of Our Lady of Guadalupe, the image of Our Lady of Ephesus was imprinted. But, unlike the image of Our Lady of Guadalupe which was imprinted on the cloak of St. Juan Diego, this image was not imprinted on Mrs. Fraser's garment, but on her mind. She described the image in great detail and the image was painted according to her description.

When I entered Mary's House to pray, I saw this image displayed in the entranceway. Mary looks like a happy Jewish mother. A mosaic of this image is now displayed in the Basilica of the National Shrine of the Immaculate Conception in Washington, D.C.

Mrs. Fraser said, "It will always be my wish that everyone might have the opportunity to visit Mary's House at Ephesus. One cannot help but feel at home there with the gracious welcome which I'm certain Mary extends to everyone who comes to her House."

This is best summed up by a poem written by a relative of Mrs. Fraser:

Mary's House

By M. Laura Leddy

Little House of Our Lady
Restored and standing anew
From centuries' devastation
On a mountainside she knew.
She came to you for haven
From a land beset with strife
Far from the stress and tumult
That threatened her holy life.

You sheltered her in her sorrows
Quietly soothing her fears
Filling the lonely hours
Throughout her declining years.

Warmth from your hearthstone fire
Its light on the walls aglow
Brought to her peace and comfort
That only she could know.

Little House she still remembers
Your gracious and loving care
And comes on light rays from heaven
To the dim lit chapel there.
Eyes have beheld her beauty
Minds have been freed from all fear.
Hearts rejoice in the message
Of Our Lady standing near.

Our Lady of Ephesus.

On April 4, 2003, at a time of tension between the United States and Turkey and during the war in nearby Iraq, a beautiful mosaic image of Our Lady of Ephesus was solemnly blessed in the Basilica of the National Shrine of the Immaculate Conception in Washington D.C. It was precisely the 44th anniversary of the vision of Our Lady of Ephesus that Elizabeth Fraser had seen on April 4, 1959.

The image is installed in a small oratory. The writing on the left wall of the oratory explains the dogma defined at the Council of Ephesus that Mary is the Mother of God. The writing on the right wall quotes chapter 19 of the Gospel of John that he took Mary into his home. John built Mary's House in Ephesus.

Cardinal McCarrick of Washington D.C. and Archbishop Giuseppe Bernardini of Izmir, Turkey, concelebrated a special Mass in honor of Our Lady of Ephesus. I was there with the daughter of Elizabeth Fraser, the visionary.

In his post-Communion remarks, Archbishop Bernardini expressed his great joy for the installation of the image. He said, "I would like to leave this oratory as a gift from my diocese in Turkey for the people of the United States. At Mary's House different faiths and cultures pray together. The Blessed Mother receives and embraces all of mankind. It is the spirit of the mother who receives everyone without distinction as to race, language or culture. The spirit of reconciliation and peace is the spirit of Our Lady of Ephesus, especially today with war in Iraq. May Our Lady of Ephesus bring peace to the world."

Mosaic image of Our Lady of Ephesus in the Basilica of the National
Shrine of the Immaculate Conception

As I neared the end of my writing of *The Gospel of Love*, I returned to Ephesus in the Spring of 2013. It was almost 12 years after my original visit there in September 2001, just after the 9/11 attack on America.

I also made a pilgrimage by ferry to the island of Patmos, where the book of Revelation was revealed to John.

Patmos is a small Greek island situated off the west coast of Turkey in the Aegean Sea, about 70 miles southwest of Ephesus. It has a population of 3000 and an area of 13 square miles. It is a rocky, arid and virtually treeless island. As the ferry approached the island, I noticed the crystal-clear waters and a variety of bays, coves, headlands and harbors.

St. John received his revelation on Patmos in a cave now known as the Cave of the Apocalypse. It is situated about halfway up a thousand-foot mount. He was exiled to Patmos by the Roman Emperor Domitian. He remained there for 18 months until Nerva, the succeeding Emperor, granted him amnesty and he then returned to Ephesus.

The Cave of the Apocalypse is located at the lowest level of the Monastery of the Apocalypse and is now enclosed in a chapel. Originally, the Cave's entrance faced the open air overlooking the Aegean Sea. It is a natural cave in the dark grey rock. It is about 15 feet wide, with a height of 8 feet and a depth of 20 feet.

The oral tradition of the island is that John often retired to the Cave for prayer. He would lie prostrate facing the Cave's entrance. One day, when he heard the mighty voice of Jesus like a trumpet behind him, he got up, turned around towards the back wall of the Cave, saw Jesus and fell prostrate at His feet.

A monk told me that John later noticed that Jesus' voice had shattered the ceiling of the cave which had caused a fissure that extended from the back of the cave on the south, north to the front where the fissure divided the ceiling of the entrance into three equal parts, symbolizing the Most Holy Trinity.

I walked down the stairs, through the Monastery to the Cave.

292

Above the entrance is an icon of St. John and above it the inscription, "How dreadful is this place! This is none other than the house of God, and this is the gate of heaven." (Genesis 28:17).

I passed through "the gate of heaven", entered "the house of God" and prayed. I prayed for the fruitfulness of my book and left a small portion of my manuscript in the wall of the Cave where St. John had received the Book of Revelation.

I prayed for his intercession for my intention. I then climbed back up the stairs, through the Monastery, to the open air where I was pleased to see a full moon rising over the Aegean Sea.

Appendix

The Prayers of the Jesus King of All Nations Devotion

The Chaplet of Unity

The Chaplet of Unity is a series of prayers recited on ordinary rosary beads. Jesus said, *"I promise to give this Chaplet of Unity great power over My Wounded Sacred Heart when prayed with faith and confidence to heal the brokenness of My peoples' lives..."* (*Journal* 47).

Recite on the large bead before each of the five decades:

God our Heavenly Father, through Your Son Jesus, our Victim-High Priest, True Prophet, and Sovereign King, pour forth the power of Your Holy Spirit upon us and open our hearts. In Your great mercy, through the Motherly mediation of the Blessed Virgin Mary, our Queen, forgive our sinfulness, heal our brokenness, and renew our hearts in the faith, and peace, and love, and joy of Your Kingdom, that we may be one in You.

Recite on the ten small beads of each of the five decades:

In Your great mercy, forgive our sinfulness, heal our brokenness, and renew our hearts, that we may be one in You.

Conclude the Chaplet with the following prayers:

Hear, O Israel! The Lord Our God is One God!

O Jesus, King of All Nations, may Your Reign be recognized on earth!

Mary, Our Mother and Mediatrix of All Grace, pray and intercede for us your children!

St. Michael, Great Prince and Guardian of your people, come with the Holy Angels and Saints and protect us! Amen.

Jesus said, *"Yes, in this devotion to Me as Jesus, King of All Nations, entreat My Kingly Heart with the prayer of this Chaplet of Unity that I Myself, Your Sovereign Lord Jesus Christ, have given you! Pray and ask for the spiritual wholeness and the healing of your own souls, for the union of your own will with God's Will, for the healing of your families, friends, enemies, relationships, religious orders, communities, countries, nations, the world, and unity within My Church under the Holy Father! I shall grant many spiritual, physical, emotional, and psychological healings for those who pray this prayer if it is beneficial to their salvation according to My Holy Will! Unity and oneness in Spirit was My Own prayer for all mankind and My Church as My own last testament before I gave My life as Savior of all mankind! As I am One with My Father and the Holy Spirit, My Will is all that mankind be one in Me, so that one Faith, one Fold, and one Shepherd will be gathered together under My Sovereign Kingship as Lord."* (Journal 50).

"I, Jesus, Son of the Most High God... promise to hold out to the souls who pray My Chaplet of Unity the Scepter of My Kingship and grant them mercy, pardon, and protection in times of severe weather and plagues. I extend this promise not only for yourselves, but also for

individuals for whom you pray. Any harm or danger, spiritual or physical, whether it be to soul, mind or body, will I protect these souls against, and clothe them over with My Own mantle of Kingly Mercy." (*Journal* 54).

The Chaplet of Unity may also be prayed as a novena, nine times in succession. This can be done at one time, hourly or daily.

The Novena in Honor of
Jesus as True King

This simple Novena is a most generous gift from Our Lord. Jesus gave these extraordinary promises to His servant:

"My little one, every time you say the prayers I taught you in connection with My image as 'Jesus, King of All Nations', I promise that I will convert ten sinners, bring ten souls into the One True Faith, release ten souls from Purgatory and be less severe in My Judgment of your nation, the United States of America. My little one, this not only applies to your nation, but also all other nations. My child, each time you say these prayers, I will mitigate the severity of the chastisements upon your country." (*Journal* 41).

The Novena consists of praying once a day, over a period of nine days, a set of one **Our Father,** one **Hail Mary** and one **Glory Be,** recited along with the following Novena Prayer:

O Lord our God, You alone are the Most Holy King and Ruler of all nations. We pray to You, Lord, in the great expectation of receiving from You, O Divine King, Mercy, peace, justice and all good things.

Protect, O Lord our King, our families and the land of our birth. Guard us, we pray, Most Faithful One! Protect us from our enemies and from Your Just Judgment.

Forgive us, O Sovereign King, our sins against You. Jesus, You are a King of Mercy. We have deserved Your Just Judgment. Have mercy on us, Lord, and forgive us. We trust in Your Great Mercy.

O most awe-inspiring King, we bow before You and pray; may Your Reign, Your Kingdom, be recognized on earth! Amen.

Jesus said, *"I desire that this Novena be prayed on the nine days preceding My Feast of Christ the King, but I encourage souls to pray this Novena at any time throughout the year. My promises will be granted whenever it is prayed."* (Journal 194).

Novena of Holy Communions

This Novena consists of offering nine consecutive Holy Communions in honor of Jesus King of All Nations. Jesus said, *"I desire that the faithful souls who embrace this devotion to Me... make a Novena of Holy Communions. They therefore shall offer me nine (9) consecutive Holy Communions, in honor of Me as 'Jesus, King of All Nations'."* (*Journal* 220). Jesus indicated that by "consecutive", He meant nine Communions, uninterrupted, one after another, that the souls would receive. They need not be on nine calendar days in a row, just each Communion received, one after the other.

The powerful and unprecedented effects of this Novena were shown to the visionary, Jesus' "Secretary", in a vision. She saw Jesus gazing up to Heaven. Nine times He gave a command and an angel came to earth. Jesus explained: *"My daughter, for those souls who will offer me [this] devotion I will bid an angel of each of the Nine Choirs, one with each Holy Communion, to guard this soul for the rest of its life on this earth."* (*Journal* 223).

Jesus wants us to pray the Novena for others, and explains its necessity at this time: *"This Novena may be prayed with its promises for another soul and that soul will also receive additional angelic protection. The praying of this Novena for communities, nations, and the world, will also call down My angelic protection upon them. Because of the many evils in these end-times, it is My desire that you pray to Me to send My angelic hosts to guide, guard and protect you. This is then My solemn promise."* (*Journal* 224).

In His great generosity, Jesus granted that, in addition to the angelic protection, one may have a separate, unrelated intention for this Novena. He promised: *"What they ask for in this Novena, if it be according to My Most Holy Will, I will surely grant it. Let these souls ask from Me without reservation."* (*Journal* 221).

Consecration to Mary Mediatrix of All Grace

Jesus asks those who embrace this devotion to consecrate themselves to His mother under her title as "Mary, Mediatrix of All Grace." His servant recorded Jesus' words:

"My beloved little daughter, your Lord and God comes to you to give you a message of great importance. I desire that the souls who embrace My devotion to 'Jesus King of All Nations,' make a special consecration to My Most Holy Mother under her title of 'Mary, Mediatrix of All Grace,' which it has pleased Me in My Great Love for her to give her. People MUST acknowledge her indispensable role as the Mediatrix, the Channel, of all of My Grace to mankind. Only when this dogma is officially proclaimed by My Church will I truly establish My Reign on earth." (Journal 239).

Our Lady then appeared next to Our Lord and said: *"Daughter, know that I have obtained this prayer for my children from the Heart of my Divine Son."* (Journal 244).

Jesus then revealed the Prayer of Consecration to Mary, Mediatrix of All Grace:

O Mary, Most Holy and Immaculate Mother of God, of Jesus, our Victim-High Priest, True Prophet, and Sovereign King, I come to you as the Mediatrix of All Grace, for that is truly what you are. O Fountain of all Grace! O Fairest of Roses! Most Pure Spring! Unsullied Channel of *all* of God's Grace! Receive me, Most Holy Mother! Present me and my every need to the Most Holy Trinity! That having been made pure and holy in His Sight through your hands, they may return to me, through you, as graces and blessing. I give and consecrate myself to you, Mary, Mediatrix of All Grace, that Jesus, Our One True Mediator, Who is the King of All Nations, may Reign in every heart. Amen.

Jesus also gave this beautiful message:

"My children, I desire only your peace and happiness! My Most Holy Mother has appealed to you time and time again! She still pleads... Children, listen to your Heavenly Mother. Is there a more tender or loving ambassadress then My own mother? You see, My children, if I had come to you in My Power and Majesty before this, before My Most Holy Mother had come to you in great tenderness and meekness, you would not have been able to handle it for fear. The times have arrived, My children. Your Lord comes to you with great Power and Majesty. My Most Holy Mother has prepared My Way with the greatest of care. My children, you owe much, very much, to your Heavenly Mother." (Journal 212, 213).

The Special Blessing

The Special Blessing of Jesus King of All Nations was revealed by Our Lady when she appeared to His servant's "spiritual mother" holding the Child Jesus in her arms. The Child was plucking roses one by one from His Sacred Heart, kissing them, and holding them to His Mother's lips. Our Lady kissed each rose, took it from Jesus' hands, touched it to her heart, then gave it to the "spiritual mother" who placed each rose within Our Lady's Immaculate Heart. From there the roses were distributed to peoples of all nations for all time – billions upon billions of roses. The roses are the graces of the Special Blessing, and the passing of the graces from Jesus to Mary to her children illustrates Our Lady's role as Mediatrix of All Grace.

To Give the Special Blessing:

The Special Blessing may be passed on by anyone to others in person or at a distance in prayer. If in person, place your hands on the person's head with your right thumb on his/her forehead. If at a distance, hold your hands over, or in the direction of, the person or group and pray:

May the Reign of Jesus King of All Nations be recognized in your heart;

May the Reign of Jesus King of All Nations be lived in your heart;

May the Reign of Jesus King of All Nations be given through your heart to other hearts;

So that the Reign of Jesus King of All Nations may be lived in every heart all over the world.

I ask this Special Blessing through Our Lady, Mediatrix of All Grace, who as Queen and Mother of All Nations, has obtained it for you as a tremendous grace from the Sacred Heart of her Divine Son, in the name of the Father and of the Son and of the Holy Spirit. Amen.

Make the sign of the cross on the person's forehead with your thumb, or make the sign of the cross with your hand in his/her direction.

The gifts of the Special Blessing are the gift of receiving, understanding, and living Jesus' Word in Scripture; the gifts of intimacy with Jesus, Mary, and souls as partners in the Body of Christ; and the gift of knowing the secrets of God's love. The Blessing also grants healing and brings unity to the Body of Christ.

Jesus wants everyone to receive the graces of this kingly Special Blessing. Pray it for your family, your friends, your priests, the lost, the sick, the dying—everyone who is in need of God's mercy.

Litany in Honor of Jesus King of All Nations

Jesus told His servant, *"I promise... that whosoever shall recite this Litany of Mine shall die in My arms with My smile upon them. I, Myself, will appear to these souls as 'King of All Nations' before their death."* (*Journal* 283).

The litany responses are indicated by the letter "R" and are made after <u>each</u> invocation.

The following is the Litany in honor of Jesus, King of All Nations.

Lord, have mercy on us.

Christ, have mercy on us.

Lord, have mercy on us.

R - Have Mercy on Us.

God, our Heavenly Father, Who has made firm for all ages your Son's Throne,

God the Son, Jesus, our Victim-High Priest, True Prophet, and Sovereign King,

God the Holy Spirit, poured out upon us with abundant newness,

Holy Trinity, Three Persons yet One God in the Beauty of Your Eternal Unity.

R - Reign in Our Hearts.

O Jesus, our Eternal King,

O Jesus, Most Merciful King,

O Jesus, extending to us the Golden Scepter of Your Mercy,

O Jesus, in Whose Great Mercy we have been given the Sacrament of Confession,

O Jesus, Loving King Who offers us Your Healing Grace,

O Jesus, our Eucharistic King,

O Jesus, the King foretold by the Prophets,

O Jesus, King of Heaven and earth,

O Jesus, King and Ruler of All Nations,

O Jesus, Delight of the Heavenly Court,

O Jesus, King Most Compassionate toward Your subjects,

O Jesus, King from Whom proceeds all authority,

O Jesus, in whom, with the Father and the Holy Spirit, we are One,

O Jesus, King Whose Kingdom is not of this world,

O Jesus, King Whose Sacred Heart burns with Love for all of mankind,

O Jesus, King Who is the Beginning and the End, the Alpha and the Omega,

O Jesus, King Who has given us Mary, the Queen, to be our dear Mother,

O Jesus, King Who will come upon the clouds of Heaven

with Power and Great Glory,

O Jesus, King Whose Throne we are to approach with confidence,

O Jesus, King truly present in the Most Blessed Sacrament,

O Jesus, King Who made Mary the Mediatrix of All Graces,

O Jesus, King Who made Mary Co-Redemptrix, Your partner in the Plan of Salvation,

O Jesus, King Who desires to heal us of all division and disunity,

O Jesus, King wounded by mankind's indifference,

O Jesus, King Who gives us the balm of Your Love with which to console Your Wounded Heart,

O Jesus, King Who is the Great I AM within us, our Wellspring of Pure Delight,

Jesus, King of All Nations, True Sovereign of all earthly powers,

Jesus, King of All Nations, subjecting under Your feet forever the powers of hell,

Jesus, King of All Nations, the Light beyond all light, enlightening us in the darkness that surrounds us,

Jesus, King of All Nations, Whose Mercy is so Great as to mitigate the punishments our sins deserve,

Jesus, King of All Nations, recognized by the Magi as the True King,

Jesus, King of All Nations, the Only Remedy for a world so ill,

Jesus, King of All Nations, Who blesses with Peace those souls and nations that acknowledge You as True King,

Jesus, King of All Nations, Who Mercifully sends us Your Holy Angels to protect us,

Jesus, King of All Nations, whose Chief Prince is St. Michael the Archangel,

Jesus, King of All Nations, Who teaches us that to reign is to serve,

Jesus, King of All Nations, Just Judge Who will separate the wicked from the good,

Jesus, King of All Nations, before Whom every knee shall bend,

Jesus, King of All Nations, Whose Dominion is an everlasting Dominion,

Jesus, King of All Nations, Lamb Who will Shepherd us,

Jesus, King of All Nations, Who after having destroyed every sovereignty, authority and power, will hand over the Kingdom to Your God and Father,

Jesus, King of All Nations, Whose Reign is without end,

Jesus, King of All Nations, whose kindness toward us is steadfast, and whose fidelity endures forever,

R - We praise and thank You.

Eternal Father, Who has given us Your Only Begotten

Son, to be our Redeemer, One True Mediator, and Sovereign King,

Loving Jesus, Sovereign King, Who humbled Yourself for Love of us and took the form of a servant,

Holy Spirit, Third Person of the Trinity, Love of the Father and the Son, Who sanctifies us and gives us Life,

Mary, our Queen and Mother, who mediates to Jesus on our behalf,   *R – Pray for us.*

Mary, our Queen and Mother, through whom all Graces come to us,   *R – Pray for us.*

Mary, our Queen and Mother, Singular Jewel of the Holy Trinity,   *R – We love you.*

Holy Angels and Saints of our Divine King,

R - Pray for us and Protect us.

Amen.

HOW TO PRACTICE THE DEVOTION
Through Its Image, Prayers, Medal, Promises and Graces:

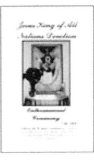

READ *The Booklet*!

THE REMEDY for our times! Newly revised. Read about the origin of the Devotion, the Kingship of Jesus, how *we* can recognize Jesus as King of All Nations, the promises and prayers of the Devotion. Read about signs, wonders, healings and conversions!

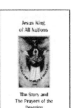

HEAR
The Story and
PRAY
The Prayers

READ *The Journal.*

The Journal contains all of the visions, revelations and messages of Jesus in this Devotion.

"One must read the full account of The Journal to have a comprehensive view and insight concerning the rich spiritual treasures of the Devotion, and the vital apostolate outlined there for our times, NOW TIMES! And get the medal!" Rev. Albert J. Hebert

Granted the Nihil Obstat which declares that *The Journal* is free of doctrinal and moral error.

ENTHRONE
The Image

WEAR *The Medal*

CARRY *The Package*

Jesus said,
"Enthrone this My image everywhere for I shall be powerfully present there ... "

DISPLAY AND VENERATE
The Image

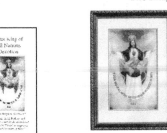

Jesus said, *"This image, My child, must become known.* ***Tremendous*** *will be the miracles of grace that I will work through this image and Devotion of Mine."*

SPREAD the
Introductory Pamphlet to
others.

309

Help the Reign of Jesus King of All Nations to be Recognized on Earth by Enthroning His Image!

"Take up My devotion of Jesus King of All Nations for in its practice you shall find for yourselves a haven of Grace, Mercy and Protection. **Enthrone this My image everywhere** *for I shall be powerfully present there and the Power of My Sovereign Kingship shall surely shield you from My Just Judgment." (Journal 418).*

Honor Jesus by enthroning His Image in your home, parish or school! Dan Lynch shares with you the Devotion to Jesus King of All Nations and then guides you step-by-step through the process of enthroning and consecrating your home, parish or school to Jesus King of All Nations. We have everything you will need to make your enthronement. Pass this tradition to the next generation to ensure continued devotion to and trust in Jesus well into the future.

| **Framed Jesus King of All Nations Image** | **8" x 13" Unframed Jesus King of All Nations Image** | **Beautiful Color Images of Jesus King of All Nations on canvas** | The ONLY **medal** revealed by Jesus for protection! This unique medal is manufactured exclusively for us. |

The Medal

Jesus said, *"It is My Most Holy Will and desire that there be a medal struck according to the likeness [of me] you have seen. I promise to offer the precious grace of final perseverance to every soul who will faithfully embrace this devotion. . . . . I promise to offer the grace of protection . . . . This will especially be true of danger coming from natural disasters."* (Journal 75).

 Jesus is on the front side of the medal. He appears crowned in majesty, with arms outstretched, grasping a large golden scepter of mercy in His right hand. His left hand is open in a gesture of mercy. Rays of light, which symbolize His merciful graces, shine from the wounds in His hands and fall on a large earth globe below His Sacred Heart.

St. Michael the Archangel is on the reverse side of the medal. St. Michael appears in flight, enveloped in glory, with a fiery sword in his right hand raised above his head. His left hand holds a pair of scales over the earth representing justice. To the right of St. Michael above his head appears the Sacred Host with the letters "IHS" and a small cross above. "IHS" is the monogram derived from the Greek word for Jesus. Drops of the Most Precious Blood drip from the Sacred Host into a chalice below and from it upon the globe.

The medal size is 3/4" x 1". Chains are not included.

Dan Lynch Productions

Our Lady of America, Our Hope for the States

♦ The only canonically approved devotion that is based upon apparitions of Our Lady in the United States.

♦ Our Lady of America's apparitions, messages and requests for Purity and Peace and her promise of Protection.

♦ The Divine Indwelling of the Most Holy Trinity.

Our Lady of Guadalupe, Hope for the World

"This book will instruct, encourage and inspire a wide variety of people in the Church and outside the Church. You may be a priest seeking new ways to call your people to a deeper faith.

Whoever you are, give this book some of your time, and it will repay you abundantly."

Fr. Frank Pavone, National Director, *Priests for Life*

The Ten Secrets of the Blessed Virgin Mary How to Prepare for Their Warnings

This book contains information from a personal interview by Dan Lynch with Medjugorje visionary Mirjana Soldo in which she disclaims prior reports about the first secret. Read the whole truth about Mary and her secrets.

"Everything is closer and closer.... God has to do something very quickly." Fr. Petar Ljubicic, designated recipient of visionary Mirjana Soldo's secrets.

Saints of the States

"This book is a wonderful contribution to appreciate the rich spiritual heritage we possess in the lives of so many heroic men and women of America. Dan Lynch traces the historical development, both secular and religious, through the centuries.

Dan Lynch has produced a very enjoyable, enriching and inspiring book. It challenges us to do in our times what these holy men and women did in their own."

Fr. Andrew Apostoli, CFR

DAN LYNCH APOSTOLATES
144 Sheldon Road   St. Albans, Vermont   05478
888-834-6261 or 802-524-5350   WWW.JKMI.COM

1. The Story of the Devotion Booklet. Explains the Devotion. Dan Lynch. $ 3.95

2. Enthronement Booklet. Dan Lynch guides you step-by-step through the process of enthroning and consecrating your home, parish or school to Jesus King of All Nations. $ 2.00

3. The Journal of the Secretary. The writings of Jesus' servant containing His revelations. $ 15.95

4a. The Story. DVD. Dan Lynch explains the Devotion and Image. $ 15.00

4b. The Story. CD. Same as above in CD. $ 6.00

5. The Story and The Prayers of the Devotion. Two CD set of The Story of the Devotion and The Devotional Prayers. Dan Lynch. $ 19.95

6. Battle for This Dogma! DVD. Dan Lynch explains the dogma of Mary Mediatrix of All Grace. $ 15.00

7. Introductory Pamphlet of prayers, promises and explanation of the Devotion. Available in bulk quantities only of:

25 for $10.00
50 for $15.00
75 for $20.00
100 for $25.00

8. Leaflet of Prayers. Contains all of the Devotion's $ 0.50
Prayers.

9. The Package. Contains *The Story of the Devotion* $ 9.00
Booklet, *Leaflet of Prayers* and an aluminum medal.

10a. Chastisements - Preparation and Protection $ 14.95
Against Them. Book. Explains the what and why
of chastisements, warnings of chastisements,
prayers of protection against them and hope for the
future. Dan Lynch.

10b. Chastisements - How to Prepare and Pray $ 15.00
Against Them. DVD. Dan Lynch.

11. Medal:

a. Aluminum $ 5.00

b. Brass (Gold, Silver or Bronze) (Circle choice) $ 19.00

c. Sterling Silver $ 52.00

d. Gold-filled over Brass $ 150.00

e. 14K Gold $1022.00

12. Walk in the Footsteps of Jesus! DVD. Join Dan $ 19.95
Lynch as he leads a pilgrimage in the footsteps of
Jesus to the Holy Land and Egypt.

13. Paper Holy Cards:

a. Jesus King of All Nations Novena $ 0.50

b. Mediatrix of All Grace $ 0.50

c. Special Blessing $ 0.50

d. St. Michael $ 0.50

14. St. Michael the Archangel Protect Us! DVD. $ 15.00
Dan Lynch explains the role of St. Michael.

314

15. Jesus King of All Nations and The $ 15.00
Triumphant Queen of the World. DVD. One-hour
television interview with Dan Lynch explaining the
Devotion, signs, wonders and conversions and Our
Lady's Triumph.

16. Images:

a. Jesus King of All Nations - 20" x 14" Beautiful $ 120.00
   double matted with gold colored frame.

b. Jesus King of All Nations - 8" x 10" print $ 6.00

c. St. Michael the Archangel - 8" x 10" print $ 6.00

d. St. Michael the Archangel - 12" x 20" print $ 12.00

e. Jesus Christ Mediator, Our Lady Mediatrix - $ 6.00
   8" x 10" print

f. Jesus King of All Nations - 2' x 3' full image on $ 195.00
   canvas

g. Jesus King of All Nations - 4' x 6' full image $ 750.00
   on canvas

Order Form
All prices subject to change without notice.

No.	Qty.	Description	Price	Total

SHIPPING & HANDLING UNITED STATES	
Value of Order	S&H
$ .00 - $ 9.99	$6.00
$ 10.00 - $24.99	$7.00
$ 25.00 - $49.99	$8.00
$ 50.00 - $99.99	$9.00
$100.00 & up	10% of order
-CANADIAN-	Double Above Rates
-FOREIGN-	Triple Above Rates

Subtotal _____

Shipping and Handling _____

Optional Donation _____

TOTAL Amount Due _____

Method of Payment to
Jesus King of All Nations:
○ Check Enclosed ○ Money Order
○ VISA ○ MasterCard ○ Discover

_____   _____
Credit Card Account Number   Expiration Date MM/YY

SHIPPING ADDRESS

Name_____

Address _____

City _____ State _____ Zip _____

Phone _____ E-mail _____

Presentation of this Book

The photograph shows the author presenting the first copies of this book to Mary Tarinelli on his right and Erin von Uffel on his left on the Feast of the Assumption, August 15, 2016, at Our Lady of Ephesus House of Prayer in Jamaica, Vermont.

(See: http://www.ourladyofephesushouseofprayer.org/).

Our Lady of Ephesus House of Prayer is an exact replica of Mary's House in Ephesus, Turkey, and contains one of its stones. The Feast of the Assumption is the traditional day of pilgrimages of Christians and Muslims to Mary's House in Ephesus, because she was assumed into heaven from there.

Mary Tarinelli and her late husband Don are the co-founders of Our Lady of Ephesus House of Prayer. She is also the daughter of the late Elizabeth Fraser who had a vision of the Blessed Virgin Mary at Mary's House in Ephesus on April 4, 1959. She described her vision to an artist who painted it. On April 4, 2003, precisely 44 years after her vision, a mosaic image of this painting was solemnly blessed and installed in an oratory in the Basilica of the

National Shrine of the Immaculate Conception in Washington DC. (See pages 347-355 of this book for more information).

Erin von Uffel wrote the Foreword to this book. She is the Vice Postulator of the cause for the canonization of Sister Marie de Mandat-Grancey and the President of the Sister Marie de Mandat-Grancey Foundation. (See: www.sistermarie.com).

Sister Marie is the nun who was responsible for the finding, purchasing and restoration of Mary's House in Ephesus. This book is dedicated to Sister Marie. (See pages xiii-xv of this book for more information).

About the Author

Dan Lynch is a former judge who is the founder of Dan Lynch Apostolates which promote devotion to Our Lady of Guadalupe, Jesus King of All Nations, Our Lady of America and St. John Paul II. He coordinates journeys of Missionary Images for veneration and Holy Hours of Prayer for Life, Peace and Protection. He is an author and a public speaker on radio and television and at conferences, missions and retreats. He is pictured here in front of Mary's House in Ephesus, Turkey.

He produced the video, *Our Lady of Guadalupe, Mother of Hope* which is shown regularly on EWTN. He is also the author of:

Our Lady of Guadalupe, Hope for the World which explains the history of Our Lady of Guadalupe and her modern mission to end abortion and bring a Culture of Life through conversions in the New Evangelization.

Our Lady of America, Our Hope for the States which explains the only canonically approved devotion that is based upon apparitions of Our Lady in the United States and contains her prayers and requests.

Saints of the States which tells the story of the development of Catholicism in the United States through biographies of its saints and blesseds.

The Ten Secrets of the Blessed Virgin Mary which explains how to prepare for warnings and chastisements that will soon come to the world.

Dan enjoys hiking, biking, kayaking, boating, sailing and fishing. He and his wife Sue live in Vermont. They are the parents of nine children and the grandparents of twenty-five.

Made in the USA
Middletown, DE
16 November 2019